Bard FICTION PRIZE

Bard College invites submissions for its annual Fiction Prize for young writers.

The Bard Fiction Prize is awarded annually to a promising, emerging writer who is a United States citizen aged 39 years or younger at the time of application. In addition to a monetary award of $30,000, the winner receives an appointment as writer-in-residence at Bard College for one semester without the expectation that he or she teach traditional courses. The recipient will give at least one public lecture and will meet informally with students.

To apply, candidates should write a cover letter describing the project they plan to work on while at Bard and submit a C.V., along with three copies of the published book they feel best represents their work. No manuscripts will be accepted.

Applications for the 2018 prize must be received by June 15, 2017. For further information about the Bard Fiction Prize, call 845-758-7087, or visit www.bard.edu/bfp. Applicants may also request information by writing to the Bard Fiction Prize, Bard College, Annandale-on-Hudson, NY 12504-5000.

Bard College PO Box 5000, Annandale-on-Hudson, NY 12504-5000

COMING UP IN THE FALL

Conjunctions:69
BEING BODIES
Edited by Bradford Morrow

All of us are conceived by bodies. Born from a mother's body, we emerge with an infant's body. Through the course of our lives, be they long or short, we exist within our aging bodies. And when our bodies cease to function, we die, and the bodies we have grown so used to inhabiting perish, disintegrate, integrate into the earth, the ocean, the air. Some believe the body hosts a soul, others don't. Either way, as John Donne wrote, "Loves mysteries in soules doe grow, / But yet the body is his booke."

Being Bodies explores the complex circumstances of our flesh-and-blood existence, the many ways in which having our own unique physicality is both a gift and burden. What we do with our bodies defines us spiritually, ethically, morally, and connects us with others, sometimes for good, and sometimes in acts that are destructive. Some of us are ascetics, others gluttons. Each of us is, in another's eyes, beautiful, attractive, even ravishing. Those same bodies are to others ugly, vile, re-pulsive. Our bodies dance, they're inked, they contain prosthetics and implants. Our bodies are gendered, though not always correlative with how we perceive ourselves. Our bodies are pigmented—we are descended from different ancestors. Ignorant of our common humanity, some hate us for our very looks. Some of us use our bodies to save the lives of others, some of us use them to murder. The body is political, musical, stoical, gregarious, ad-dicted, clean, remote. It is healthy and ill. We reward our bodies, we abuse our bod-ies, and they punish us for it. Our bodies are mortal, their days numbered. We do with them what we can and what we will.

In *Conjunctions:69*, *Being Bodies*, some of today's foremost contemporary writers address the body in its myriad forms. Contributors include Rachel Blau DuPlessis, Stephen O'Connor, Forrest Gander, Michael Ives, and Edward Carey.

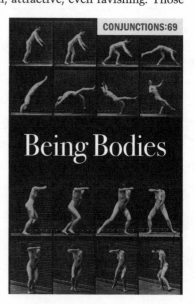

CONJUNCTIONS:69

Being Bodies

One-year individual US subscriptions to *Conjunctions* are only $18 (two years for $32) for today's most innovative fiction, poetry, and narrative nonfiction. To read danger-ously, subscribe or renew at conjunctions.com, or mail your check to *Conjunctions*, Bard College, Annandale-on-Hudson, NY 12504. For e-book editions of current and selected past issues, visit openroadmedia.com/ conjunctions. If you have questions or wish to request an invoice, e-mail conjunctions@bard.edu or call (845) 758-7054.

CONJUNCTIONS

Bi-Annual Volumes of New Writing

Edited by
Bradford Morrow

Contributing Editors
John Ashbery
Martine Bellen
Mei-mei Berssenbrugge
Mary Caponegro
Brian Evenson
William H. Gass
Peter Gizzi
Robert Kelly
Ann Lauterbach
Dinaw Mengestu
Rick Moody
Karen Russell
Joanna Scott
David Shields
Peter Straub
John Edgar Wideman

Published by Bard College

EDITOR: Bradford Morrow
MANAGING EDITOR: Micaela Morrissette
SENIOR EDITORS: Jedediah Berry, Benjamin Hale, J. W. McCormack, Edie Meidav, Nicole Nyhan, Pat Sims
COPY EDITOR: Pat Sims
ASSISTANT EDITORS: Matthew Balik, Ari Braverman, Nicholas Wetherell
PUBLICITY: Darren O'Sullivan, Mark R. Primoff
EDITORIAL ASSISTANTS: Kaitlynn Buchbaum, Cleo Egnal, Brigid Fister, Kelsey Johnson, Tessa Menatian, Charles Noyes, Jay Rosenstein, Michael Sarinsky, Chloe Scala, Leah Stern

CONJUNCTIONS is published in the Spring and Fall of each year by Bard College, Annandale-on-Hudson, NY 12504.

SUBSCRIPTIONS: Use our secure online ordering system at conjunctions.com, or send subscription orders to CONJUNCTIONS, Bard College, Annandale-on-Hudson, NY 12504. Single year (two volumes): $18.00 for individuals; $40.00 for institutions and non-US. Two years (four volumes): $32.00 for individuals; $80.00 for institutions and non-US. For information about subscriptions, back issues, and advertising, contact us at (845) 758-7054 or conjunctions@bard.edu. *Conjunctions* is listed and indexed in JSTOR and Humanities International Complete and included in EBSCO*host*.

Editorial communications should be sent to Bradford Morrow, *Conjunctions*, 21 East 10th Street, 3E, New York, NY 10003. Unsolicited manuscripts cannot be returned unless accompanied by a stamped, self-addressed envelope. Electronic and simultaneous submissions will not be considered. Do not send work via any method requiring a signature for delivery. If you are submitting from outside the United States, contact conjunctions@bard.edu for instructions.

Cover design by Jerry Kelly, New York. Cover art by Eugene Ivanov (opatov.wixsite.com/eugeneivanov, facebook.com/eugene.ivanov.artist): *Settlement North*, oil on canvas, 60 x 80 cm., 2012. © Eugene Ivanov 2017; all rights reserved by the artist.

Conjunctions e-books of current and selected past issues are distributed by Open Road Integrated Media (openroadmedia.com/conjunctions) and available for purchase in all e-reader formats from Amazon, Apple, B&N, Google, Indiebound, Kobo, Overdrive, and elsewhere.

Retailers can order print issues directly from *Conjunctions* or via Ubiquity Distributors, Inc., ubiquitymags.com, 607 Degraw Street, Brooklyn, NY 11217. Telephone: (718) 875-5491. Fax: (718) 875-8047.

Printers: Edwards Brothers Malloy, Circle Press

Typesetter: Bill White, Typeworks

ISSN 0278-2324

ISBN 978-0-941964-84-5

Manufactured in the United States of America.

TABLE OF CONTENTS

INSIDE OUT:
ARCHITECTURES OF EXPERIENCE
Edited by Bradford Morrow

EDITOR'S NOTE

TO BE ALIVE IS TO encounter architecture. From the most solitary hermit to the most gregarious urbanite, survival itself fundamentally involves negotiating constructed spaces—huts, houses, high-rises. Architecture often plays a defining existential role in our earliest perceptions. To have roofs over our heads is desirable to most all of us, no matter whether they are made of quarried slate or rummaged cardboard, of woven wheat-straw thatch or forged corrugated steel. Childhood bedrooms, whether our own or shared with siblings or even with one's parents and grandparents, stay imprinted in our memories long after we've ventured out into other rooms. The architecture of the neighborhoods in which we grow up, be they urban, rural, or suburban, also shape who we become. Every building has its own narrative that begins with an architectural idea—an office where we work, a church in which to pray, a prison to avoid, a hospital for healing. And beyond functionality, architecture strives as often as not to be aesthetically pleasing. To challenge expectations, to honor tradition, to be new.

In this issue readers will come upon walls, and the people they protect or separate. They will discover pyramids and caves, castles and bars, seaside hotels and roadside motels, a tiny haunted house and a mansion on a Miyazaki-esque island floating in the sky. A mother and son visit a fractal museum in Maine, only to have their lives irrevocably altered. On a boarding-school farm in West Virginia, a troubled boy has his first unexpected sexual encounter in an isolated room. A band of weekend urban archaeologists who salvage artifacts from buildings about to be demolished make a grim discovery but, because they're trespassing, face the dilemma of whether to report their find. A girl obsessed with bridges eventually creates single-strand spans that defy the laws of physics.

Throughout, we see the many ways in which the very materials we fashion into architectural structures reflect our deepest selves and are vivid physical extensions of our imaginations. To borrow a phrase from poet Elaine Equi, "We mark our place and it marks us."

—Bradford Morrow
April 2017
New York City

The Limestone Book
Joanna Scott

I ONLY CALL IT A BOOK because he called it that. He said it was the greatest book ever written, and he was sorely sorry he didn't have a copy to share with me.

He was the old man who had taken up residence in an abandoned encampment alongside the tracks. How long he'd been there, no one could say. Sanitation workers found him one morning after a night of heavy snow. With his eyes hidden behind the frosted glass of his Wellsworth spectacles, his arms rigid on the rests of an old chair, he gave the appearance that he would never move again. One of the workmen reached out and poked the figure, producing from him a sharp inhalation. Startled by this unexpected evidence of life, the men lurched backward, tripping over the gravel ballast, and falling into a heap, one on top of the other.

The stranger, obviously alive, said nothing. He didn't need to speak. He presided over the workmen like a judge, giving them the impression that within the span of a few seconds they had been found guilty and just as promptly pardoned, leaving them forever beholden to the stranger for their freedom.

Once on their feet again, they took turns asking the stranger questions. Who was he? Where was he from? Had he been left behind when the police cleared a band of vagrants from the area in December? The stranger refused to explain himself, though he did not resist when the sanitation workers picked him up by his elbows. Stiff as a mannequin, he let them carry him the few hundred yards to their truck. He made no complaint as the men fussed over him, lifting him into the passenger seat, draping him in a blanket, blasting the heat in the cab, and setting out in the direction of the hospital.

Once his spectacles had thawed, the pale green of his eyes glistened like well water reflecting the noon sun. The black cashmere of his ragged coat—Italian made, we would learn from its label, with fine flannel fabric for the pocket bags—gave off the scent of damp fur. Between the satin of the lapels peeked a red bow tie, neatly knotted.

At the hospital he was undressed and clothed in a gown, poked

8

with needles, infused with saline, and then added to the duties of the financial counselor, who, failing to extract any useful information from him, not even his legal name, was pleased to learn from a nurse about the existence of a wallet.

The wallet, discovered in the inside pocket of his coat, was of a vintage metal kind. Inside were more than enough large bills to cover the patient's hospital expenses. General care for the patient was ramped up. The attending physician called in specialists, and a neurologist diagnosed Wernicke-Korsakoff's Syndrome due to excessive alcohol consumption—this despite the fact that no trace of alcohol showed up in his blood tests.

I was assigned to his case after the patient had been transferred to the rehabilitation facility and installed in a room of his own. It was determined that he did not match the description in any active Missing Person report. A short article about him ran in the local newspaper, but no family came forward to claim him. As far as we knew, he had no family. We assumed that he was alone and had fallen on hard times. My job was to assess his resources and needs, and place him in a permanent residence.

When I first saw him he was standing by the window. His room looked out on the frozen lake. At a later time, he would call my attention to the view, noting that between the thin ceiling of clouds and the snow-covered ice, there was no differentiation. With the added tangle of leafless branches on shore, I was reminded of a painting I'd once seen—I don't remember the artist—of penciled lines scrawled on a white canvas.

He was clean-shaven, with a head of silky white hair cut in a side-sweep style. His suit, in a dark Scotch-plaid pattern, looked like it was made to fit a much larger man. There was a yellow stain above the top button of the jacket. I noticed that the leather of one loafer had cracked open at the toe. I was surprised he hadn't suffered from frostbite.

He had his coat folded neatly over his forearm, as if he were preparing to leave. He announced in a voice that was surprisingly strong, given his emaciated condition, that he had been waiting for me. I explained that we weren't going anywhere and asked if I might hang up his coat. He used the word "cordially" when he accepted my offer.

I surmised from his bearing and polite manners that he was far more cognizant than the report had conveyed. I began to suspect that his amnesia was, at least in some part, feigned. My approach changed within a few minutes of conversing with him. I saw that earning his trust would be a delicate process requiring patience. He was an educated man with a philosophical disposition; at first he preferred to discuss anything other than himself. He wanted to know what I thought about Facebook and electric cars. He asked if I had ever been to Disney World (yes), and whether I was married (no). He was interested to hear about any books I'd read that had a lasting effect on me. His interrogation of me continued through several meetings. In this way, Guy Fraiser prepared me for his own story: only after I had nothing left to tell was I ready to listen.

Over a cup of tea, he admitted that Guy Fraiser was a pseudonym. He wouldn't reveal his real name. He kept other secrets, more minor, such as his current age, and the name of the village where he was born. He insisted that these things weren't important.

His family raised goats and manufactured a crumbly cheese that was famous in the region; it was Guy's chore to gather the stinging nettles that his mother would boil down to make the rennet. He described how he liked to climb into the mountains to search for the nettles. One day, he climbed up to a narrow shelf below a limestone outcrop where he had never been before. A mound of soft aeolian sand offered him a tempting place to rest and take in the view of the distant sea, and he had begun to level a seat for himself when the sand gave way beneath his hand, creating an opening to a hollow interior. He dug at the hole and soon was peering into a cave so deep that he couldn't see to its end.

He went home and returned the next day with a lantern and two friends from the village. The girl, Pilar, and the boy, Matteo, were siblings and belonged to a large extended family that had made pottery for generations. Guy secretly hoped to marry Pilar, and so he put up with her older brother, though Matteo was known for his bad temper and the body odor that wouldn't wash off, no matter how much soap his mother used on him.

Though it's not exactly relevant, I don't want to leave out anything Guy told me, so I will mention, as he did, that though he had known Pilar all his life, he first realized she was beautiful when he saw her standing in the village square, holding the hand of her little cousin. The two girls had stopped to watch a traveling musician play his accordion. Pilar's hair was pulled back in a single braid; she wore loose trousers colored a blue that matched the sky, and a cotton blouse, white and frothy like a cloud; her cousin wore a polka-dot dress. Both girls wore patent-leather buckle shoes without socks. They stood facing the musician, listening intently as he squeezed the bellows of his instrument. Guy, who was just eight then, watched Pilar from the side and knew he would love her forever.

When, four years later, he convinced Pilar to accompany him to explore the cave, she invited her brother Matteo to come along. Matteo carried the pole of a broken broom to use against any bats that dared to swoop too close to them, and to smash the scorpions he predicted would be nesting in the crevices.

Matteo was a bully and a jughead, and Guy couldn't hide his resentment when the boy proved right about the scorpions. The children saw them glistening red against the brown of sand and dust, their pincers waving, just inside the entrance. Guy tried to convince Pilar to continue past them, but she wouldn't budge, not until Matteo took charge. He attacked with his broom, grinding the end of the pole against the nest. When he was done, the scorpions had been smashed to confetti.

The children pressed forward—Guy first, carrying the lantern, then Pilar, then Matteo. The dome of the cave gave them ample room, enough to stand at their full height, except where clusters of waxen stalactites hung low. The steady drip-drop of seepage echoed through the hollow space. In the rear of the cave, they saw evidence that other people had been there before them. Pilar found a piece of hammered metal that looked like a spearhead with the sharp tip broken off. Guy found a short length of rope that turned out to be made of leather.

They had grown up hearing legends about pirates who had buried treasures in caves and never returned; their three young hearts pounded hard at the thought that they would find a chest full of gold. They kicked and scraped at the floor, but the limestone was hard beneath the crusted sand. Disappointment replaced hopefulness as their efforts resulted in nothing but bloody knuckles and bruised toes. What good was a cave if it didn't contain gold! Matteo swung the broomstick, knocking Guy hard on the knee—on purpose, Guy was sure, though Matteo claimed it was an accident. Guy held back his tears so as not to reveal himself to be a weakling in front of Pilar. Matteo's fury grew, his greed insatiable. He banged the broom against the wall, releasing a loud stream of crumbling stone. Guy thought the cave was collapsing around them, and he threw his arms around Pilar to protect her. His lips touched the back of her soft neck. Even as he cursed himself for putting his beloved in danger, he believed he would die happy if he died right there, with Pilar in his arms.

She wasn't ready to die and pushed him away. The limestone stayed intact above them, and Matteo, who gave off a stink of rotten eggs, howled with laughter at Guy's fearfulness. Guy was pleased when Pilar told her older brother to shut up, and then he was broken-hearted when she said she wanted to leave that stupid cave and never return.

Guy lifted the lantern, preparing to light the way back toward the entrance. But then, behind a cloud of settling dust, he saw a new hole in the cave wall, opening to a separate space. He held the lantern closer to the hole and caught sight of a smear of rosy color on the slanting surface of an interior wall: a secret room—the perfect place for pirates to leave their treasure! He let Pilar hold the lantern so she could see for herself. Matteo pushed in front of her and began clawing at the hole, Guy joined him, and soon they had an entrance wide enough for the three children to squeeze through one after another.

The chamber where they found themselves had a vaguely rectangular shape, with vertical walls slanting to a peak. The low ceiling was free of stalactites, the floor as smooth as polished marble. In the light from the lantern, the ocher color Guy had seen through the aperture slowly gained definition, revealing identifiable shapes. Circles became eyes, the joint in the stone formed a nose. Lines connected over a boss of rock into the hulking body of a bull. On the wall ahead of the bull were forms stained red, shaded with chalky white and yellow, with lyre-shaped horns, their legs tapering to delicate black hooves; in these shapes the children recognized a herd of ibex. Overhead, wings with apricot-colored rosettes belonged to a bird in flight, with a snake held in its beak.

There must have been fifty or more figures painted on the walls, preserved in the deep chamber from the destruction of time. Some of the animals bore scratched symbols on their hindquarters—a form of ancient writing, Guy believed. What was the story they were telling? How much he would have given to know.

I slowly came to understand that this was the great book Guy Fraiser had wanted to tell me about, a limestone book made of symbols and illustrations that were impossible to decipher with any certainty, yet were rich with infinite meaning.

The children's awed silence gave way to cries of astonishment. Even brutish Matteo appreciated the import of their discovery. They felt themselves to be in the presence of something more sacred than the saint's tooth encased in a gold reliquary in the village church.

These ancient pictures were older than any saint. They were as old as Adam and Eve. Maybe they had been made by Adam and Eve themselves, and they told the story of paradise! The children had found their treasure, all right, and they wanted the world to know. They took their amazement out of the decorated chamber, out through the long passage of the cave into the open air, where they whistled and hooted with the news of their discovery as they scrambled down the slope.

"It is never enough," said Guy, sipping the tea that had grown lukewarm while he was talking, "to experience the magnificence of a beautiful thing that has been lovingly made. We must share the experience. We must cry out with joy, sound the bell, invite our friends to see what we saw and feel what we felt. Delight matters little until it is communicated."

I was picturing the illustrations Guy had described, imagining myself in his place, feeling the thrill he had felt. I was increasingly hopeful that I could persuade him to tell me where the cave was located so I could visit it myself one day. I was dismayed when he reached for his coat and announced that he had a train to catch. Where he intended to go next, he would not say.

He asked me to call him a taxi, and while we were waiting he finished his story in some haste. He explained that after he and Pilar and Matteo had roused the drowsy villagers from their siesta with their shouting, a crowd of dozens made their way back to the cave. Everybody who saw the drawings was appropriately impressed. Soon word of the discovery spread across the region. The local authorities set up a booth and began charging an entrance fee. Archaeologists came to investigate and published papers arguing about the age of the paintings. Claims were made regarding the ownership of the cave, graft was exchanged, and magistrates were accused of corruption.

Then the war broke out, and no one cared anymore about primitive paintings on the walls of a cave. At the age of just sixteen, Guy joined the Resistance and was charged with the task of carrying messages across the border. He went into hiding when he learned the Germans were looking for him.

"For two years," he said, gazing past me toward the window, "I traveled from town to town disguised as a girl and protected by sympathetic families, who pretended I was their sister and daughter."

Just then an aide poked her head into the room and announced that the taxi had arrived. Guy slid his arms into the sleeves of his overcoat and adjusted his bow tie.

"There isn't much more to tell," he said as I accompanied him down the hall. For the first time, I detected a note of bitterness in his voice.

Only after he had been driven away in the taxi did it occur to me that he was spending his remaining years traveling around the world and repeating the same story over and over, as if by telling he could revive what had been lost, a quixotic effort he must always have known would fail.

This is how his story ends:

When he finally returned home, he found his village in ruins. The streets were deserted except for an old man idly poking at the rubble with a pitchfork. Guy recognized him as the village schoolteacher. The teacher gladly accepted Guy's offer to drink from his canteen. After gulping what was left of the water, he stared into the distance with the blank expression of the shell-shocked. It took lengthy coaxing to get him to explain what had happened, but finally Guy learned from him that the teacher had survived only because he had been enlisted by the Allies to serve as a translator, and so he was far away when the Germans arrived. The villagers took refuge in the cave Guy had discovered, a cave so famous by then that even the Germans knew of its existence. It was easy enough for them to guess where the villagers were hiding, and before retreating north ahead of the Allies, the German soldiers lined the entrance with powerful explosives. The whole side of the mountain collapsed from the force of the blast.

The Kite Room
Andrew Mossin

Let the stars of the twilight thereof be dark,
let it look for light but have none.

—Job 3:9

ON A SWELTERING AUGUST MORNING in 1967, my father took me to live with a family who ran a small boarding school on a property known as Wild Goose Farm in Shepherdstown, West Virginia. I was eleven years old; had been transferred from one public school to another within the DC school district where we lived; had spent six months of the previous year in foster care with a family who lived in a row home on Porter Street, a few blocks from my house; and had been caught three times for stealing toy cars and fountain pens from the G. C. Murphy on Wisconsin Avenue. After that happened, my mother told me the next time I'd be sent to Junior Village, a youth detention center in the Shaw neighborhood of DC. There was talk at first of a boarding school on the Chesapeake, then possible relocation to another foster family for a time, until finally Wild Goose Farm ended up being the alternative. After much searching and debate between my parents, my mother found an ad in the *Washington Post* for a boarding school in West Virginia. She showed me the ad one day in the spring and I didn't think much of it, just stared at it until my mother took it away from me and put it back in the drawer of the escritoire. A few weeks later, my father told me that we would be visiting the farm in June, just to see. He said it might be necessary to give my mother some rest for her "bad nerves."

Mother, a former British journalist who'd come to the United States with my father, a Polish refugee, from England after World War II, had named me Edward partly because it was my father's middle name and partly because it sounded a bit like Shakespeare's Edmund from *King Lear*. I never liked the name, but allowed that, for my mother, it was her way of connecting me to my father, both of us at once needed and unwanted by her. My mother would often quote me the famous lines from *Lear*, "My father compounded with my mother under the dragon's tail, and my nativity was under Ursa Major; so

15

that it follows I am rough and lecherous," and would say to me it was fitting, given my own uncertain origins as an adopted son. I heard different stories from each of my parents about who my "real" parents were; sometimes that they were survivors of the Holocaust who'd given me up for adoption so that I'd be raised by non-Jewish parents, sometimes that my biological mother was an itinerant Gypsy who had been living in poor conditions in a small town in Hungary after the war and had no way to raise me on her own. Whatever the truth may have been, I held on to the talismanic figure of Edmund, as if he were always watching over me, watching out *for* me, the names twinned in my mind, reversible, changing places with each other: Edmund and Edward, Edward and Edmund. I climbed into bed some nights saying the names together and apart, the one I was and the one I wasn't, moving back and forth in a line until they formed one sentence, one person, a kind of unity that might protect me.

My father suggested we visit before committing to the farm, so on a Saturday in June we made the drive from Washington to Shepherds-town. I later learned that Wild Goose Farm had been constructed in the 1830s as a plantation house with a row of icehouses in the back and two buildings for curing meat, all of them built by West Virginia stonemasons more than a quarter century before the beginning of the Civil War. The farm had been designed by Richard Shepherd, the grandson of William Shepherd, the founder of Shepherdstown. As described by F. Vernon Aler, who wrote a book on the history of Berkeley County, West Virginia, and visited Wild Goose Farm in the 1880s, the property proposed a space of distinct, pastoral innocence and gentry-like charm: "Passing up a long avenue of well-grown and carefully selected forest trees—beech, linden, maple, and others—we approach the mansion. Here on a knoll, embowered 'mid a profusion of waving willows, stately poplars, and quaking aspens, stands the residence, built in a quadrangular shape, with two extended wings— a pretentious frame structure of a comparatively modern architec-ture. . . . We enter through a Gothic porch, a spacious hall, leading to the parlors, which are simply but richly furnished—skillfully reflect-ing mirrors and choice paintings adding to the pleasing effect."

The property we first saw that day hardly resembled Aler's descrip-tion, though a few geese could still be spotted roaming near the pond in front of the main house and two horses paced together in the pasture that could be seen from the front porch of the house. The house itself had fallen into disrepair over the years, the front balcony showing its age, a few of the front railings missing and the paint on the wood-paneled siding having splintered so that it was brittle to the touch and came off in my hands when I pulled off a piece as we were walking alongside the east-facing portion of the house. Even the paving shale that led up to the main entryway had chipped, each one having cracked into two or three separate pieces that rested like small gray islands in the moist soil.

Yet the farm, for all its broken-down aspect, still had a strangely compelling quality in the late spring light as my father and I walked around the property for a few hours and spoke to Mr. and Mrs. Ross, who were caretakers of the farm for the Capertons, the family who had owned Wild Goose since the 1940s. Most of the other boys had already left for the summer break at that point, though we were introduced to the Rosses' sons, Phillip and Robby, and an older boy, Jordan, who had been sitting on a tractor by himself as we walked across the front yard past the pond.

"Why don't you come over and meet our guests?" Mrs. Ross called out to Jordan. I watched as he got down from the tractor and climbed over the fence and made his way over to us. He was tall with a military-style crew cut, dungarees, a stained T-shirt, and shoes that looked like they didn't fit.

"Nice to meet you," he said, glancing sideways, and held out his hand to my father first, who shook it awkwardly, then to me. His palm was rough over mine and he had a small scar just above his ring finger that he later told me came from baling wire.

"Edward's coming to stay with us in the fall," Mrs. Ross said.

Jordan looked over at the tractor and played with a piece of wood about the length of his hand. "That's nice," he said, then to Mrs. Ross, "Ma'am, I'd like to go back to work, if you don't mind," and she shrugged and said, "As you will, but don't forget we're having supper early tonight," and Jordan nodded toward my father and me and walked back toward the pasture and climbed over the fence and made his way through the hay bales that had already been piled up in one corner of the field.

As my father and I roamed the property that day, I remember feeling some odd kinship with the place, as if it proposed an alternative home space to the one I would be leaving. And at the same time, walking past the chicken coops and horse stalls, I somehow understood as I hadn't before what my mother meant when she had told me one afternoon that I'd be living on a farm in West Virginia for a while to learn "what hard work really looks like." When was I coming back? My mother looked off that day and didn't offer anything conclusive. "Just a few months, maybe longer," she'd said, her hands resting on a tea towel in the kitchen while the clock above showed it to be 3:32, the only time the clock had shown for months since neither my mother nor father knew how to fix the electrical wire that had come loose and now dangled off to one side.

We left to drive back to Washington late that afternoon and my father said, "It seems good, don't you think so?" and I looked out into the still bright June day as we passed a truck stop selling beer and cigarettes for seventy-five cents a pack and said, "Yeah, I guess." My father and I didn't speak for much of the rest of the car ride home. When we got back it was past dinnertime and the house was quiet and I went up to bed without supper, while downstairs I heard my father banging a pot on the stove as he prepared his dinner of frankfurters and beans.

By the time I returned to Wild Goose Farm in August, there would be seven of us, all boys: two, Phillip and Robby, the sons of Mr. and Mrs. Ross; Jordan, whom I'd met; and the other three from families living in Washington, Virginia, Maryland. I was given to understand that the reason we were at the farm in the first place was that we were all "troubled" in one way or another. It was mostly a quietly received understanding we shared with one another, as if we'd been brought together for this one purpose, to become somehow other than what we were: a group of boys whose families couldn't or wouldn't keep us anymore. *Here's the only place you've got, it's home, like it or not.* I don't know if I viewed this period as punishment or welcome escape from the home I shared with my parents. Probably a little of both. It was as if my mother were saying to me, *You are living on borrowed time, you have only so many more chances to prove yourself worthy of our love before we give you up altogether and that will be the end of what we have to give, the end of our love.* At least that's what I heard in my head, her voice softly accusatory and oddly comforting at the same time.

In my recollection of those days it's the shades of blue and green that come to me most often. The wind moving through the open balcony window of the Rosses' bedroom and the smell of eggs, bacon, and grits that permeated the entire house each morning. In the afternoons after school (we were taught by a thirtyish teacher who showed up to work each morning in a bow tie and neatly pressed slacks and whose favorite book was Thor Heyerdahl's *Kon-Tiki*), I rode down the mile-long driveway on the post office bike I'd been given, then back up to the area on the side of the house where Mr. and Mrs. Ross parked their cars. I would ride in a circle, counterclockwise, clockwise, counterclockwise, clockwise, steering nowhere, moving in one direction, then another, and as I rode I'd hear the hens in the chicken coop and Joe, the Rosses' black cook, calling out to us to come in for supper, and then the squalling cries of geese that ran loose on the property.

Parked in the carriage house was a 1958 Chevrolet pickup truck that had once been Mr. Ross's working vehicle on the farm. The doors had been removed and the tires had long since rotted out on the rusted rims of the wheels. Some late afternoons and evenings after dinner, I'd climb in and pretend to drive, imagining the route I'd take past Martinsburg into the mountains and the counties to the west and north of us. The seat's nylon cover was torn away, revealing foam and springs, so that they scratched against my bare legs as I sat with my left leg barely reaching the gas pedal and clutch, and when I pulled the gearshift down on the steering column it made a wet popping sound that cracked in the still air of the carriage house. Mr. Ross used to say to me the truck had traveled more than two hundred thousand miles in its day, had been able to drive through any kind of weather so that he swore it possessed near-mythical powers, and I believed he was telling me the truth. Sitting in its cab, the eastern pasture visible in the dip through the chestnut and maple trees that lined the stone wall surrounding the front of the house, I'd read from the tattered copy of the New Testament I'd stolen from the Ross family library downstairs off the main dining room. Sometimes I'd read from the same parts my mother had once read to me, Corinthians or Romans, more often from the Gospels, and I would read silently to myself, the words passing my lips in silent syllables, near soundless, so that movement of my body came near to its accidental center, as if I could watch myself inside the cab and hear the sun moving past us and get creation's draw all over again through the liberties of this ghost language that filled the cab. "Truly, truly, I tell you, if one is not born from above, he cannot see the Kingdom of God. Nicodemus said to him: How can a man be born when he is old? Surely he cannot enter his mother's womb a second time and be born? Jesus answered: Truly, truly, I tell you, if one is not born from

19

water and spirit, he cannot enter the Kingdom of God. What is born from the flesh is flesh, and what is born from the spirit is spirit. Do not wonder because I told you: You must be born from above." Looking out from the cab of the truck, the day passing into blue dusk, I'd sit with the pages of the book open on my lap, and there'd be the barking of one of the stray dogs the Rosses had rescued, followed by the bleating of one of the two goats kept on the farm, and as the morning doves sang from the trees just beyond the carriage-house walls I'd notice that a kitten from the new litter had wandered under the porch of the house and not far distant from where it went, the porch lights would come on and the roses on the trellis near the eastern part of the house would turn black inside the outlines of fading light.

When I stopped reading, I'd often observe the low-flying bats whooshing past in the tranquil light of early dusk and then the cascading rip of voices from inside the house and dinner being made and Mrs. Ross standing on the porch like my own mother in a blue-gray dress and cheap pearl necklace and her demeanor would be that of some vigilant matron and she'd stand the minutes it took to see through the failing light that I was still sitting in the cab of the vehicle and would call out to me then to come in. And sometimes I would and sometimes I wouldn't, preferring the solitude of the abandoned truck to what was awaiting me inside, and would continue reading from the text that lay in my lap like a soft bundle of wet fabric. "This is the judgment, because the light came into the world and people loved the darkness more than the light because their actions were wicked. For everyone who does bad things hates the light, lest his actions be discovered; but he who accomplishes the truth comes toward the light, so that it may be made clear that his actions were with God." When I closed the book and made my way up to the house, I could feel a low breeze against my legs and arms, like cool water spreading over my body, and Mrs. Ross had already turned to go back inside and behind me the pasture fell away from view into the late shadows of evening.

One night after dinner I wandered down to the library on the first floor at the front of the house, something that was forbidden to all of us, except for the Rosses' two sons. As I entered the room, the light was coming in from the gallery windows that fronted the portico and there was this smell of old leather and tobacco and wood smoke. On the shelves of the ceiling-to-floor bookcases were a set of *Chambers's Encyclopaedia* with the date 1874 stamped on each volume's leather spine, naturalist histories of the Shenandoah Valley, several books on local flora, and leather-bound editions of Dickens, Thackeray, James Fenimore Cooper, and other writers I'd never heard of. Situated between the gallery windows was Mr. Ross's desk, a large oak affair that looked like something a wealthy lawyer might own. I sat down in Mr. Ross's leather chair, from which he'd greeted all the new boys one morning, indicating that we were here for hard work and the kind of book learning that we hadn't yet had but would grow to appreciate. I slid open each drawer and viewed their contents of chewing-tobacco containers and old coins and stamps and fingered a few of the coins, some of which had dates on them from just after the Civil War. In the bottom drawer, I found a wood-handled hunting knife with the initials J.L.R. carved into the handle. I opened the knife so that the silver blade shone in the light coming in through the windows, then closed the blade and shoved the knife into my pants and went back upstairs to the room where we all slept and stuck the knife in the bottom drawer of my dresser.

The next day Mrs. Ross came around as we sat in the playroom adjoining the kitchen and asked if any of us had something to tell her. No one said anything, until finally Jordan asked her why she was asking. Mrs. Ross turned her gaze over in my direction, then back to Jordan and the others, and said, "Something's missing from John's library desk, and he wants to know who's responsible." The five o'clock chimes of the clock in the hall went off as we looked around at each other and Mrs. Ross took a notepad out from her pocketbook and said, "Here, if one of you knows something you can write it down and leave it on the table."

A few days later Phillip was in our room going through everyone's things and brought out the knife from the bottom of my drawer.

"Where'd you get this?" he said.

"I don't know. I've never seen it before," I said.

"You're a liar. A liar and a thief."

"No, I'm not. I don't know how it got there."

"I expect my mom will have some answers for you when she sees this," Phillip said and went downstairs to find Mrs. Ross.

She never did come up and later that evening before dinner I went outside and it was like darkness but not, and I rummaged in my bag for a piece of licorice and went down to the stone wall separating the western and eastern pastures, and looked over to the barn where I'd

21

once found the sloughed-off skin of a rattlesnake. I listened for the other boys and Joe, but no one was around. I walked slowly back up to the house and looked through the window and saw everyone assembled around the table for dinner, and Jordan caught a glimpse of me through the window and smiled back and then put a forkful of food into his mouth. When I came in, Phillip and a couple of the other boys snickered and made the gesture of a knife passing across a throat and then it all got silent again when Mrs. Ross came in from the kitchen and Joe behind her said, "The boy need a plate?" She motioned for him to take the plate into the other room, where she had me sit down as Joe brought a plate of food in for me, lima beans and minute steak and a side of applesauce, and I heard the sharp quiet of the boys in the other room while I sat and ate by myself.

After dinner as we were getting ready for bed, Mrs. Ross came up with a set of sheets, pillow, and blanket and said, "You'll be sleeping upstairs on the third floor for a while," and I looked at her and said, "For how long?" and she said, "For as long as I say, until you accept responsibility for what you did."

I took the linens in my arms, walked out of the room, and saw Jordan as I passed him in the hall. He gave me a look that said he was sorry but he couldn't do anything for me. When I got to the third floor, I threw the sheets and pillow and blanket on the floor, flopped on top of them, and listened to the TV going in the Rosses' bedroom downstairs. The third-floor rooms were mostly empty now except for a few old steel spring mattress beds set against the walls and some metal bureaus that were pushed against the corners of each room. The low ceiling of the middle bedroom came down in odd fashion so that you couldn't fully stand up in some parts of it but had to bow down, careful not to bump your head. When you looked out of the windows, what you saw was the lay of the land as my mother used to say, you could see all the way across the farm's pond to the barn and the fields beyond, and out past them I knew that there was a train that came early in the mornings, because Mr. Ross caught it from Martinsburg to work in Washington each day and came back on it each night.

One of the dogs was barking in the yard, and I saw the stars through the windowpane that had been handblown at the end of the nineteenth century so that everything appeared as if curving away from you, as though you were looking through a prism and the light was reflected back to you from objects that no longer held their place in the world.

*

After I was sent to the third floor, the other boys understood and acted accordingly. One afternoon I went down to the icehouses and Phillip and his brother, Robby, followed me along with two of the other boys, Charley and William, lanky kids who'd come to the farm from Hagerstown, Maryland, and Alexandria, Virginia, respectively, and who generally kept a low profile through the days we were together. When they caught up with me, Phillip said, "You'd like it if we left you alone, wouldn't you?"

"Yes, I would," I said.

Phillip took one of my arms and Robby the other, while Charley and William stood nearby, neither one wanting to get involved but not moving away either, as Phillip and Robby pushed me down onto the ground.

"Do you admit you took the knife?" Phillip asked.

"I never took anything."

Robby spat at me, and his spit felt hot on my cheek.

Phillip twisted my right arm behind my back and said, "You sure? You really sure?"

I shook my head and felt tears coming down my face, and Phillip pushed his knee into my back and said, "You can steal other people's stuff and cry about it? You've been takin' stuff from everybody: me, Robby, even Jordan."

I could see Jordan, standing just a bit farther out from the group, and his arms were at his side and his eyes were nearly shut, it looked like, from the sun or just because he couldn't look.

And it was as if I were already dead, already underneath the ground, as one then another would come to dig me out. Only it wasn't a digging out but more like a burial, so that I felt like all their hands together were laying my body down in the earth covered in chicken shit and goat dung, and Phillip pushed my face into it again and again, until I stopped moving and his brother said, "Let's go, he's got nothin'." Jordan stood there without saying anything but starting to move away from the other boys, like he knew there was nothing he could do but was doing it by standing there. I caught his gaze, then turned back to face the inside of the icehouse, where years ago, I'd been told by Robby, a kid had hung himself from one of the beams, though who the boy was and when this happened or if the story was anything more than apocryphal I couldn't have said.

When I came back to the house I passed Joe on the way up the stairs to the third floor, and he looked at me and said, "Son, what you get yourself into?" and I said, "Nothing, I just fell." He watched as I went up the stairs and said, "Dinner's in an hour. You best clean yourself up." When I went into the bathroom, I saw that my shirt had been torn, the new one my mother had sent from a new department store in Washington, and my face was smeared with chicken feathers and dung.

I was looking for a protector, someone to look after me. It seemed the days fell dark, black light, shallow light, down to the doorframes, and I'd be caught after dinner staring into the yard and Joe would come out and say to me, "You not in bed yet? You get on inside before Mrs. Ross comes out," and I'd look off and his hand would gently nudge my body toward the stairs at the back of the house and I'd go up the back stairs to the third floor of the house, which is where the family that once owned the house in the 1930s had kept their children at night. There were owls in the trees you could listen to all night long and in the daylight breaking over the farm there was mist rising from the pond and the hollowed-out frame of the carriage house where I went each evening after dinner. But there was no one there and when I looked down and heard the voices coming back up in the darkness, those of Mrs. Ross's or one of the other boys, it was like a journey was being taken without me and what I meant to know, what I needed to know, was where I fit, what I could do to be part of some family.

Even as I was kept apart from the other boys and rarely permitted to spend time with them beyond class and mealtimes, Jordan was becoming like an older brother to me. He had turned fifteen that summer, his face girl-like and pale as I remember it, his skin fairer than mine, his cheek bearing a small scar under his left eye from a childhood injury. His hands were delicate boned, with a fineness that I associated with my mother's hands, and as he spoke they would move through the air as if to emphasize a point he was making. Often, I'd notice the tapered paleness of his fingers, which always seemed to be working with a piece of rope or string or whittling small bits of wood with his hunting knife, as he had started teaching me to make kites from balsa strips and colored tissue paper and string in one of the empty rooms on the third floor near where I slept. He called it the kite room, had been coming there since his first days at the farm, had made it a workroom for building his kites, though no one else referred to it that way. During one of my first nights on the third floor, I'd found Jordan at work on one of his kites and when I came into the room, he looked over at me and said, "How you holding up, kid?" and I said, "Best as I can," and he said, "Yeah, that's probably right," and turned back to his kite. I sat and watched him for awhile and asked him how long it took to make a kite.

"Depends," he said.

"On what?"

"Depends on the kind. Regular triangle kite you can finish in an afternoon. Box kites take longer, need more time to get all the parts to fit the way they need to."

I came over and watched him working for a bit longer before he turned and said, "You're not going to take anything, are you?" and I said, "Why would I do that?"

"Just be sure you don't," he said.

I looked out the window, then back toward Jordan, and said, "I wouldn't do that," and he clipped a piece of nylon from a length of balsa.

"No, I don't think you would," he said.

Not long after, Jordan started spending more time in the kite room, and I'd come up to find him already at work. "Here," he'd begin, "you cut the strips of wood with this," handing me a small saw, "and like this you trim the strips as you need. Then you put the glue on each end and attach them, forming a T," and he would direct my hands with his, so that we were making the T of the crossbar together. "After you've done that," his left hand directing my hand into place over the crossbeam, "you apply some more glue onto the strips like this," tracing with his index finger a seam of white glue down the balsa strip, "and you fold the paper over the edges like this, making sure to cover the area between top and bottom of the T with the tissue, careful that you don't tear it while gluing it into place." His hands and mine would smell of glue afterward, and we'd wash together in the bathroom and return to the room to look over our work.

There wouldn't be words between us most days, not really, we didn't seem to need to say much to one another, and sometimes he'd come over to me and put his arm around me and once he bent his body into mine and kissed me on the lips so that I tasted licorice and tobacco after and I didn't move one way or the other, just watched his hand move through the light like a small diaphanous fan, ribbed and smooth at the same time. Over a series of afternoons, he'd told me about his life before he came to the farm. He'd grown up in Annville, Pennsylvania, a small town in Lebanon County. He could barely remember his father, Ray, who was gone by the time Jordan turned four, though Jordan was told by his mother, Leanne, that Ray had once been a math teacher at the local high school, and every year on the holidays and for Jordan's birthday there would be a card from him, sometimes with money inside, sometimes not. Jordan and his mother lived together in a four-room house down a street of other sloping attached homes built around the turn of the century. Leanne worked as a bartender at a restaurant in town and sometimes played music in the area on the weekends with friends from high school who'd remained, working part-time jobs and living in apartment shares or with their folks. Jordan said he wasn't sure who the men were who came back to the house sometimes, a few who stayed as long as several months, some less than a week. Eventually he understood that his mother would just live this life until she didn't anymore. Some days she wouldn't get out of bed until he'd returned from school and he'd go upstairs to find her smoking and reading the paper and he'd get in bed with her with his school clothes still on and sometimes they'd fall asleep together like that, neither one of them waking until it was well past ten. She'd ask, "You hungry?" and sometimes they'd go down to the kitchen and make something to eat and sometimes they'd just remain in bed and she'd light a cigarette and pick up a book from the floor and continue reading while he fell back asleep next to her.

Those were the ways they lived, Jordan said, nothing much else to it. He went to school, came home, watched TV in the living room until Leanne returned from work or sometimes didn't, went to bed when he felt tired, woke up when it was still dark, went to check in on his mother. Sometimes she was there, sometimes not. One night she came back with a man she'd met at work, Dan, a contractor who worked over in the Harrisburg area. Dan wasn't sure what to make of Jordan, a kid who didn't play sports, didn't seem to like girls or go out much, just wanted to be left alone in his room. In the summer Jordan turned fourteen, Dan moved in and it was a short time after that that he and Leanne announced to him one day they'd found a school in West Virginia for him, a place he'd learn to do the things necessary for him to grow up into the kind of man he needed to become. "You understand," his mother had said to him, "you'll learn things, be with boys your own age, it'll be better for you." Dan didn't say much, played with a socket wrench he'd brought in from his truck, finally offered that what his mother meant was he needed to be in a place where he could learn the kind of things young guys learned. Dan's voice trailed off, while Leanne stood by the sink washing plates from dinner, and Jordan nodded, said it was OK, he got it, and his mother wiped her hands dry and came over to him and took his hands in hers and pulled them to her chest and said, "There's nothing I wouldn't do for you, you know that, right?" Jordan said, Yeah, he understood.

He went back down the hall to his room, where his things were already laid out on the bed for him to pack, it was that fast a turn, and he didn't go back out into the living room until he'd filled his old army surplus rucksack with everything he was going to take, and when it was full he sat on the bed and looked back out the window where the light was orange and crimson now, failing in gentle bands down the sides of the houses across the street.

The next day, a Sunday, the three of them made the two-and-a-half-hour drive south down 81 through Chambersburg and Waynesboro through Hagerstown to Shepherdstown and Jordan said that when they crossed the West Virginia state line he'd started to tear up and Leanne reached back from the front seat and said, You'll be OK, I promise, nothing bad's gonna happen to you, they're nice people, you'll like them, I promise. Jordan said it was hard light coming through the cab window at that hour and when they crossed the Potomac into Shepherdstown he saw the river shining all black on its surface and he felt his mother's hand go from his like rope being pulled through slick palms and began to hum to himself, softly, nothing he could recall but the sound hung between them as Dan glanced down at the map on the seat between them and his mother took a cigarette out and lit it and flicked it out the cab window after one puff.

He hadn't gone back, he said, hadn't seen his mom since he'd come to the farm a year ago, though he heard from her from time to time through letters she sent, occasionally some money tucked into the envelope, never much more than $10 but enough, he said, for kite-making materials and sometimes a pack of chewing tobacco. As far as he could tell, his mother was happy, settled with Dan, in her life in ways that made sense to her and had to make sense to Jordan, regardless of what he might otherwise have thought or wanted to believe.

I'd come up early one morning to fish with Jordan, left my room to walk down the pasture path out to where the creek bed was and the water stagnant and shallow, barely moving, and when Jordan saw me come through the trees he'd said, Don't be stupid, there aren't any fish to catch here, put your rod down. It was just after daybreak and no one else had come down and he said, "You should be careful if they find out."

"I don't care, let 'em," I said, and he shook his head but didn't say anything.

I was still catching my breath from running down to the creek and he said, "Doesn't matter, the fish are gone."

"Then why'd you come?"

"Because it's peaceful here."

"Yeah, that's true but why come out here when there aren't any fish?" He leaned over the creek bed like he was going to fall in and pulled his hand from his pocket and said, "It's easier, you know, if you don't think so much."

I didn't say anything but held onto my pole and let the lure float just above the surface and watched the nylon play out until the lure was downstream a ways. When I turned around Jordan had unrolled his bedding on the ground and was staring out over the creek.

I said, "What you doin'?"

"Lettin' the light do its thing," he said.

I took my rod and put it on the ground next to his and leaned over and he handed me a piece of bread and some cheese he'd brought with him and said, "It's all I've got but take some," and I said, "Thanks," and took the bread and a piece of cheese from his hand and saw the line of light come up across the horizon in one pink band, as I spotted a minnow moving inside the stream.

Jordan sat up and said, "Leave it go," and I watched it go silver and black over the stone surface as he took a knife out of his pocket and cut into the small block of cheese and passed me another piece.

"You see," he said, "there's this way we can connect to what isn't ours. It's all about seeing where you don't live yet, then coming to it and living there for awhile until you can say you're ready for anything that comes, you could die there and it would be OK. It's all about the way you let it let go from you and you go to it, so it's like you're underwater, and it's always going to be what you aren't that's most important, the part of you that isn't, that's what you listen for and move toward, that's how you know where you are in the world."

I was part of what wasn't, he said, and he trusted me for being that, for being that thing that wasn't expected or known and I knelt down and skimmed a rock off the water's surface so it broke across the surfaces in several places at once. I let the water slide off my wrist and when I took it out of the water it was slick from the creek and I let another rock go in one arc over the dead near silent creek bed and when I looked up I saw the empty space where Jordan had been waiting for me.

One afternoon after we finished building two new kites, his a yellow-and-orange box kite, mine a traditional diamond kite of red and white paper, we went to the window together and looked below to see Robby and Phillip Ross in the pasture, helping some of the other local boys from Shepherdstown bale hay, their white T-shirts moving above the hay bales like sails on a moving tide, and beyond them were the fields that led to the road we took to go into town. I was watching them disappear as I'd done countless afternoons before and remembering as I watched them how hard it had been at times to stay here, how many times I'd wanted to run away, not sure where I'd go, who would come find me, where I'd end up. And in that calmness, like someone who could see things going on and didn't need words, Jordan took my hands in his and patted then kissed one then the other, and I let him press them together. He said this was what good friends should do, they should show each other how they felt. It wasn't much, the touch of his hands on mine was warm and comfortable, like my mother's hands moving over mine in the cold so that she'd warm them with hers, saying, "Cold dannies" as she did so.

"How do you feel?" he said, and I looked over at our kites then into his green eyes, one of his lids lower than the other like my own low left lid, and I said, "You're my friend."

"That's right, I am," he said and he took me into his arms in a bear hug, then turned me slowly like I was being enfolded and encircled at the same time, and we seemed almost to fall together onto the floor, his body falling on top of mine. I saw a crease of light beneath the door that was shut now, then the folds of light from the window that was partly open so that a cool breeze came over me as Jordan laid me on the mattress. His hand slid under my belly and he undid my shorts and pulled them down around my ankles, and I could hear him behind me unzipping his pants and pulling them down too, and then he spread my legs apart and asked, "Is it OK?" and I watched the dust motes floating above my head from the sunlight coming through, and I said, "Don't make me wet," because I remembered reading about how boys had fluid that flowed out of them when they got excited and I didn't want that feeling down there. He pushed himself

29

into me and it hurt at first, then I let go and he was inside me, and there was the smell of cornflower all around me, and his hands held onto mine as he jerked forward and backward and as he moved on top of me I kept looking across the room where the light was now falling across the boards and saw a brass nail head that needed to be struck back into place. I felt something burn inside me and pulled away and Jordan held onto my torso for a moment then pulled away and when I turned over he was already putting his pants back on and had made his way to the other side of the mattress.

"Did I hurt you?" Jordan asked.

"No, it's OK," I said because I knew that he'd meant no harm, that what he'd done was something he viewed as a secret between us, a kind of bond we could share. He kissed me on the cheek when I sat up, and I turned away from him so that I was facing the window and saw that it was getting still and quiet outside as it always did on the farm this time of afternoon. And outside it was sort of a half light that fell over the landscape, and I saw myself in it and the room was filled with shadow and the sun was low across the trees, everything was going back to its settled place, and later I would go outside when everyone else was asleep and look up into the morning sky and watch the meteors come flying across the horizon like flares that wouldn't stop. I remembered the story of Cain and Abel I'd read in Sunday school and how short it was that they lived before Cain slew Abel in the field and the light was hard that day on Cain's back as his face was averted from God and he knelt down low to the earth and saw his brother's blood flow into the wet ground and the stars came high over his head and the light was complete when he saw what he'd done and heard that his crime would not go unpunished, he would be an exile for the rest of his days, never to cross homeward again.

Over the next several weeks, the kite room became a kind of sanctuary, an unreal space without borders or time or connection to the world below. Often, I went there by myself and waited for Jordan to come up and I'd sit with the kite-making materials and hear the doves in the eaves long past morning. I wasn't made yet; I wasn't an "I" yet. I felt more like something made of paper and string, like the kites Jordan and I made, I was exactly like the kites, able to fly above the house where I'd been left, above these rooms without walls, this space that occupied my senses but left my body incomplete. And once I recalled the words of Isaiah: "Wash yourselves and ye shall be clean; put away the wicked ways from your souls before Mine eyes; cease to do evil; learn to do well. Seek judgment, relieve the oppressed, consider the fatherless, and plead for the widow. Come then, and let us reason together, saith the Lord: Though your sins be as scarlet, I will make them white as snow; and though they be red like crimson, I will make them white as wool." And when I turned my body around, I knew that I was put here to wait. But for what?

One night followed the next in those days when I was still being kept apart from the other boys and left to spend nights by myself on the third floor, brought down for meals and lessons during the day, then sent back up. I heard the birds passing overhead, the sounds of a house that wasn't at rest but moving toward it as each day completed itself and a new one came to take its place. Resting on my bed through those long nights I listened for those who might come to get me, to take me back to wherever it was I belonged. From my bed, I stared off into the dark and the door that was left ajar and heard sometimes the passing overhead of a plane, then nothing. Downstairs was a world I didn't know and above me the heavens were marked by small points of light set back against a background of black fabric. And when I lay down again it could be nightfall or the morning after. The wind could be southerly or westerly, and above the door jamb was the insignia of a family who no longer lived here. When I went out onto the landing and smelled the light filled with the heaviness of bacon fat, I would trace the wall seam with my eyes down to the first staircase, then the second, watching myself as one visits another from across the room, watching myself descend then disappear into the darkness of the rooms above.

Drifting off to sleep then no sleep, I laid awake and said to myself, it's coming to an end, this is all coming to an end, and it seemed perfectly strange, strangely perfect, the world underneath, like a watery space that was always there, always ready to receive you, and there was this opening, like the crawl space underneath a house, where you could go and taste the earth in your mouth again and smell the food being cooked above you and the light that found you was this restorative kind that seemed almost to lie down with you, to keep your body and head still when you heard movement up above. And sometimes I'd imagine my parents' home in DC and drift back through its rooms as though each space was as familiar as the lines on my hand. But other times nothing felt familiar when I journeyed back and I'd lie awake counting back from a hundred and hear the birds in the trees and I'd remember the foster home I'd been sent to and the night

I'd told one of the foster kids staying there with me about death because I'd come to understand it, the way you went quiet and there was this darkness around you, this perfect enclosure outside of time or space. Erin was the girl's name and she was all of six years old at the time, I think, and I remembered coming up to her room one night after dinner and telling her good night and not to be afraid of the dark, it was a good place to stay with nothing to fear. Sitting on the bed beside her I could tell she was frightened, and I said, "It's like dying, you go to sleep and don't wake up, that's all."

She'd started to cry, "*No no no*" as I said these words and I tried to comfort her but her eyes welled up with tears and she screamed for her mother.

I heard her mother rush up the stairs and when she came into the room she saw Erin sobbing on the bed and threw me off the bed so that I fell hard against the wall.

"What did you do, what the hell did you do to her?" she said, as I sat on the floor against the wall and saw Erin's tear-streaked face across from me like I was suddenly staring at a coloring book from which all the pages had been torn out.

"Nothing, ma'am," I said, "I just tried to explain that we're all going to die, that's all," and her mother said, "That's not something you have the right to tell my daughter, Jesus, look at her," and I looked over at the wall and got up from the bed and walked into the room where I stayed and lay down while in the other room Erin's mother was comforting her saying you never have to worry baby you never have to think about such awful things they aren't going to happen ever you don't worry.

Jordan disappeared for a while, I don't know for how many days, but it seemed like a week, maybe more. It was late autumn by this point and the leaves were nearly gone from the trees and the white columns of the old plantation house had the appearance of rubbed marble in the light that came hard across the front most afternoons. Jordan had left or was taken away from the farm for reasons that I never learned. When he came back, it was late evening, and I saw him sitting by himself on the side of the house, in his lap a hunting rifle, and he was fingering the barrel when I came up and sat down next to him.

"Where'd you go?" I said.

"I've been around." Jordan looked over at me and smiled, but I wasn't sure.

"Around where?"

"Hereabouts."

"Yeah?"

"Yeah."

"You mad at me?"

Jordan shook his head and reached over to take my hand, and he said it was getting time for him to leave the Ross farm. He'd gotten word from his mom that Dan had moved out and she couldn't afford the school anymore. I said that was a shame. He didn't look over but kept his gaze steady on the few geese left on the farm, and he ran his hand through his hair a couple of times.

"Yeah, but it's OK," he said. "I knew this would happen. Maybe it will be better with me at home this time."

"It's like a gift you've got back again," I said. "You must be glad you have a mom who is there and needs you."

"Yeah, sure, but you . . ."

I cut him off and said, "It's not right now, but it will be one day." He just nodded.

Inside, it was near dinnertime, and Jordan played with the barrel of the gun while I looked over at the pond where a year before there'd been this light, like a spreading, soft core of yellow across the surface, and now there was a dull silver hue to the water, as if water and pond weren't the same thing, as if one transformed inside the other but wasn't the other.

We got up to go, and I followed Jordan down the path behind the carriage house that led back out to the fields of the southern pasture. As we walked, I followed the power lines with my eyes and heard our footsteps in the wet grass moving in unison.

The last time I would see Jordan he came up to the third floor after dinner, and he sat on the bed opposite mine.

"I don't want you ever to forget that I'm your brother, no matter what," he said.

It came to me as he sat there that I didn't know what a brother was, had never had one, even as Jordan had adopted me in the kite room like I belonged to him.

"We're both orphans, I guess," I said, "like we don't have a proper place in the world."

He laughed and said, "It's not so much about being orphans, it's more like a road trip. You get to one place and set up your stuff and

33

stay a little while and then it's time to move and do it all over again."

I thought what did it mean to have a brother in the world, my mother was my sister and friend, my father was my messenger and caregiver, I had no brother, no one to say I was theirs but those who said they were mine.

Jordan looked over at me when I didn't respond.

"What you need to realize is that, whatever else, there'll come a time when you and me will make sense," he said. "I never wanted it to be something you thought was wrong or bad."

"I know," I said. "I don't."

He glanced down at my hands.

"They've grown, they look more like a man's hands," he said.

I smiled and said, "I don't think so. They're still kids' hands, as far as I can tell."

I didn't even think they showed calluses yet from the farmwork we'd been doing through the fall, and part of me wished that they did.

Jordan pulled out a five-dollar bill.

"I bet you in a year you'll have a girlfriend," he said.

"I don't think so," I responded. "Have you ever had a girlfriend?"

"Not really, but I did some stuff with this girl once."

"Did you love her?"

He was silent, then said, "No, love wasn't part of it."

"I'm afraid I'll never find anyone," I said, "at least no one who stays."

He smiled and said, "It'll take time, for sure, but you've got plenty of that. You're all of, what, eleven, right?"

I laughed, and we both laughed a little.

Jordan took my hands in his and stroked them and came to sit beside me on the bed and passed his right palm through my hair and said, "Why don't we just lie down together?" He smelled like talcum powder and I noticed for the first time several razor-thin scars at the base of his wrist and I said OK and he smiled and said he just wanted to lie down for a bit this last time and when he put his arm around me I turned to face the wall and saw the light go dense then pale across its surface and his hand reached over and pulled me into his body where I lay crumpled like a rag doll next to him.

When I woke in the middle of the night, Jordan was gone, and I walked through the rooms of the third floor looking for him and when I came into the kite room he was resting on the floor against the wall with the last box kite we'd made together held against his chest and I came over and took the kite from his arms and placed it on the work table and knelt down and adjusted his shirt collar that had been bent over and placed his arms one over the other like I'd seen them do with dead people in movies. I couldn't hear him breathe but knew that his breath was there nonetheless, shallow and slow but there all the same, and left him to go back down the hall to the room where I slept.

I sat on the bed and stared out the window and waited for the sound of the B&O freight that passed through town each night, and when I woke next, it was daylight. I walked down the hall to the kite room. There was no sign of Jordan, only the kites we had made together.

At holiday break, my father picked me up from Union Station and drove me back home in the cool winter darkness of DC. When we got to our house, my mother was outside sweeping the front stoop, and when I came up the steps, she put the broom down long enough to come over and give me a hug and said, "Go inside, you'll catch your cold," and I carried my suitcase into the house that smelled of fireplace ash and soup on the stove. I went up to my room where the bed was made just as I'd left it in August.

When I came down, I saw the car was gone from out front, and my father had left. I asked my mother where he'd gone, and she said, "It doesn't matter, let me look at you." I stood in front of her in the living room, and she said I'd gotten taller, my features had changed, become more adultlike. I said I was the same, nothing had really changed. She lifted her glass and said, "We'll see." I followed her into the kitchen and out on the back porch where she said, "This is where I sit most nights waiting for you to come home, like the lost dog Sheba in that movie we watched together." I said, "I am home," and she said, "Yes, you are, yes you are." We sat there for a time on the porch looking out over the garden that was covered in a light frost, and she said, "What do you want to do tomorrow?" I said I didn't know, maybe see what was playing at the Uptown. We went back inside, and she put bowls of beef barley soup on the table for us, but didn't eat anything herself, just let her bowl get cold and sit in front of her while I ate.

"You'll need some warm clothes to wear back on the farm," she said. "I heard from Mrs. Ross you didn't bring anything warm for the cold weather." "No," I said, "but I'm OK, I can wear the sweater you got me." She said, "We'll see if we can't find something at Kaufmans'," and pushed her plate away from her and got up from the table and went into the front room, where she sat down and pulled the bottle back from behind the curtain, forgetting I could see what she was doing, and said, "I'm more tired than I thought, they said I should get more rest, but your father—" She lifted the bottle of Scotch to her lips and took a swig. "Your father is losing his patience with me, I don't think it's fair but that's what I get for marrying the man when I was still too young to know better," and she took another swig from the bottle and put it down, and said, "Come over here, darling, let me look at you," and set the bottle back behind the curtain before going on, "I'm just not resting enough is all. I've only so much energy left, not enough, no doubt, not enough, but you and I will have some time now to do things, won't we?" The question hung there between us, and I didn't respond but sat on the couch beside her as the light from outside shifted, becoming grayer.

She glanced around the room as if looking for someone else, and I said to her, "What is it?" and she said, "It's nothing, I thought you were going to—" then paused and said, "It's good you've come home."

My mother stood up from the couch slowly and carefully, and I put my hand out to steady her, but she waved me off and said, "No, my darling, I'm fine," and went into the hallway and up the stairs. I could hear her go up the landing and down the hallway into her room and close the door and throw her shoes off and lay herself on the bed. When I went up a little while later, I imagined she'd already fallen asleep, the light was out from underneath the door, and I couldn't hear anything from inside her room. I went down the hall into my room and took the last kite that I'd made with Jordan out of my suitcase and put it on the windowsill so that the fine white and red paper caught the light. I lay on the bed watching the kite for awhile until it became like a phantom bird I could follow through the night sky, and the higher it flew, the harder I had to look to see it until finally it disappeared altogether.

When I woke, the kite rested unmoving on the sill, and I lowered the blind and let the darkness enfold everything around us.

Archipelago and North
Claude Simon

—Translated from French with an Introduction by Louis Cancelmi

INTRODUCTION

CLAUDE SIMON IS BEST KNOWN as a novelist, in particular as a "new novelist"—therefore a formalist—with a gift for crafting long, super-subordinated sentences with a painter's eye and engineer's precision. Though the Nobel committee awarding him the 1985 prize for literature cited his "deepened awareness of time in the depiction of the human condition," they might as easily have praised his careful attention to *space*. He was an artisan both in method and effect, and his training as a painter contributed significantly to the visual style of his writing, on vivid display in these prose poems, where story, without dissolving entirely, gives way to layers of memory, perception, and imagination, producing an almost cubist transcription of reality.

Neither *Archipelago* nor *North* was published in French during Simon's lifetime. Les Éditions de Minuit brought them out in 2009, thirty-six years after they appeared in the journals *Åland* and *Finland*. The author first visited Scandinavia in the summer of 1963, when he gave a conference in Lahti, Finland, and both poems presented here have something of the travel journal to them: the geography and history, the natural and manmade habitats, and in general the sense of place they convey, are all depicted with an attention and intensity that imply direct experience. That said, they in no way resemble mundane (or even extraordinary) reportage. They are, rather, reformulations, "assemblages" of the material from which they were composed. The result is highly structured but at the same time lush, even sensuous, and in keeping with the rigorous experimentation of Simon's major narrative works.

With *Archipelago* and *North*, Simon gives us both architecture and its photo negative, neither scaffolding nor space alone but a synthesis of the two, and a kind of demonstration that the artist's subject cannot be disentangled from its form. Architecture, on its most basic level, is the creature's response to the demands of nature, a manipulation of natural forms undertaken not only for the sake of survival, but in hopes of making nature habitable, useful, beautiful. The more extreme the environment, the more exposed are the limits of order, and the more apparent the tendency of nature (and of time itself) to reconsume the interventions and fantasies of human ingenuity, reduce them to mere traces. These poems, while providing an account of such tendencies, might also be read as creature responses themselves: artificial structures through which Simon negotiates an alien landscape, illustrating, demarcating, and organizing its spaces in order to build—image by image, word by word—a new and elaborate whole.

ARCHIPELAGO

like perforations at first, here and there, as though beneath the fabric of parallel meadows woods fields stretched another sky, symmetrical to the one the plane is flying through, yet darker, a lightly purpled blue

or gray

shimmering dull glare backlit like metal mirrors studded in the grass

lemon-yellow reflection now and then running quickly over the surface when the sun

optical illusion setting them in light as though not holes at all but puddles of mercury scattered in faint relief upon the darkened earth

one that barely forces the adjacent road to change its course then another larger one (the road turning off veering upwards curving coming back on the left following the edge of the river curving in the opposite direction and returning then to its rectilinear trajectory) then nothing more: only the fields the woods the little gleaming rectangles of roofs, then another, just a pond this time, then a fourth then five then ten the earth now spangled ripping itself apart dissecting itself so to speak

rag tattered with a thousand cuts

as though the plane were flying over one of these paintings one of these tessellations where from right to left one color gradually takes the place of another invading it by increasing fractions each element in equal tension with the center of the canvas then

the opposite now: strips drawn out in long parallel strands (what a marvelous glacier tons of years withdrawing slipping slowly away . . .) their darkness against this sparkling expanse as far as the eye can see

columns processions of pilgrims advancing a fantastic armada driving toward

millions of years of bluish strata crawling edging forth in a tremendous silence inhabited by tremendous groans the polished granite thousands of islands thousands of gulfs bays creeks where the oyster-colored ocean swells

water lilies ringed with light dissipating upon a slate-gray backdrop drifting

archipelago APXI–ΠΕΛΑΓΟ : referring originally not to these innumerable specks of scattered earth but on the contrary to the vast sea

as though the sense had inverted itself Container for the contents the reverse of Greece (and likewise the two flags one a white cross against blue background the other a blue cross against white background) Like a photographic positive and its hourglass negative the top on bottom where the void is full language inside-out like a glove the seams here beginning to bulge sudden thunder in these silences flower of fire with a yellow heart blooming vermilion petals battles for these straits as well these passages Swedish ironclads Russians with iron-laden vessels advancing through these cold white iron seas

fin-land suo-mi : marsh-land

imagining them peopled still with fabulous beasts half-man half-fish as in these paintings where pinkish lines on whitewashed backgrounds depict creatures through their torsos a medial bone the curved ribs on either side of which flaring like harpoon barbs

discalced Franciscan monks zealots come from where to build a sanctuary here with stones of pink lilac cyclamen blackish brown its roof covered in scales to depict the scourging the judge in his plum-colored robes washing his hands to sculpt these clusters of clotted blood

vines climbing the sides the palms the feet pierced with nails grapes hanging from them

the sea the whole archipelago climbing toward us One after another beginning with the most distant the islands sinking disappear one of them a low-lying one barely undulating rose up grew larger concealing the previous ones it scrolled past quickly to one side water splashing up under the floats His enormous sailor's hands thick flat fingers square nails rimmed black with grease stopped fiddling with the levers and gadgets on the instrument panel with its various black dials and various black switches among which they had been dancing skimming over them delicately as over a complex and feminine form the din of the motor stopped when he was close enough he jumped deftly onto the rock and wound the rope around one of the stakes on the landing

silence clumps of alders rowans scarcely shivering and these long grasses like pink feathers in the distance forming blurry pastel clouds helmets and arms these too made of iron they probably set foot on these same rocks piled out of hobnailed skiffs girded with baldrics beneath their brown frocks before painting upon the limed surfaces the white vaults between the multicolored palms of the archways these strange amphibian creatures

two escaping from the toothy maw of some swamp monster neither fish nor men nor women with their flat enormous feet still fins one of them endowed not with breasts but teats like a female cetacean's whose vulva is said to resemble a woman's same softness

silence the water spreading in layers without breaking over the polished granite surface retreating leaving it wet a whale's flank lilac

grapes of blood

or still creviced: not rock but thick leather of an old pachyderm furrowed with wrinkles with fissures with interlacing gashes left by a chiseled knife

pier of loose planks all askew resting on a first cambered rock and tinted gray by the water the frost the sun another branch of water the undulating silence of pallid cattails then the stone underfoot silence

only the muted creaking of the rope straining and slackening the wavelets licking the floats the little red-and-white hydroplane un-moving poised on the water like a long-legged insect

and yet cannonades for someone from these rocks some fortress built from massive chunks of the same rocks guardian of these silences these mazes these scraps

some of them rather large with paths roads houses with green roofs red walls with white crosses From the plane the recently harvested or turned over fields where tractors had passed through leaving par-allel grooves as though some enormous comb had set about tracing them rounding the corners embedding here and there some rock or some jade-green copse like those sacred gardens in Japan where raking the sand is a matter of ritual fawn-colored fossilized sea its parallel waves frozen around stones dropped here and there by a fastidious deity

others hardly big enough for a few trees three pines a silver birch

lapping silence

others still without even a tuft of grass ground down barely breaking the surface of the water petrified fish low enough even for a single wave to cover them washed over and again endlessly revarnished thousands of silences

thunderous flowers of fire bows loaded with iron great sails their figureheads plunging before them through the straits the pleats of their sculpted skirts flapping in the wind their impassive painted wooden faces raised toward the sky one hand concealing one of their paint-smeared breasts their chalky masks made up pink their blue earthenware eyes their thick coal-tar locks floating beneath the bowsprit the water separated by the bow into locks of foam

like sacrilegious thunderclaps answering one another in the silence echoing among the ice sheets the rocks the empty sky

Englishmen Frenchmen too redheaded barbarians with thick side whiskers Bretons with large ribboned hats with short coats short hands even thick fingers with thick nails splintered by the rigging

all the wildflowers umbels campanulae miniature daisies wild oats yellow or gray-green lichen like loose change clinging piled on top of one another ink stains daffodil spreading over blotting paper dotting the lilac leather of the rocks

engraving that shows them busying themselves around hefty black cannons on a wooden gun carriage loaded with iron harnessed with cables contorting with the recoil hefty shortish admiral with oakum sideburns wearing a cocked hat a telescopic spyglass whose copper glints in his right hand the thumb of the other on his chest between two buttons of his tunic

    thunder and fire

    then silence again nothing but the crackling of fire now and then a beam caving in with a splash of sparks the surfaces of the walls the battlements their enormous stones cyclamen pink strewn among the silent dead

    seasons, castles

    the flagship gliding slowly between the islands beneath the complicated scaffolding of its spars and rigging some queen of sculpted ice at its prow the empresses with their blue and white blue and red names Alexandra Kristina Katherina their dresses snow-white and gold fluttering about their thighs their snow-white faces a bit fleshy cruel proud sovereigns of the steppes of the woods

    princesses with archipelagoes for their dowries with beds of islands upon islands

    of forests upon forests vast as continents

    quarreling with one another contending with the usurpers from the South

    straits

    isthmuses

    water lily islands

    lakes of mercury

fish islands

processions of islands

marshes

caravans of islands on the tinplate sea

inlets

pallid cattails

the fish men with snow-white bodies with pink bones the females their teats drawn in salmon pink on the white of silence

NORTH

once I arrived the setting sun like an orange hung above the frozen white sea incandescent disk without warmth unmoving as though caught between the interwoven branches of naked trees in a salmon gray satin sky the facades on the harbor with pediments and colonnades painted delicate colors pastel blue ocher in the whiteness of the ponds the tugboats had opened channels of black water

but never until now . . .

capital of the frigid North

HELSINGFORS blue red yellow finished with a flag F flapping in the wind swaying S, HELSINKI snapping on the K like those triangles of ice shattered by ship prows and which the nocturnal frost had probably soldered together again or maybe a cold so deep that as soon as the vessel passed, springing back in the swirls of wake knocking together, had solidified like this chaos of grayish slabs like stars like saw teeth climbing one on top of another their tips the wavelets of black water licking their oblique planes

screeching black-hooded seagulls their black feet landing for an instant on the tarnished surface arguing with one another furious then flying away all at once

spiral of orange peel floating rising and falling among the other detritus bits of wood corks wisps of straw brown things glommed together in rippling sheets

but I had never until now entered . . .

another time the orange sun still fading bit by bit turning pink in the pink midnight sky where long twisting russet streaks stretched out left there as though by the bristles of a paintbrush haze or smoke from the tall parallel red-brown chimney stacks the dockside cranes tangled together standing out in black against the painted sky

and what time? one o'clock in the morning maybe white horse in the milky June night the fog in gray scarves stretching dragging over the meadows between the dark woods occasionally they would thicken and the automobile would seem to plunge into an impalpable wall where the light from the headlamps dwindled the horse glimpsed for a split second unmoving as though hanging in the air like in a slow-motion film along the road behind the fence surrounding the unreal colorless meadow the animal too out of some Nordic legend in the half-light part of the same unreality as the night itself then it disappeared Further on still deep in the countryside a man and a woman in dressy attire also unreal she wearing something like an evening gown going to or coming from where what ball with neither automobile nor house in sight only these same scarves pulling themselves to pieces putting themselves back together again driven on by imperceptible movements dragging their bellies over the grass gray with dew myriads of pearls

but I had never . . .

squares where solemn gentlemen ceremonious and severe were seated on bronze chairs dressed in bronze suits bronze ties with bronze-black mustaches gazing out before them with vacant eyes

. . . until now entered this youth this old age I thought

always somewhere glimmering a thousand specks lighting up going dark again between the trunks a lake

but this was not really the North yet only something that This melancholy

rising up among the wildflowers the insane and poignant vegetation of fleeting summers expecting to see it come apart little by little clear off in pieces crumble away the massive house as though gnawed at by invisible termites a secret melancholy its rococo gables its passageways its craft-worked balconies wooden lace yellowed with time between the pallid greenery like those old women with their dried-out skin mummies draped in fading rags

airy ball gown all you could see its bright spot floating against the backdrop of black woods and the white as though phosphorescent trunks of birch trees

but only its edge its ornamental border was dressed in bronze in lace frills as though to

then I was there: little by little the woods lost their geometric contours their edges no longer carved off in straight lines by the fields by the enclosures now they rose and fell their peaks resembling flames soon between them there were no more spongy greenish patches their limits blurred where black streamlets turned in on themselves the hills began to peel back you could see the mallowy skin of the earth then there it was I walked on I made my way into the world's old age the thousands the dozens the hundreds of thousands of trees cut down by storms uprooted lying among the vertical boles among the new eruptions of sap certain of them leaning still clinging to a younger one and no more rock no more grass no more flowers no more road only the sandy yellowish-brown path between the soft undulations of dunes blanketed with moss with gray lichens

and so on all the way to Sevettijärvi and so on all the way to Kandalaksha and after Kandalaksha Arkhangelsk and after Arkhangelsk Vorkuta and after Vorkuta Igarka and after Igarka Salekhard the plains the plateaus the mountains of Verkhoyansk those of Chersky so on all the way to the Anadyr Baikal the Chukchi Sea far very far farther than a man could walk if he walked his whole life the forest always the forest only cut off from the marshes from the ponds with their turquoise waters their amethyst waters their sapphire waters from long motionless rivers from giant estuaries from tributaries flowing flakes of gold from violent rapids

never until now

I made my way into the world's childhood Separated from the forest top by a band of reddish light a mountain of clouds was rising its summit lined with a silver fringe

dazzling

cemetery where no lumberjack has ever

tangled skeletons lying among the living with their fantastical roots like crowns of daggers their spasmodic twisted limbs silver gray I walked silent as lichen silent as sand (there exist likewise, it is said, whale cemeteries strewn with bones) the ones cut down by the most recent storms still intact hard others would crumble when I set my foot upon them crushing others still they were nothing anymore but vague swellings of earth already covered over with the same

47

lichens their trunks already three-quarters subsumed returning to the humus the earth from which they had sprung giant hoary stricken down weakening bit by bit collapsing hugging the landscape of the dunes sinking in gobbled up swallowed

centuries

before then I had never been inside old age inside the world's cemeteries: budding expanding impetuous crossing the steel of winters summers without night autumns then fur-lined winters again more summers more autumns then lying down cracking decomposing food for the roots of those who in their place

matrix of trees

under the mountain of clouds the bloody fringe took on a soot-brown cast their summit hemmed with light rising bit by bit a wall now of blackish blue

cradle of forests

the rapids' waters progressively darkened in the end they were completely black too ink where the manes the galloping chargers of foam were now like snow the birches on the opposite bank paler and paler under the black sky as though all the light had gathered together in these swirls these simmering pools the discolored foliage the rain began suddenly to fall violent ferocious mixed with flashes of lightning on the desolate banks on the thousands and thousands of dead pines sprawled out spasming

red-orange light in the bar too, absorbed by the dark woodwork clinging to the sculpted sides of the glasses the women's naked arms like bright die castings that they themselves illuminated

understanding why there was something of the southerner in this somewhat affected somewhat stiff decorum that they did their best to uphold as though the wild and splendid Far North were protecting itself trying to raise up a barrier a facade behind which

expecting to see some Chekhov character come out of there some gentle and gloomy melancholic man with a goatee and pince-nez wearing a frock coat he would appear on the veranda under the gingerbread trim come down the worm-eaten steps settle into a rattan chair on the well-raked gravel and pretend to open a book while by the windows with their artistically scalloped canopies the paint flaking off you could see women coming and going in their stiff-collared summer dresses with their leg-of-mutton sleeves ribbons in their hair their almond eyes their cheekbones protruding slightly their faces stamped with repressed passion the silvery birch leaves flickering noiselessly the slender silver-pink trunks sprinkled with black spots, like horizontal mouths, like wrinkles, or wounds

onward I went into the world's childhood its old age my steps falling without a sound

he watched me approach his body in profile head turned toward me topped by heavy branching horns covered in the same fur as his gray body stump-shaded black I stopped we stayed like that for a moment he with his contemplative horse face his softish mouth his gentle eyes then he turned away indifferent haughty went off at a leisurely pace then fell into a jog trot moved away among the scattered trees skirting the heaps of dead branches without a sound elegant and solitary in the vastness of the woods his gray coat appearing and disappearing between the boles soon I had lost all sight of him

or a cemetery for reindeer perhaps for gigantic animals lying there in whole packs their tangled horns knotted and gray which the frost the winters glaze over bit by bit

I also saw two enormous hares with white-furred bottoms with long ears one darted off straight through my feet practically I had bent down to pick up a root the shape of a candelabra

(and this strange shrubbery thorny bushes of nails crisscrossing every which way gathering in some places into parallel bundles organ pipes I found on the ground—what blacksmith what carpenter had been here . . .—hedgehogs with mobs of rusted quills stuck together by a lumpy flow of molten metal fire working with air and water on something extracted from the bowels of the earth . . .)

I stroked a dog reddish brown with its pointy muzzle like a fox's with its pointed ears its tender eyes images showed how they would trap bears under trunks loaded with heavy polished stones wolves left cruelly hanging by one paw snagged in the fork of a tree or foxes their backsides clasped in a slipknot hoisted upside down by a counter-weight to the top of a pole

I'm told that a bit farther on between the banks of sand at the edge of the great river that flows to the North there lived a very old man (I asked his age and they told me: same as mine) who'd only ever left to go to war and who afterwards had returned to this place where he was born where he had always kept his home where he had lived back when there were no paved roads (or for that matter any roads at all) no planes no electricity no propeller-driven sleighs no Honda motorcycles like the one his grandson has no Johnson outboard motors rocking on the backs of long outrigger canoes no heating oil no oil-fired stoves no prefabricated huts like the ones in Minnesota or Wisconsin no shop stalls where you could find standard fish hooks toothpaste insect repellent scope rifles magazines with naked ladies in Kodacolor on the cover antibiotics chocolate clothes hangers washing detergent back when there wasn't any pharmacist either or any doctor making rounds by seaplane or helicopter no television no post office no canned vegetables no . . .

the river flowed peaceful slow describing large winding turns the sky was gray the water was gray a cold wind was blowing the grandson wore a light T-shirt with something in English printed on it and rummaged around the outrigger's motor the boat hauled up on the bank He said the last time he was happy with how the fishing went was ten years ago he'd spent every night out on the river and every salmon he caught weighed more than thirty pounds the fox-dog ran toward me wagging his tail rubbed up against my legs then lay down on his back tucking up his forepaws so I could stroke his belly

white arms like runnels of milk one of his companions got up and bent over she walked ahead of him toward the dance floor her arms were like snow

they said the old man could tell me how they rounded up the reindeer through the hailstorms at the beginning of winter how they corralled them into the pens of gray crisscrossed poles how they marked their ears with the owner's brand how they wouldn't be cared for when they were ill how they'd die without a word how they would bury the dead on the only island with sandy ground because the only shovels they had were made of wood how the water level rose once and unearthed the skeletons and how they had to bury them all again how they would put chunks of reindeer meat and dried fish on another island as an offering to the gods and how the neighboring tribe had crossed the frozen lake to steal the meat and the fish how they had sacrificed other reindeer whose bones you could still see in the crevices between the rocks how the moose that lose their horns every year like the reindeer do hide them so carefully no one has ever been able to find them how . . .

then the rain stopped the woods darkened again the water of the rapids as light as foam the river pocked with black rocks a horizontal reddish flame appeared flickering just over the ground went still at the base of a pine tree departed just as quickly its long tail waving behind it the squirrel reached the foot of another tree stopped again seemed to sit there and reflect a moment turning his head to the right to the left then vanished in a few short hops A yellow stripe was trailing now above the trees as I was writing it drifted slowly to the right the northeast the storm had destroyed a pylon and there was no electricity but I could write by this soft glimmer it was past midnight

white in the sleepless night it looked like one of these heavy warhorses out of an Uccello painting its breast rippling with muscles suspended in the air midstride for an indeterminable length of time

51

perhaps carrying an invisible princess from a Norse tale her arms of snow her dress of fog

I wasn't going to see the very old man by the river

everything returned to normal as the north receded the edges of the woods became rectilinear again as though dammed up tamed the glutinous marshes disappeared

the milky night filled the street too, light coming from everywhere and nowhere there were dark silhouettes of men here and there leaning against walls against the trunks of trees silent waiting (for what) as though sleep here were impossible great white birds flitted about perched on the deserted road took a few steps flew off again all together without a sound the owl of Minerva takes wing at nightfall

I thought the old man had the right not to say anything to be left alone over there by the edge of the great river flowing steadily toward the frozen seas

since I'd stopped stroking his belly the fox-dog looked at me questioningly with his gentle little eyes then he got up shook himself and went off toward the woods

supple streams of milk one passed over the shoulder of the man she was dancing with

on the lawn the man in the bronze suit was still welded to his bronze chair wearing his bronze tie looking out gravely before him his hands resting on his thighs

white almost bluish

great cadavers of trees all pointing the same direction through the endless days the endless nights some look like gigantic insects from before the flood skeletons millipedes wending along on their twisted legs

seven or perhaps eight sitting there their legs hanging over the edge of the dock in front of the arrangement of pastel-blue facades the reddish domes of the Russian church the same charming and interchangeable girls as in Amsterdam along the Seine or in the East Village impossible to distinguish from the boys all with the same long blond hair wearing the same faded jeans nonchalantly swinging their bare feet their heels strike the stone some of them turn their heads look at me without seeing me two of them have guitars

the boat for Leningrad was already casting off turning itself around in the middle of the lake with extreme majestic leisure its chimney belching scrolls of smoke On the white stern the invisible setting sun the absinthe sky above the dome of the cathedral leaving a vaguely golden reflection

one of the boys started to strum his guitar and hum It's a guttural language at once violent and tender somewhat reminiscent of Japanese with its vowels its consonants doubled drawn out hanging as though from posts from the strokes of the hard letters the Ts and Ks like stanchions like fractures Their way of saying Ahhrha . . . as the Japanese also do to signal their interest their astonishment

almond-shaped eyes faintly slanted

on the record sleeve you can read the lyrics One of the songs begins like this

Miten mielellâni miten mielellani
puhuisinkaan suuresta ilosta
Maan ja taivaan mehuista
ja rakkaudesta

same as any other song the meaning of the words I imagine has no importance Only the sounds they make their music when I turned around the boat from Leningrad had disappeared (with that lightning quickness of slow-moving things: there then no longer there the next instant the time it takes to turn one's head it seems) As though it had been erased as though it had never existed the lake was empty a cool puff of wind rippled over the water which suddenly came and splashed beneath the bare feet the little boats moored there started banging together

the wind subsided picked up again subsided again then little by little bolstered itself tousling their long hair like blades of grass one of the girl-boys slipped a sweater on The wind blew in from the north the more it settled in the colder it became

Quartet
Cole Swensen

RICHARD LONG WALKS ACROSS ENGLAND (1997)

That the body becomes architecture as soon as it starts to walk:

Witness:

It is witness to the day. To the torque, which is the sun, which is walking away.

Richard Long, in his intricate maps, free of detail, and meticulously tracked: the arc of the hand in the act:

and then off it walked across the page. Exit. Nave.

Took it with it. An apse across what expanse, expanded by

1. A white horse
     carved into a hill of chalk

2. A broken tree
     at once our house

3. A red field
     the essence of a window in that
     that is its distance—architrave

4. A falling bird
     —recognizable curve—more nave, nave, who
     could ever forgive

5. A line of horses in a spine
     that the body could not outbuild
simply by sight

Cole Swensen

tried the walker
to be that animal
of accidental citadel
or make it up in time.

FAN AS ARC AS HOLD ME ON

based on the premise of the curve:

                                that the curve is the first move.
Leibniz, clinamen, on
          and all that arcs therefrom:

would culminate in a fan. In a relatively minuscule and fragile notion all

nothing but gesture: that the arc ended

in a flick of the wrist. Every arc is a window—

Witness:
Cone Collection: *Black Chantilly Bobbin Lace Fan Leaf*, 1908

the little built
          divides the sun
the little split
          sieves the wind

designed by Georges Martin
and manufactured by Compagnie des Indes,
Belgium and France.

Claribel and Etta Cone traveled extensively in Europe
inveterately collecting
yearly from the early 1900s to the late 1920s
with a sideline in lace.

Bobbin lace is based
                    on a distinct architecture
                    determined in advance
with a trace
        of the bee
                    in houses built of cavities

the most important part of any structure is its emptiness
through which
                    what slips
as with any room
                    builds the throng.

Once held in a hand, the hand swung
back and forth against the equal architecture of wind.

7P., CUIS., S. DE B. . . . À SAISIR
(3 BD, 2 BATH; DON'T MISS OUT!) (1984)

To fold the roam into something you could

get lost within, and this is how

something opens into space that one can hold.

And could held be:

                    Begin with a stair

then a door

a window just behind
                    the future
is emptying a room
                    the room itself

57

Cole Swensen

leaving through

the radiator below the window

          and all the ghosts are children.

and the window swings shut

in front of everything green.

          Called Dream or at least that was what
was written on the mirror.

And beyond the window, again the park, again the same

sense of something shut
          and the panes repeated in light
stained across the floor.

          Goldfish in the kitchen
          Goldfish on the lawn

and the window swings open

          now its panes the light divide

and the tree within that light
          flying in the wind which rises in the wind
tearing things
          that opened a window in the wall
and the feathers
          come and go across the woman, old.

The feathers are the snow you held for years until it shut.

Cole Swensen

Ô SAISONS, Ô CHÂTEAUX (1957)

seen from a window by a hand

striking a match

lighting a candle in the middle of the day,

the candlelight working

its way through the sun carefully

trembling on the stairway carefully turning

symmetry to birds of prey.

(They say the "wings" of the château)

(when they are trying to get away.)

The sound of rakes combing gravel.

Exotic birds alarming gardens

and the labyrinth at its center,

so precisely divided, it divulges a fountain

also combing
also raking;

we hear the rake in the split of it, the slit

in the crack of it, the crick,

green,

even tryst-green, blitz-green, and built

as a ruin; all châteaux were built as ruins

and so patiently we waited.

Augustus Pugin, The Grange, Ramsgate, 1843.

Father and Son
Robert Clark

WHEN I WAS LIVING IN LONDON St. Pancras station was always in
view. You could see its spires and towers from the doorstep of my
flat and pretty much from anywhere in Finsbury and Bloomsbury.
I thought it was magnificent—the greatest Victorian building of all—
but as with my affection for much Victoriana, I was a bit sheepish
about it. I never quite knew if it was truly magnificent or simply too
much. John Summerson, one of the essential architecture critics of the
twentieth century, split the difference and called it "Sir George Gilbert
Scott's tawdry masterpiece." He also admitted to finding the building "nauseating" and I think I know what he meant: that there was
something queasy making in looking at it; on the one hand, the sense
that in its height, its ascending piles of ornament, and ceremonial,
even liturgical style, it's worthy of awe; on the other, that one's being
suckered by its scale and pretensions into admiring what is ultimately in bad taste, not magnificent but vulgar. It is, after all, not a
cathedral or a seat of government, but a train station with a luxe hotel
stuck on front. Scott had been commissioned to build the new Foreign
Office in Whitehall, but the government refused to countenance his
Gothic Revival design. It's said that he recast his ideas for that project
in St. Pancras, built in 1868, employing them there with some bitterness, perhaps with the sense that the station was indeed a lesser,
tawdrier piece of work.

   That couldn't be said of the dozens of churches and cathedrals
Scott built nor of the Albert Memorial, which perhaps even more
than St. Pancras was the most Victorian piece of all Victoriana. It
confounded me: was it monumental or overbearing, stunning or
elephantine (and there are elephants, in tribute to Britain's colonial
possession of India), an expression of national grief or of bloated sen-
timent? It could have been any or all of those for me; what it was for
the Victorians themselves I can't say and I wonder if they could; if their
mixed feelings about faith, progress, family and gender relations, and
paternal authority were summed up in this manifestation of confusion; the jumble of ornament and motifs, an art fully convinced only

of its desire to ascend and make a weighty impression on the earth, but toward what? I went to photograph it once but only shot close-ups of the elephants: the thing in toto was too much; it would have been preposterous were it not also somehow diffident, a monument not just to loss but, it seemed to me, a sort of failure, an imperial gesture touched by perplexity.

Scott finished up the most prominent and doubtless richest architect of the Victorian age and launched a dynasty via his son George Junior, and grandson Giles Gilbert, who designed Liverpool Cathedral, the Thames powerhouse that now houses the Tate Modern, and, not least, the ubiquitous red telephone kiosk found throughout the nation. But it was George Junior who interested me most, the one whom architectural historians said was the most gifted of the three, who most deeply plumbed the possibilities of the Gothic Revival and foreshadowed those of modernism. Unlike his father, he didn't produce many finished buildings and only a handful of those still stand. He was an intellectual magpie and a wayward Catholic convert. He died alcoholic, broke, and insane, estranged from his children just as he had been from his own father, in a bedroom in the St. Pancras Hotel. He was, perhaps you would say, my cup of tea. I'd read everything (which was not very much) about him and went to photograph his places.

George Gilbert Scott Sr., Albert Memorial (detail), London, 1864–76.

George Junior is supposed to have built seven or eight churches and chapels, a larger number of houses and rectories, and some college buildings. He went to work in his father's practice after attending Eton, supervising some of the firm's projects and church restorations. Working on one of these at Cambridge, he was inspired to enroll as a student, earning a "first" and then a fellowship at Jesus College after winning a prize for an essay, "The Intellectual Character of the First Cause, as affected by Recent Investigations of Physical Science," which aimed to defend the idea of divine origin of creation against Darwinism.

Unlike many Victorian sons—especially of successful fathers—Scott wasn't a rebel or antiauthoritarian, at least not in a conventional sense. His politics were Tory and became more conservative over time and, as the essay showed, his Christian belief remained intact. It was, in fact, the deepening and intensifying of his faith—ending in Roman Catholicism—that would make him a black sheep. It also informed his architecture, which rejected the High Victorian style of his father and his generation for a more austere late medieval English Perpendicular Gothic he felt was better suited to worship as conducted by High Anglicans and Catholics. But it was precisely the churches that embodied that approach most successfully that were gone, damaged by bombing in World War II, considered beyond repair and pulled down. That wouldn't stop me from photographing them, or rather the places they'd stood. I was beginning to like photographing such absences, or at least not feeling frustrated or overly disappointed by them. It seemed to allow me to make a special claim upon them: to be seeing what other people couldn't, to be peering into a world that belonged solely to me.

Just then, I went on a date with an art historian, a specialist in Victorian photography, and after we'd had coffee at the Tate Britain—communing with some daguerreotypes and a couple of whopping Turners—we agreed to meet up at a Scott church in Camberwell in south London. I think she was just as keen as me; it was she who'd known about the church and had always wanted to see it.

We meant to meet on a Sunday but it was raining hard. I told her not to bother coming, that we'd do it another time. But I went by myself and I cannot say why. I checked the timetables and saw that the closest train station was Denmark Hill, close by the site of the house John Ruskin, the art and architecture critic, grew up in. It was a place I should photograph.

I knew the house was gone, that it had been razed and most of the grounds turned into a public park. But I wasn't prepared for how absolutely it had been erased, the site now a street of turn-of-the-century suburban villas on a faceless road with only a car wash and a filling station standing out against the rain and the gray. I found a tiny marker indicating where it had once been and stood next to it, sopping, my camera sheltered under my coat, staring down a driveway bordered by shrubs, a big Mercedes parked at the end.

I never got to the church, which, it turned out, wasn't by George Junior at all but by his father. My date's source had been wrong. As ever, where Junior's work wasn't obliterated it was misattributed and, still more, overshadowed by his father's—eight hundred buildings against Junior's dozen or so—his father's houses and edifices of every description that constitute an outline of Victorian society, which made up the stages and scenery of the Victorian novels I loved and my nineteenth-century obsessions: his churches, of course—143 either designed or rebuilt—to hold all that faith and unfaith; forty workhouses for the likes of Charles Dickens's father and everyone else who failed to have money; Reading Gaol for sexual and gender misfits like Oscar Wilde; and four lunatic asylums to hold, among others, his son, George Junior.

Of course, the site of the Ruskin house too hadn't really been Ruskin's place but his father's. There are always fathers—even (maybe especially) in their deepest absences—but to me nowhere so strikingly as in the Victorian age with its beards and seers and Old Testament thunderers and "driving" amassers of wealth, overseen by a small but formidable woman who adored her husband, Albert, like a daddy's girl does her daddy, who had him memorialized on an uncanny, perhaps absurd scale by George Junior's father.

A few days later, I went to Ramsgate on the English Channel and there too George Junior had been slighted, this time in converse fashion with a building of his own mistakenly attributed to his father. It was a chapel in the municipal cemetery on the fringe of an ugly neighborhood. The cemetery had a long drive that led straight down to the chapel, which was shaped like a squared cross with a tower at the center. The tower, though, was taller on one side than the other, topped on the left by a smaller secondary tower. To the right of this was a window, off-center. It seemed to me that this arrangement should throw the balance of the whole structure off. So should the fact that the windows on the wings on each side of the base of the tower were also out of kilter and of different shapes and proportions. It ought to have seemed lopsided and clumsy and hodgepodge, but it didn't. It was a rebellious building, flouting the rules of Victorian Gothic, his father's architecture, and getting away with it for reasons I couldn't put my finger on. I tried to go in but the door was locked. I photographed a piece of exterior wall, a downspout, and the trees behind the building. Their limbs ran all in one direction, away from the sea, contorted by a perennial wind that wasn't blowing that day.

The other reason I'd come to Ramsgate was to visit The Grange, the home of the architect Augustus Pugin, though it was less a house than a compound, around which Pugin had grouped a church, cottages, and a full-fledged monastery, a village within the larger town. Pugin was the main founder of the Victorian Gothic Revival and George Gilbert Scott's chief inspiration: "the thunder of Pugin's dreams" had been his creative epiphany, Scott said. For Pugin, Gothic was more than a style; it was a complete manifestation of England, of English culture, of medieval communitarianism built around social cohesion, obligation, labor and craft, and charity, with the church at its core. Pugin was a brilliant architect and designer—he'd been the cobuilder of the Houses of Parliament—but, still more, he was an aesthete and a passionate Catholic convert, a man in constant pursuit of beauty and the divine. As an acquaintance wrote, "He rushed into the arms of a church which, pompous by its ceremonies, was attractive to his imaginative mind."

I went overboard at The Grange. I photographed inside and out, in black-and-white and color: hallways, roofscapes, fireplaces, a bed and its coverlet in the master suite, a flagon and an empty holy water stoup by the door of Pugin's private chapel. I shot until I ran out of film, until I was sated. As with other Victorian buildings that had drawn me in, even obsessed me, after a while I felt overwhelmed, swamped in detail, in crockets and pointed arches and saturated polychrome and gilded decorations. I was submerged and the water was pouring in; an attic full of accreted gorgeousness, a jumble of marvelous doodads and bric-a-brac was closing over my head. Walking back to the station, I knew that I now had seen a place I'd sought for a long time, that it had been beautiful, and that, oddly, dully, I had no desire to ever return.

Pugin's counterpart inside the church was undoubtedly John Henry Newman, the famous High Church Anglican priest whose conversion to Roman Catholicism and elevation to a cardinalship stunned the Victorian world. Medievalism and the Gothic were the artistic and cultural expression of the "Oxford Movement" (in which Newman had been the leading figure) that returned the English church to its pre-Reformation roots and cultural centrality. In fact, much of the opposition to the Gothic Revival was based less on aesthetic considerations than the fear that it was a stalking horse for Roman Catholicism, as was the case with the rejection of Scott's first design for the Foreign Office. Privately, Pugin would doubtless have admitted this.

Victorian faith was under threat from two opposing sides: Darwin and the phenomenon labeled by Thomas Henry Huxley "agnosticism" on one and, on the other, defections to the Roman church by prominent figures like Newman, rationalism and neo-medieval piety that jointly pressed upon a national Anglican Church increasingly incapable of inspiring even the most rudimentary faith. For every expression of religious doubt or renunciation by people like George Eliot, Ruskin, and Virginia Woolf's father, Leslie Stephen, there seemed to be a conversion to Catholicism by a prominent Victorian academic, writer, or clergyman, sometimes at the hands of Newman himself, who had received the likes of Gerard Manley Hopkins, among others.

Another would be George Gilbert Scott Junior. His father had been a devout architectural follower of Pugin but had never felt the need to follow him into the Roman Church or even High Church Anglicanism. It was George Junior—a rebel against Pugin's strictures on late medieval style—who "went over," though reading his biography, I began to feel that his conversion was less spiritual than temperamental, that Junior's general pessimism arose from and in turn fed a sense of failure, of lassitude, and creative stasis, a sort of disassociation: "Old work was *real* . . . ours is not real, but only *like* real," said one of his contemporaries, Norman Shaw. But as with his political conservatism, Catholicism did seem real, insisted on its own eighteenhundred-year-old tradition as both authoritative and unalterable. And without it his creative work could only be empty: "a blank skepticism, or an arbitrary agnosticism, have never, and never can, originate any advance either in art or in any other department of practical life."

In 1880, George Junior was introduced to Newman and shortly thereafter attended a morning mass celebrated by Newman on his behalf. Afterward he

> had not walked fifty yards down the street before as it were a
> momentary flash of thought passed through my mind and I
> saw in an instant that all the difficulties, uncertainties and
> indecision of years was but a phantom, and that my duty was

clear as day. I experienced even then no emotion, no surprise, I was not only cool but even cold. Simply all my old difficulties fast tumbled down, in a moment, like—so to speak—a house of cards, and I had quickly made up my mind to become a Catholic before I reached the second street corner.

George Junior's family was appalled, relieved only that he had waited until after his father's death two years earlier. Beyond the social embarrassment that came with his conversion, there was its impact on the family architectural firm (now managed by his brother), dependent as it was in large part on commissions from the Anglican Church.

To George Junior himself, his conversion seemed utterly rational, even practical, but in the eyes of others it was a manifestation of mental instability and those closest to him had reason to think this. His drinking—"alcoholic drink is . . . the properly & divinely designed beverage of man," he'd said—was resulting in unexplained absences, night wanderings that sometimes ended in the company of prostitutes or in arrest. In 1881, he had his first bout of mania and within another year he was committed to the Royal Bethlem Hospital—Bedlam—afflicted with paranoid delusions. On release, he was arrested several more times while carrying a knife for protection against his imaginary persecutors. His family applied to have him permanently committed, but he fled to France before the judge could issue a ruling.

George Junior had long stretches of lucidity during his exile: "I am in a rather droll position . . . hav[ing] been declared legally a lunatic, incapable of managing my affairs in England, while here in France I have been examined by the official medicals, and have been pronounced with equal certainty to be perfectly sane." But returning home there were more arrests and hospitalizations. In January 1888 he was committed to Saint Andrew's Hospital for Mental Diseases at Northampton for the Middle and Upper Classes. There his room overlooked the hospital's chapel, designed by his father.

He made several attempts to escape and was eventually released, only to relapse into his customary bouts of drinking, mania, paranoia, and run-ins with the law. He worked sporadically, mostly on his final project, the Catholic cathedral in Norwich, which his brother finished when George Junior became incompetent again. In sum, he had produced thirteen buildings in his career against his father's eight hundred.

After 1894 there are few records or evidence of his whereabouts. But by 1897 he was inhabiting his final quarters, a room in the St. Pancras

Hotel, his father's masterpiece. He died there, according to the death certificate, of "acute cirrhosis of the liver and heart disease" and of "exhaustion syncope," heatstroke and dehydration. His sons, who would only recall having met him once before, were brought to his bedside. Whether he received last rites from a priest isn't known or still less what he might have made of dying there, of all places. He was poor by then—he'd been cut off from the family fortune, his father's fortune, long before—and I suppose it was a cheap room near the attics, among the castellated chimneys and crocketed pinnacles and spires.

My own conversion—now twenty years ago—was remarkably like George Junior's, less felt than arrived at as a necessary, logical, and inevitable destination. It was a kind of intellectual assent—enthusiastic to be sure—but I don't recollect much sense of freedom or peace, of mercy having befallen me and sins being wiped away, of loving God and of him loving me. What I liked was the beauty not only of the content—the music, liturgy, architecture, and art—but of the form, the organic, self-containing tradition and belief that seemed to go back as far as I might see. That too seems much like George Junior, the comfort of a self-sustaining and self-evident order, a stay against meaninglessness.

It's easy to connect all that to fathers, or, in my case and the case of so many Victorians, the absence of a father, or a father whose presence was felt by way of money or reputation or a shame in not being equal to his measure and it's on that account that he's gone. So you might replace a father with God the Father, with an institution that's gently authoritarian, that corrects and instructs without anger or injustice. You might feel safe there, maybe for the first time ever.

But it's also not much of a leap to connect the role of father in Victorian times not only to conversion but to the lapse and loss of faith, and to a broad and deep sense of loss, of failure, of reality having been emptied out. God the Father disappears or perhaps is in some unwitting way killed, an obstacle moved out of the way by the son, as in the myth of Oedipus, as Freud—another Victorian—would assert. God left us, abandoned us, but that, in truth, was our desire; God had to die and we had to kill him. His simultaneous love and oppression, his tender but iron hand, was too much to bear. In that view, to wish to have him back afterward would be, in the inexorable flow of history, a fool's errand, for all the efforts of a Scott or someone like me.

68

As I said, my conversion was twenty years ago and not long after I made a trip to England. I located the village where my ancestors had come from. It was called Somerton and what I found was a crossroads of twenty or so houses, thickets, and meadows, and, in the meadows, sheep. There was a church too, and although there was no one around—no one in the whole village apparently—it was being kept up: the grass in the graveyard was freshly cut and I supposed I had ancestors buried here, though there were no monuments or stones with their names. Not being of much social standing—fleeing to America to try to improve their lot—there probably never were.

The church—St. Margaret's by name—is at least a thousand years old, though there's no saying when my family turned up there. The oldest parts of the church date from the 1100s and there's a blocked-up doorway in the Romanesque style that preceded the Gothic. The baptismal font is nearly as old.

I suppose that given how much of my conversion was based on aesthetics—on chant, on beautiful hints of hidden mysteries—I was a convert of the same sort as Pugin or George Junior: I'd become as much a neo-medievalist as a Catholic; what they'd said about Pugin's conversion—that it was "attractive to his imaginative mind"— was exactly true of me too. I thought about Somerton while I was in Ramsgate; although Pugin's compound was altogether magnificent and stately and St. Margaret's was altogether humble, they both manifested what Catholics called the sacramental, outward signs of inward, invisible, spiritual things, intimations of God, of ultimate beauty and truth. But I was afraid I couldn't see them anymore, that my religion was or had become abstract, academic, maybe sentimental, a kind of nostalgia for feelings I'd never, in fact, felt. That, maybe, was where my interest in the Victorian era had come from, when the decisive battle of faith versus doubt was fought by people who could express themselves only in architecture and novels and sensed from the start it was going to be a failed enterprise. Maybe I was looking for a way to be a believer who was also a doubter, instruction from a father/mentor who could show me how to do it and then leave me to go my own way, maybe to prosper, maybe to become a more contented failure at both faith and art.

One day every man turns around and sees that for all the struggles he's made to live with being a son, he's become a father or at least an old man despite himself. George Junior's sons came to him as he lay dying in his own father's building, his house, so to speak. His life was concluded—he couldn't, as a son can, regard it as a work in progress that might be turned around or amended or justified—and now there would be a reckoning, a toting up of what must be regretted since it was too late to atone for. His sons stood at his bedside and there was nothing he could be in their presence but a father entombed in the encrustations and brick his own father had built at the height of his powers. Did he say he was sorry, and if he had, what would that have amounted to?

Of course, George Junior had already converted and presumably was still a believer on his deathbed. But he was unconscious when his sons reached him and they wouldn't have the satisfaction of seeing him confess his sins as he took his last breath and perhaps feel their own resentments and wounds ease, if only a bit. Maybe they forgave him anyway, shamed him with their mercy, or—who can say?—allowed him to die at peace with himself. If nothing else, two of them became architects, and good ones too.

George Gilbert Scott Sr., Midland Grand Hotel and
St. Pancras station, London, 1866–78.

I took the train to the Northampton General Lunatic Asylum on a squally Sunday afternoon to take pictures. The name is now simply St. Andrew's Hospital although it is still a psychiatric facility. I'd done a little more reading about it before going and learned that Virginia Woolf's cousin James Stephen had been a patient contemporaneously with George Scott Jr., committed for the same manic depression she was afflicted with, which ran in her family, and in those of Turner and Ruskin and so many other Victorians.

The grounds were beautiful, a classical terrace of wards overlooking a vast lawn. When I arrived, there were a dozen or so people playing croquet—inmates, I supposed. At the lawn's far edge I saw the chapel George Junior's father designed. It would be visible from any of the wards and so Junior could have seen it whenever he looked out. I wondered what that was like for him: this manifestation of his father's incessant productivity and mastery of the conventions of Victorian Gothic that George Junior hadn't fully succeeded in overturning. Or maybe it made no impression because his experience was by then entirely internal, a knot of paranoid fantasy. People were trying to poison him, assassins had been hired; he had more pressing things to worry about than the insults and accusations of his father's chapel.

Or maybe—and this is how I believed it must have been—he'd have looked out and the chapel would have stared back, shaming him. Alcoholics are habituated to shame as are sons of eminent men (and maybe all sons to some extent). There were trees around the chapel, big conifers that cast pools and rivulets of light flowing in the direction of the wards. Gazing out, George Junior would have seen them approaching, serpentine, mirroring what he'd conjured up in his own brain.

He had no choice about being committed to St. Andrews, but in his next and final home he embraced the same dialectic—son and father, art and shame—even more profoundly, taking a room inside the St. Pancras Hotel, deep within his father's oeuvre, swallowed up by it until what proved to be the very end.

The photos of St. Andrews came out underexposed; that shifting light played tricks on my meter, or that is how I excused myself from the failure; that's what I would have told anyone who might take me to task me for it. And now I am thinking of an extract from the diary of General Charles George Gordon, the hero of the Fall of Khartoum, another failure the Victorians had turned into a triumph by means of sentimentality and grief, written as the Sudanese enemy was beginning its siege, the things that were on Gordon's mind as he was preparing to die. He quoted the Bible: "The eye that mocketh at his father and despiseth to obey his mother, the ravens of the valley shall pick it out, and the young eagles shall eat it." And then he added, "I often wonder whether they are destined to pick my eyes, for I fear I was not the best of sons."

One of the crucial things that separated the children of Victorians from their parents' generation was their indifference to the opinion and regard of their fathers; in Bloomsbury and other outposts of the modern movement, they made, in fact, a virtue of rejecting most of what their fathers thought most important. They (and perhaps we, or at least I) didn't much care about or for what their forebears did— or built. It seemed to them self-evident that those fathers' posterity culminated in nothing so much as the slaughter of the 1914–18 war. They, the Victorians, had been in deadly earnest, held to deadly sureties that sent their sons and grandsons to the trenches, flung buttresses and pointed arches backward in time toward what they would have liked to be true, toward buildings that "were *real*," as George Junior's colleague wrote, knowing that "ours is not real, but only *like* real." The ravens would come regardless, whether anyone deserved it or not.

The Botanist's House
Kathryn Davis

MOSTLY, SHE NEEDED TO PUT it all behind her, and by "all" she meant all of us, as well as the events of her life, what people call memories. The moment we were out of sight she opened the door to the tall house with the steep roof and went in. Right away it was as if she had never been inside a house before; even the noise the door made closing behind her seemed not to have been made by wood sliding against wood with an accompanying burst of air, but instead signaled the presence nearby of something previously unknown or imagined, something large and shifting around in a space too small for it, breathing heavily through the mouth.

Little bug, little scrub, little bead, little need. The Botanist knew she was being summoned. She was floating again, that much was for sure, her eyes like burnt holes in something not like a blanket but more like herself and consequently a lot worse to look at.

Up a long staircase and onto a landing. The windows were shut tight yet if she looked back she could see smoke seeping from the crevices, as well as from hundreds of small objects on shelves along the walls, unrecognizable, glinting as if in the light of a fire but there was no fire, no stove, no candle, no light at all. Meanwhile the smell of smoke occurred to her like the image of a little girl in a smocked dress playing jacks, *not* a memory but an idea. It was exactly the way she worked when she was botanizing: there would be the smell of hyacinth and there would be an old lady reaching for something just out of reach. There would be the taste of a cranberry bean and there would be a young man sharpening a pencil. You couldn't interrupt these operations of reaching, of sharpening—they were each, in their own way, eternal.

The thing is, we couldn't save one another. The Botanist was in danger but there was nothing we could do. Ditto the Archivist, borne on the increasingly powerful current, headed for the rapids where the Rock that Cries had ended many a life. We hadn't heard about this yet but we were going to. There was nothing we could do. Once you were in the Savage Domain there was no escaping the Beast. Meanwhile we sat on our cloaks under the capacious beech tree, eating meat and drinking wine and planning what to do next, as if the operation we were involved in, however it might be described—Déjeuner sur l'Herbe, maybe, or fiddling while Rome burns—was not, likewise, eternal. As if we could have any say about the outcome. As if we couldn't see the little brown dog curled on the grass at our feet.

The Botanist floated along the second-floor hallway and up the final flight of stairs to the third floor. Was it true, what they said? Once you went up you never came down? Little bug, little bud, little hug, little judge, little mug, little rug, little BUD. LITTLE BUD! On and on she drifted along the hallway, her obedience ferrying her past many doors, all of them closed tight, all of them with smoke seeping through the cracks. It is true that smoke is often used to create a barrier of aromatic vapor through which the air that carries sickness is unable to penetrate. Get out quickly, go a long way away, and don't be in a hurry to come back: that was what the doctors were prescribing—the ones who hadn't run away themselves, that is.

The family who used to live here had been beset by *X. cheopis* or rat fleas, pests known to be happiest (if pests can be said to be happy) during unseasonably mild, damp winters, which this one certainly seemed to have been. The family consisted of a mother and father and a boy, but when the boy got sick from sleeping in the bedclothes his father acquired in trade for a rooster, they left him behind. They left him behind for dead—that was the spirit of the age. The Silk Road ran in front of their house; everyone was using it, for commerce or as a means of escape. Some travelers relied on word of mouth, some on cairns or blazes. What everyone had in common was lack of destination.

The boy wasn't dead, though. When he awakened, the place he was in was as dark as the deepest well. There seemed to be a log fire burning in the middle of the floor—though how could that have been? He was still inside his house, wasn't he? Inside the house where he'd been born and suckled and weaned? The bedclothes too seemed to be arranging themselves without assistance. The trader had stuffed them with rat flea–infested feathers and hair; as the boy watched, the stuffing reassembled itself into a large creature that glistened like a pearl.

"Come to me," the creature said, but it wasn't talking to him.

The sun went down and for just one moment the sky was bathed in golden light. Then the Botanist opened the door and came floating across the threshold.

Inside she saw the boy sitting by the window, though he wasn't exactly a boy. The person sitting by the window was older than he'd looked from below, older and bigger, and because he had wrapped himself in his cloak she couldn't see the swellings on his body, but she could smell the sickness on him. What the Botanist saw, smelling it, was the Fairy beckoning the Prince to join her in the Garden of Paradise, even though she'd told him it was the one thing he was forbidden to do. The Fairy said if he joined her there and kissed her, Paradise would sink deep into the earth, which is where it was located in the first place.

In assembly, if you so much as thought of talking to your neighbor while the principal was telling the story of the Garden of Paradise, you would be turned to stone. The Prince drew back the branches and saw tears welling in the Botanist's eyelashes. "I have not sinned yet," he insisted. Even if everlasting night were to descend on him like the lid of his own casket, a moment like this would be worth it. He kissed the tears away from the Botanist's eyes and then he kissed her lips, whereupon there came a sound like thunder, louder and more dreadful than any sound any living thing on earth had ever heard before. The chill of death crept over his limbs. The cold rain fell on his face, and the sharp wind blew around his head.

Down by the river we all heard it.

The man behind the concession stand doused the fire while a child in a faded green pinafore began closing up shop. Both of them looked around nervously, as if they were being followed. In the Keeper's kitchen, the cake, which she had recently put into the oven, fell, but it took her a while to realize this, since the oven door was closed and it was an old oven, without a light. The cake was a One-Two-Three-Four Cake, the kind she used to make us for our birthdays, until she made one with a spoiled egg in it for Mother.

What lightning bolt devoured everyone? What earthquake? There had been a crowd of us but now we were almost one.

In the river the Archivist felt raindrops hit the side of his face each time he turned his head to breathe; at length he stopped turning his head, no longer feeling the need to do so. The Poet used to make fun of how afraid he was of everything but she never understood what a good swimmer he was; at Saint Roch he had been captain of the swimming team.

Now, in the water, he was naked, the wound on his leg completely healed, his flutter kick more muscular than ever.

The river charged over rocks and around fallen logs; it surged and eddied and funneled; it leapt into the air and then dropped a great distance in a waterfall, spangled and unfettered, foaming and loud into a moss-lined pool. The Archivist's eyes were wet and he could see perfectly without his spectacles. Or, more accurately, he could see perfectly except for a spot in the middle that was nothing. Of course that's where she was, in that spot, monitoring his arrival. That's where she always was and always had been, in the spot he couldn't see. It was what drove the Poet mad, finally.

The thing is, he wasn't himself or what he thought of as himself, just as the farther we walked along the trail, the less we knew of what we thought of as ourselves. It was disconcerting, our titles having been so deeply imprinted in us as to become identities. The Cook hadn't cooked anything in a long time; the Iceman had abandoned his quest for permafrost. If the Archivist was going to turn into something like a fish, no one was going to find it strange. It was all right, as long as he eluded the lure.

Meanwhile the beech tree provided us with protection from whatever was falling from the sky; beech trees allow very little light or much of anything else to reach the ground, appropriating it all for themselves. The tree was being imperial but we didn't know that, its imperial behavior limited to trees and not people. In this way we could be certain that we were people and not plant life, though as was the case with the Archivist, it wasn't always possible to register a transformation as it happened. Some of us were putting forth branches we couldn't see called fear branches, like a tree whose space is being commandeered by a beech.

If the Botanist were here she could have explained what was going on. But that was how she'd always been, drifting away in pursuit of something better than anything we could offer, a keg party or a rare mushroom, a doomed boyfriend or a clump of lady's slippers. Besides, we never paid attention to scientific explanation—none of us did, aside from the person providing it. The Astronomer walked up from the riverbank with an armload of fish, their tall dorsal fins shedding water like stars. The fish constellation isn't very bright, he told us; it's hard to see with the naked eye. As might be expected, we weren't interested. The Astronomer said we should use what was left of the concessionaire's fire to roast the fish if that infernal child would let us, and this was a side of him we hadn't been aware of—a side of him that, unlike the scientific information he was quick to dispense, actually caught our interest.

The Cook was sound asleep on his back, grinding his teeth.

We don't have that much time, someone said.

Our sense of urgency was strong, even though we didn't know where we had to be, or when we had to be there.

In the third-floor bedroom in the tall, narrow house, the Botanist was lifting the person from the floor and putting him into bed. He weighed almost nothing. He was as light as a feather, almost as if he was already dead and gone and what she was lifting wasn't his body but his soul. He looked at her beseechingly and she shook her head *No*. Brushing the hair back from the forehead, drawing the eyelids down over the eyeballs. They don't know my story, she was thinking, so they can't put their fingers into it and ruin it they way they've done to all the other stories. Except for the Cook, whose story was the shortest—as he had reminded us repeatedly—everyone had already told their tale.

Now she would suck the air from the sac. Extract the lights on their string of silk. The Silk Trail was far shorter than the Silk Road but the distance it covered was far greater, the compass of a human life.

Five Provence Poems
Elizabeth Robinson

VILLAGES-PERCHÉS

Safety lives high above itself, protected from what it needs.

It sees what it sees, sees

a cave in its flank.

Time, really: a strategy reconsidering itself.

Time: a narrow street whose height

doubles back.

Sees a bird in flight below it.

Sees a body in a vineyard taking grapes.

Road narrow with caution, height softening

in the cave.

Feels its knuckles burn, scraped on the fortification.

AFTER MONTSÉGUR

We voyaged into an architecture of nonexistence.

The shape of the fortress, the very

shape of the castle.

Perfection creates invisibility.

We voyaged into the same domicile
we warded off: perfected ruins.

The shape of a structure

is itself belief. Not yet,
but soon

re-embodied.

To be unsexed, blanched by simplicity,
and rise high in one's own architecture
over the terrain.

Crendenti, perfecti.

Only those abolished from the false haven
of their own bodies might lift a flare.

For to be a castle is always to be burned alive.

NOTRE DAME DES GRÂCES
[PLAGUE CHAPEL]

Wayfarers expect no sanctuary. Therefore

the structure itself is shallow, infectious.

The pilgrim seeks nothing but to get away. Destination

would have been a mortar, Yersinia pestis

would have offered itself frankly

the way arrival is an altar

that creases into itself. The way,

long since foregone, light arrives

drapes the floor, warming

the rat droppings.

The chapel is an attenuated

circulatory system. Within it, the bite itself can hardly

penetrate skin, portal. It had its own way:

to flee is to confuse destination with departure.

To bless is to hallow with blood.

The grace of

nowhere else to go, a flea, a soft

dispersal.

VILLAGE DES BORIES

Cabane when inhabited.

Sol de cabane when not.

Architecture:

Beehive

Double-skin

      terms of endearment

Hut when it is inhabited.

Earth of hut when not.

Goats, fowl,
spider, moth, exile,
grain, migrant

Architecture whose structure
is inviolable and whose interior
is temporary.

Those who have no place to stay

may ration place here.

DOLMEN DE LA PITCHOUNE

Time is a false start.

The pronoun begs for intimacy—her, you,

I, myself.

Space replete with time,

hollowed in the earth, hidden

by a road—road

      compassing time, to move

askance of space because askance

is intimacy, how the earth

recurs to itself in stone.
Small offerings, small floods.

Called *the little one*

Misremembering the interval, like

a capstone irregular with space.

She comes back to its shoulders

as though it were a body. Darkness

an unguent on a wound, on the road,

on the mortar that crusts and falls away.

Leson

Gabriel Blackwell

LESON, IT SEEMS, IS STUCK even in his words and cannot think of
another way to say it, so he repeats to this doctor the refrain his brain
has lately taken up: I am stuck. Can you help? To which question
what can a doctor answer? Maybe see a specialist? The unit's diagnostic program, confused by Leson's complaint, had sounded its chime
and sent him here. Now this doctor was sending him elsewhere. No
one respects the gravity of my condition, Leson thinks. It is clear
Leson will have to come up with a treatment of his own.

This doctor, though, is a professional. He has been trained to operate the appropriate diagnostic apparatuses. He affixes nodes to Leson,
auscultates and palpitates and prods Leson. Leson plays along. He
coughs, turns, coughs again. He keeps his head straight. He feels a
tiny prick. The doctor tells him—though not in so many words—that
what is wrong must be inside. Leson, he says, I know a good man.
Here, in the colony. He recommends psychiatry. But it seems impossible to Leson his fault could come from him. When inert matter does
not move, he thinks, no one blames its lack of motivation. No one
claims the stone at the mouth of the cave is depressed when it refuses
to roll away on its own. No, what Leson needs is a lever, a harness,
a gantry, and so he describes his stuckness again, and then there is
only silence in the examination room. Leson thinks of the other
patients in other rooms. The doctor thinks of the same thing. Down
the hall, a squeegeeing sound starts up. A very large woman is bleeding from her eyes, and a nurse, annoyed, is brushing back the tide with
the sole of his shoe.

In the end, the only things Leson gets out of his visit are a bright-
blue blood pressure cuff, a pad of prescription forms, and a thin metal
instrument he cannot identify but which has a pleasing smoothness
in his hand. Though the latter two items had, at the time he'd taken
them, suggested future uses, Leson cannot say why he has stolen
the blood pressure cuff. Perhaps the color? It was not even the one the
doctor had used on him. At home, he puts it on, adjusts it. The bladder
inside inflates until it pushes against his arm, displacing the flesh

around his blood vessels until some essence of Leson rises to the surface to be measured and studied. His arm tingles. He experiments with keeping the cuff inflated for longer and longer. There is a residual tingling in his arm after. He puts the bulb down but leaves the cuff where it is. Perhaps, he thinks, he can inflate himself, squeezing the world around him until it reveals its answer. After such a prolonged absence of ideas, even this seems like a plan.

Such expansion, Leson thinks, would be besides strangely appropriate, for his dissatisfaction, the feeling of emptiness that had preceded his dismissal from the service and the subsequent stuckness, had come from feeling no sense of forward motion, progress, regress, or change. He could find no purpose. Now Leson would fill and move forward at once, and, best of all, he would avoid the need for any endogenous motivation. He had seen a frenzied zealousness driving men forward in the passage and on the front, but, even though he had been engaged in the same work, he had never been able to find that same thing in himself. After a time, his commanding officer, slowed no doubt by this enervation, had finally summoned the disgust necessary to discharge him. There had been no warning—just, out of nowhere, a detail was dispatched to clean out Leson's bunk; idle hands, they'd been told. Soon after his dismissal, his family too had dissipated in the vacuum.

Leson, naturally, looked to his screen for answers. With more time to himself, he could take in yet more of this world, fill himself with its signals, and, with the help of the screen's perfectly simulated voices and textures, even perhaps become an expert on the human condition, a man of the world. Or at least, Leson thought, a man of the colony. Why not? A man of the world might not only be one who could move about that world freely and without fear; perhaps a man of the world could also become so through expanding into that world, a colony unto himself. But even after hours of continued exposure, Leson, saddened, instead felt only the same sense of stillness. He did not feel full, not even a little sated. The only colonists that ever appeared on-screen were test subjects kept in crates in a conspicuously small section of the screen, illustrating the effects on the human body of various native remedies—the rest was all passage worms, the front, the passage. Leson would have learned more staying in the service. Leson, though, could take a hint. He wrote down the names of the tested substances, transferring the information to the prescription pad any time he heard *significant weight gain*. He was not so different from others, he thought. He could learn to accept help.

He presented these slips to the dispensary, and the dispensary in turn issued stapled bag after stapled bag, filling a plastic tub and then another. The man there warned Leson of the side effects and complications. A line formed behind Leson, and grew, and grew. Do not take these with these, or these with these, the man there said. Weight gain, the man there said. Impotence, the man there said. Suicidal ideation, the man there said. Leson could barely carry all of the bags away.

Once he was home and had started his regimen of pills, suppositories, ointments, medicaments, and injections, it seemed to Leson his time was better spent—his sense of well-being was thrown off even further, true, but he found that all the things on the screen, even those he'd seen before, held interest once again. He felt fuller. His sensations were once again sources of deep and abiding fascination to him. In fact, his raptness was such that he did not doze or sleep at all; without sleep, he did as much viewing as two Lesons. He may also have been speaking aloud to himself—shouting?—he could not tell. Every now and again, his neighbors complained. Leson, knock that off! Leson! Leson, do you know what time it is? He would still himself, remain silent: Yes, Leson knew what time it was. His screen was set to the correct time, just like anyone else's. He had decided it was better not to respond for now. All of what he did at this early stage was only preparation, after all; before any outreach could begin, one should have reach, range. And so Leson would first have to grow. Silently, he took another pill.

Leson's regimen inflated himself around himself. In fitful daydreams, Leson imagined fibers twining around each other into wicks of muscle, calcifications of tissue, subduction zones under his skin rising in ridges. The growing pains, at times, were unbearable. There was fat, and there was muscle, and there must, underneath it all, also have been new bone. There were shelves of Leson, lobes, where once there had been only sheer cliff faces. He grew a tenth of an inch, in all directions, then another tenth, and another. The scale went around once, twice, and then continued, so that Leson had to do math in order to weigh himself. His waist expanded, sure, but so did his wrists, his fingers and toes, his neck, his ankles. All of his joints ached. He was losing shape, becoming blobular. Even if it had not been confiscated, he would no longer have been able to put on his jungle suit. His head did not fit in the bathroom mirror anymore.

*

The seams of Leson's colony suit split when he sat down, when he bent over, when he reached for something across the table. He could see through to his overstretched skin. Would it too split when it had reached the limits of its pliability? Leson set his index finger to one of the iridescent striations that had appeared on his left arm and, with his thumb and middle finger, brought together skin that once hadn't needed to be brought together, directing the unit's automatic first-aid station to suture him where he held himself. He had some trouble extricating his index finger after.

The result was underwhelming, looking necrotic and empty to Leson, like the result of a brush with a miniature passage worm. Leson thought to retrieve the instrument he'd taken from the doctor's office—though it was not the use he'd foreseen for it, Leson could hold two opposing ideas in mind at once. He placed the needle end of the instrument against another one of his striations, pinching the old skin back together and once again directing the automatic first-aid station to suture him whole. Where his first pocket had been clumsy and loose, this new one seemed more like a pore opening onto the world. Permeability seemed a laudable goal to Leson then, something to which to aspire. He could afford, he thought, to let in more of the world, to grow through a kind of osmosis.

And so things continued with Leson, pocket by pocket. When the station had run out of binding, he considered how best to invite in the world. He settled upon stuffing his pockets with the grime that had accumulated near the baseboards and behind the furniture, all that now remained of his life before the stuckness. In time, these new catchments he had sewn into himself would foster new organisms, and this, Leson feared, would be uncomfortable, itchy and inflamed, but he thought of this as the cost of being in the world and he very badly wanted to pay his dues.

Leson paused in his labor, looking out of the greased window. A passage worm slithered past, big as a unit, ganglia drifting in the atmosphere. Leson scratched at a hillock of himself and a pouch spilled open. Something inside drifted to the floor and scurried away. Men from the patrol passed, careful, paranoid. Leson thought of chipped concrete, of gravel, of sawdust. Slowly, he rubbed a dried eye. He had once been a stalk and now he was a pile. But a place must change to accommodate its inhabitants, Leson thought.

What Leson ate was made up mainly of powders and formulae, as it always had been, but, when it seemed he had reached his outermost boundaries without any resolution to his condition, he decided he'd have to branch out into the supposedly inedible flora of the colony. He worried about the things he would not be able to keep down, on their effect on his growth, but he knew something new was needed.

Because these things needed to be treated before human teeth could rend them, Leson stewed what he found in the cultures he'd cured in his pockets and pores. The resulting mixture disturbed the stuckness of his insides, it was true, but the effect was not freeing, exactly. Still, Leson did continue to grow, through a kind of lasting, uncomfortable bloat. He felt, at times, like a termite mound. He could not supervise its members' comings and goings.

Time passed. On every passageway lever and disposal button, every wall and gate and trailing up the ramp of his unit, there were bits that had once been Leson, leavings, outpourings of his slow flood. He had thus found himself in an intractable dispute with the colony's health official and the unit's superintendent, both squeamish about entering his quarters, having been warned away from the unit by its fleeing former residents. There is something very bad happening there, they said. Very bad. People are falling ill, Leson, the super told Leson. They are being evacuated. Leson, slug-like, lolling and ecstatic with mood-altering substances and the shivering of another fever, smiled from his place on the carpet. These people brought with them some part of him wherever they went, and so yet another bit of him must have been freed. Open up in there, Leson! The colony health official is here with me. Instead, Leson inched forward, slowly barricading the door with his bulk. He felt as though about to burst. Leson! We'll have to get the patrol.

So now Leson's world has closed around him. Like his unit, his life has walls, a ceiling, a floor. He has not seen the star in months, has not breathed unrecirculated air. He has heard voices, but he is no longer sure they aren't his own. His thoughts trend in a single direction. Perhaps they always have.

And so Leson groans, having grown to perfectly meet his unit's measurements. It is almost a rumbling, this groan, the man has become so large. What it is not is a word. Outside, the superintendent has fallen ill, as has the colony's health official. All of the curious, in fact, all those who came to see Leson, are swelling. The unit's two remaining families—Leson's neighbors—disappeared in the night, and there is no one there to hear his grief. Leson is alone in his enclosure. Who knows what has become of these neighbors? Somewhere, in some other colony, a medical center is dealing with something that does not yet have a name and that causes an unaccountable augmentation.

And back in Leson's colony, the patrol is finally mustered. They arrive at the unit with their machines and immediately begin dismantling the structure. They do not know they are there because of a former serviceman. They do not know there is anyone at all inside. The front cannot wait for answers, and so the patrol does not ask questions; while the unfasteners work, passage worms cross the passage into the colony, and the jungle spills through the cordon with them. The first floor of Leson's unit is gutted and the parts are sorted and recommissioned, but, one by one, the patrol too falls ill. Soon their excavators and unfasteners and sterilizers stand idle next to the skeleton of the unit. The only walls that remain are Leson's, and, with the others ripped away, the murals of stain on those walls are all the more evident. From the outside, Leson's unit looks like a square of thin paper barely holding back some oleaginous substance. There is a noticeable convexity to the walls and the floor, even the ceiling. Those who pass think it is probably best not to think about it.

Out on the streets of his colony, all over, Leson's former neighbors blimp, go lopsided like overripe fruit. No one walks; some are rolled here and there, but it is arduous work, and the well become weary at it and then fall ill too. The elements bear down, but only the largest shelters can be occupied. Rows upon rows of units stand empty. Passage worms roam the streets, cleaning the bloated and occasionally boring holes through them with their ganglia.

A boy, seemingly abandoned by his guardians, looking like nothing so much as an immense, greatly enlarged tongue, reposes in the square outside Leson's unit. His skin has transcended see-through; it looks instead as though turned inside out and combed. Others might come along and help him—if there were others—but alone he cannot move himself, and so he has been there in the square for days. Rain has collected in the crevices of his body. Passage worms swish past, taking away parts of the units to either side of the boy. A broken unfastener stands upside down on the beaten dirt of the terrarium, and part of the low fence around the terrarium has come down. Something inside of this boy has collapsed too, some important inner faculty. The sounds he is making would have embarrassed him before, when he was well, but they come out all the same. A moan, not words. In his bloodshot eyes, rolling back in his head and then returning to focus somewhere above the plane on which other creatures still operate, one can just see his apprehension of the passage worm opposite. He has never been this close to one.

The boy does not recall how he came to be here, or what he might have done to deserve this. Is he the superintendent's boy? The health official's? Leson's? Who does he belong to? Did someone roll him here and then disappear, or did he himself make his way here before bloating? His limbs don't reach the ground; he could neither crawl nor claw his way anywhere now, so he is here, for good or for ill. Is Leson's unit his home, behind him, on the square? Is that why he is here? The passage worm halts, its ganglia flickering in the light. The moons have risen in the sky, but the star is still shining. Somewhere inside of the boy's body, an enlarged organ is pushing aside some fraction of the faculties needed for continued functioning. Struggling, he takes a breath. Somewhere inside of the boy, something is giving way. A stasis has been reached in the colony. It does not favor the colonists. The jungle's squid-like diaphanous bats descend, secrete their essences, extend their proboscises, and gently lift the boy up. He disappears into the twilight. A strange, chunky rain falls in his wake.

Perhaps disappointed, the passage worm closes on Leson's enclosure. One by one, its ganglia press against the wall and wipe some part of it away, like jets of water playing on dusted glass. Leson, uncovered, weeps to see the world again, the trail of the boy leading upward into the sky. Out flow his tears, and, along with them, the blood pressure cuff is finally delivered from inside the vastness he has become. The superintendent, the neighbors, the colony health official, the doctor, the patrol, the officer who'd discharged him—all of them and others slide out of Leson as manikins or manifestations of his grief. Their sloughed-off skins, like deflated balloons, drift lazily in the flood of jellied stuff pouring out of Leson and joining the boy's effluence. This sludge is violet, yellow, blue, red, and all of the shades in between, all colors at once, distributed across a spectrum or in an indefinable single band, depending on where one stands with regards to it. This sludge is thick enough that the unfastener stands up in it,

Gabriel Blackwell

but magnetized, in motion, is drawn onward by the passage. The runoff makes its way across the colony, carrying the furnishings of Leson's unit and all the other things it picks up on its way.

As Leson empties and joins the boy in their combined current but before he is finally spent, turned inside out by the force of his expectoration, before, that is, what was once him floats on top of the last dregs of what he had taken in, trickling along behind the rest on its way to the passage, perhaps he wonders if he has indeed been freed, or if his container has merely changed its shape to match his own. But then it is over and Leson's skin gets hung up on the terrarium's low fence and flaps under the last of the torrent, as though waving goodbye to it or else dismissing it.

The passage worm, dragging itself just a bit too close to the former enclosure, accidentally impales this Leson skin on its anterior ganglion. Without intending to, without even noticing, the worm rolls into the current and hoists the last of Leson like a flag above its exostructure. Leson, what is left of him, flies for a moment before disintegrating simultaneously at every point touching the ganglion.

One imagines this scene as a scene of triumph. Leson isn't left to do so. Somewhere, though, something has finally moved. What is owed Leson?

In Distrait
Monica Datta

THE TRAJECTORY OF THE RAIN had begun to rotate so quickly that by the time Xq finished university it poured in parallel with the Earth's surface; when the silver nitrates of the Far Orient sprang into the atmosphere to mitigate the drought, they left a fine filigree skeleton for the water molecules but no one imagined the rain would in fifty years' time move in orthogonal slabs of translucent gelatin, like the swiveling carpets and dry cleaning Xq had seen in old photographs. The saturated rugs slapped and shook the library for its secrets; the glass screeched soft.

Xq took every stair in the well—pausing at times to pull down the croaky beady lamp chains—oscillating seasick into and away from the building so it accordion-filleted the encircling birch forest like a field of distended hives. The wall panels corrugated round, broomstick branches with snapsnug shelves; the upper floors bled from a wide stair—soft rosewood and cold-blooded purpleheart—in cheesecake tribute to the Laurentian Library, falling like a doomed card house in midcollapse. The walls were a heap of failed parachutes, heptagon dying to pentagon dying to triangle; the floors a glossy, garish peacock that suited only the cacophonous café at which one could drink cavity-inducing spiced tea and shatter stray molars with hard salted chickpeas.

Out the window cedar courtyard walls, smoky in rain and sun, draped brittle, like concrete. A motorcycle jacket of Cranbrook brick in Roman slabs and leather-tanned mortar sealed the volumes with glass toothzipper of covered terracing without which they might form a bad bank, despite the glossy reclaimed mango timber door and verdigris yarmulke. The monsoons of the upper Midwest had churned the trees to arches; the sky dark blue at midnight, tufted with cotton flowers.

And then there was the forest enclosed within the courtyard that threatened to spread its roots and perform a bouleversement on the whole building; Xq's eldest sibling, Zq, had spent months in blazing forty-nine-degree summers chunking asphalt gasps, purging dry earth

91

to accommodate an actual forest of birches and poplars in the interior courtyard but if one wanted a building in the bleeding forest one should put it in the bleeding forest but nearly all the trees were in Distrait, cars and homes given a lavish burial by the same Woolfian nature deity wailing over the youth who inspired the Corinthian order.

No: no forest in Hameçon, restored to dignity from its consonant-rich Lechitic ending; the population—as well as that of Islande, its west bourgeois mothwing (by ordinance all bourgeoisies were west)—had increased a hundredfold over the past seventy years; the city limits of both municipalities were chamfered and filleted in the early sixties to make precise elm-leaf imprints within Distrait's ex-metropolis. There were now two million denizens in two square miles, pushed high into the atmosphere by a twentieth-century Far Oriental sarcoma of capsule homes and—hat tip to the city council—medina walls that were not allowed to cast a shadow over Mayura Bari. Rooftops uncoveted: falls so grisly they weren't anymore; humors vaporized clean.

At midcentury Mayura Bari replaced the meager public library on Caniff before being annexed by the national university system. It was now the largest specialist institution of any kind in North America and attracted scholars from all over, said Zq. But no one needed, in an ocean of vinyl, oxides, and concrete block, an elephantine ode to books bankrolled by the Sinhalese plutonium tycoon whose private home was a LEED Antimatter skyscraper in downtown Islande; not one with nearly all the books in lickable vitrines, not one that mandated entry via a silent, shoeless room in which one washed one's feet in a fountain deep enough to drown in.

Only a foot deep.

One whole foot!

Audiences sat for gatherings and presentations on the bare floor except in spring and summer, when, in circles, under Tagorean ordinance—signed by a salwaared white wraith called fucking Purnima—they unfurled in the swelter of the outdoor courtyard teaching and feeding one another fruits and nutmeats respectively in the mold of Jacques Rancière and infant blackbirds. Everyone blamed the young architect of Minor Oriental origins who disappeared before the project was completed and was never found; the marketing copy—around the hockey-puck plan and the punctured-soufflé section as well as the molluskwhip exploded axon—stated the design hybridized the Minor Oriental house with elements of twentieth-century Finnugrification

(Saarifinger; Neo-Birchthumb) in adapting the High Victorian colonial typology to the hard, bright froideur of the upper Midwest.

In spurning the old language it honored all who found refuge in the north.

Zq said, *There's no water. That fountain bleeds rust.*

Xq, a student of mythology, offended easily at its misuse: after all, the water eventually came back. Though ungifted as a linguist and ultimately uninterested in scholarly work, Xq found the classical literatures of the Minor Orient countered thirteen years of Jesuit schooling—at the request of their grandparents even though they weren't Catholic *parce qu'il a fallu des rites* and one should be allowed to shake off the Protestants after four hundred years—yet they offered similar reverence for ceremony without the tyranny and signifiers of the past, much to the consternation of Xq's friends of Minor Oriental ancestry in Minor Oriental Analysis. A cathedral of the republic appealed to Xq, who became a librarian.

That evening, in the meditation hall, Xq shut the fine louvers to flick the summer rain and heard a last rush of water from downstairs as V^{fx}, the gardener, scrubbed down after a long day. Almost alone, Xq began to doze against the glass wall, which sloped so far into the courtyard it was like becoming a swallow. The floor grumbled, then music: gnashing then Tinkerbell flute before zapstatic *off.*

Muttering and the bumbling clicks of someone who couldn't lock a door, from the adjoining studio. No one was supposed to be there till Monday. Xq knocked.

A young voice—English? annoyed—demanded, *What.*

What always startled Xq, who had been taught one said only *pardon. Who's there?*

A muttered staccato of profanity unfurled with the locks. Crossed arms sneered, *Your boss said I was coming.*

K'b? You're not supposed to be here till Monday. Who let you in?

Yeah.

There's a motel a quarter mile upward. Many of our residents return with chunks of wall.

All booked. The nearest vacancy is hours upward. There's nowhere else to go.

There are tent rentals all over Distrait.

The borders close at ten.

You can make it.

It's raining.

Till October.

Xq ducked under an armpit through the studio entrance. The high-ceilinged garret triangular-screamed into a nun's cornette. Like the meditation hall, it had a window that leaned into the courtyard till it committed to a sharp angle, pinpricking into the copper roof. The draping walls were useless—poor acoustics, no pinup space—and misused panels of cork on wheels had been knocked over with rightful anger. Rosewood glaze glared bright in the night. Around the slop sink hung wet underclothes. The geriatric Murphy bed, dressed already in a damp sleeping bag, slumpcreaked against the wall. An unbelted rucksack lay spent and empty like a bear trap. Its beached contents included two drills, a small electric saw, several sets of knives—oils, clay, utility—among limp, feety polyester shrouds.

I'm K'b, by the way; the anti-sculptor.

Xq nearly snapped, *Of course, The* Anti-Sculptor; *The* Only One before again catching the sharp flashes of metal, and suggested, instead, that of course it was possible to stay till Monday.

My name is Xq.

Thanks for your lack of integrity.

Xq asked, after opening and closing a dry mouth, *How was the flight?*

Shite, but what have I to compare it to. I squandered an exit when I was sixteen on my gran's funeral on the Isle of Skye. Turned out it was the previous week. Now I've like got three exits left in my whole life, and if they're anything like this, I just don't want to go anywhere.

Couldn't you apply for more?

No I'd've had four left but like all the drills and shit you know make me scary. On the way over I had a transit visa through Inverness, which apparently forbids all knives from England? Not just the ones made in England but any exposed to English air and soil. They didn't take them, though. Hope they don't dock me on the way back.

Xq said, *Last month the English Embassy threw a celebration on the Northwest 439th floor of the main complex. It was one of the most miserable half hours I've spent in a long time.*

K'b scoffed. *Everyone else is happy with mold and six exits. That's the trap. Six is all you get. Doesn't matter if you walk through the walls. You're allowed to leave the country and return six times in your life.*

I've never left the country.

Yeah, but, like, in winter you could cross the frozen river and be in another country. And you're Europeans. Might help you through the day. K'b jerked a thumb at the rest of Hameçon, whose hivemass oozed rust in the light of dusk. *Is this the favorite color?*

Xq said, *Green is scheduled at ten.*

Well, don't miss it. Shouldn't you go home?

I'm not far.

Sit down, said K'b. *I hate when people stand.*

I was going to find some dinner.

K'b shrugged. *At the newsstand I got tendon gums and ramp foam. Have some.* K'b yanked the soggy bedding from the mattress and flung it to the floor, then threw on top of it six silver packets before unscrewing a water bottle.

Thanks, said Xq, arms stretched wide to snap a tendon gum in half before dunking it in the still cold water. *These are great: I haven't had one in years. My colleague tried to bring some and was stopped at border control.*

They got rid of the pork ones a few years ago. K'b shrugged. *I'm surprised you were OK with my proposal. I'd never have come if you'd asked me to alter it.*

Hameçon is very excited about architectures of inversion in the spirit of the twentieth-century American artist Gordon Matta-Clark, stuttered Xq.

I liken cutting square-foot holes through every wall in the building to poundsfleshthievery.

Xq blinked. *I don't remember that part. I suspect you won't be able to do it.*

William Bunge exhaustively studied one square mile at the center of the city. I can't cut one-square-mile holes through the walls because the building isn't large enough.

You'll need permission to do that.

It's important that all buildings in Distrait mirror similar processes of destruction. I think of Distrait like Beirut a hundred years ago: the bullet holes were its brand. Beirut now? Nothing, France: everything France; Distrait France. If money's the only thing stopping you I say stop.

Ten years old when the Canton de Distrait joined the EU, Xq was startled when, the day after, all the textbooks were pulped in the disused railyard only to be replaced by flimsy Solresol facsimiles. The archdiocese was denied exemption or even a stay. Over the next ten years, about 59 percent of pupils—unable to master the new language—were dismissed from school and became, the newspeople said, Generation Silasila. Although this massive absence caused a substantial construction delay, they were prohibited from working and had no recourse to any public assistance including the use of roads and water. Xq's second-eldest sibling, Nz, haunted the elevators. Not even the Name Changes Department knew where Nz had gone.

K'b was gone.

Xq went through the other studio door, which opened to the end of the collection (999, Supraterrestrial Polity) and gasped at the drifts and dunes of tempered casing that buried the floor, along with the odd bloodstained iceberg crunch, and the angry islands of paper and leather and cloth, splayed open; broken bindings flayed the pages to gullfeathers. Shelves squared in murder chalk.

K'b wielded a hatchet—and it was evident from the tense, feeble grip that, consistent with the portfolio review, craft was not a major strength of the exhibited work—heaving pensively like a desert hound, hair plastered to the brow. Xq's every thought and feeling ever evaporated, replaced by a slow freezing of the nose and outer extremities and an ostrich-egg cracking of the sternum like glass holding blood boiled to gasoline, skull pressed through the nose. *Stop*, creaked the throat.

At the stair on which K'b stood began the vast Minor Oriental Event Recordings section (950s), facing south, jutting outward from the building to an exterior glazed stair, hanging into the forest so that it became a half sunroom. Pensively—and hatchethanded—K'b panted, *the city council approved the library a year after Silex ran out of water. Still none. Eighty years onward.*

There was water here. Everyone came.

Your whole country is killing its own people so that swarms of foreigners, maggots and vultures and rats, can slither into the cracks of what no one wants.

Xq clung to one of the corrugated birch panels, whose contours were as wide as a handrail, designed, ostensibly, to be grasped in futility and desperation during an earthquake and tried to creak *I'll call the police, you can't do that,* and *please stop* but no sound came out.

All this glazing wrapped around brick, like an octopus choking its victim, in an abandoned place, rewilding, ruralizing, back to bury the dead. Dakshineswar colors. Maybe this place will get a tongue-lashing from Kali, who owns all the monsoons and must now be a Muslim.

Xq sputtered, *This is not legal.*
Can't be a Muslim: the stairs are Spam, the tinned lunch meat.
I like it with rice and soy sauce and maybe mayonnaise. Did you
know this year was its 150th anniversary?
What's that got to do with anything?
That some things are better ground to a bloody pulp. You see,
becoming European has done nothing for you. American arro-
gance is nothing like French laïcité. Americans know all culture,
any culture—even their own—is a threat. The fastest way to de-
stroy a culture is to destroy its culture: Mao knew. Hitler knew.
Well, that's why they built a library, said Xq. *Distrait had a hous-*
ing surplus.
Which has been buried because they knew better than to give it
to parasites taking residence before the animal dies. Emigrants are
privileged, even the desperate ones. A grand makes you a cock-
roach king. They're investors, really, in waste. They want what no
one wants. That's what they did to every ex-industrial wasteland
a hundred years ago and now we're out of Europe and live with
the Pakis, for whom you built a monument.
That's not what happened.
I have two Minor Oriental grandparents. World's worst people.
If they know they're crawling around on a graveyard it's victory.
K'b nodded at Xq. *Doesn't this bother you? Your own people have*
been here against their will for hundreds of years, came here, built
a city, saw it ruined, and now the government is burying it?
This is a place of refuge for anyone who wants it. You have no
right to speak for my own people.
Refugees who make it out are the most privileged. You think the
worst off have the guts to flee in the dead of night without? You
just lie down and wait and pray it ends.
The rain curved so milkily it refracted the clouds; Xq remembered
when, as a child, rain fell almost straight from the sky—crying, according to the clergy, at their misdeeds—and one might primly hold
up a metal rod, pinching nylon in a simple frame, as protection.
I didn't mean to offend you, said K'b. *These are the simple truths*
of your reality. They are painful. But there's nothing more right-
wing than compassion. You don't have the right to civilize.
Ask Greece about their missing marbles, said Xq.
Everything's a bloody marble!
Rather literally, K'b believed everything was a marble, the result
of a childhood spent between the Exhibition Hall of Evolutionary

Wonders—K'b's parents were professors at the nearby Emperor's School of Scientific Hegemony—and, across the road, Bert and Vic's House of Antiquity by these aforementioned grandparents of Minor Oriental origins who felt very strongly that the ungrateful and poorly educated recipients living in the Minor Orient could not understand and did not deserve the noble interventions of English neoclassicism, which just may have done the Romans one better in the orderliness of circulation and contemporary marble work. The Earth itself was a marble, and marble looked like skin and limestone was in abundance and therefore practically the same, and so it was easy to piss away the future like any joke, like you could just shake out the bag and start again.

This was not what K'b was doing: *what K'b was doing was, emphatically, not a joke.* Everyone could keep their idols. When coal, by popular demand and years of American advisory, began to regrow, the modern art hall—which had in turn rapidly metastasized into a shopping center—was restored to its previous power-station glory. It was there that K'b's cutting exercises began: to unveil every layer of history from the prior two hundred years. When a friend told K'b about the residency at Mayura Bari, they laughed: of course Americans would discover the ancient Orientalist impulse in themselves just as Distrait threatened to eat itself, its seven-lane motorways haunted by the—literally!—faceless, overrun by bears and elmweeds, bleeding slowly from paper cuts and deaf from German measles, each with two guns (only a median of course; France hadn't fully sunk in its Communist claws).

Tears from adults sickened K'b. Xq was dying on the top stair like an opera-ballet waterfowl, clinging to pieces of splintered rosewood like it was the flat surface of the earth, howling like a broken jackal, elephant elbow skin punctured by tiny glass filaments. *Why did you do it,* it squeaked.

Destructive processes are natural.

People stay here when there's nowhere to go.

Vulnerable enough to be brainwashed.

It's not about brainwashing.

The problem, said K'b, *is that architecture gives birth to the city; without it the city would not exist: separations, thresholds, crossings, borders. This is not a building, but a tiny, demented country. Distrait is defined by its lack of architecture: wild animals. The people of Hameçon are legless hens. The people of Islande are humans. Not to me, though.*

Xq sat up. *It must be nice to be the only one to see the world so clearly.*

I think for myself. The neoliberal economy of the early twenty-first century collapsed and left the world in shambles. It's a travesty that its idols still exist.

If you take a hatchet to the shelving, won't that get in the way of your project, to cleanly cut square-foot holes?

K'b looked dumbly at Xq. *That wasn't what I proposed. I want to destroy the archaeology of neoliberalism before it becomes archaeology.*

So you're not only a violent sociopath, you're a bore.

That means either a lot or very little. Can I boil some water? The gums are a bit stale. Best to sip the broth.

K'b slipped down the stairs two at a time in thick blue socks, looking very young. Xq stood up slowly and stayed several steps behind. They lumbered into the lobby where the harpstringed glass wall tapered behind the circulation desk and the turquoise floor giggled at them. A wide, severely angled doorway to the courtyard in hard purpleheart contrasted with the curve of the sloping birch wall.

Xq presented some water from the machine behind the café counter but K'b refused it and said it must be boiled properly, filling a large copper vessel with rust and straining out the fine iron sediment before the liquid went into a neutralizing device and finally into a kettle that seemed not to have been used in a decade. Xq admitted the process resulted in a fantastic cup of hot water, enjoyed, on its own, without tea or tendon.

Despite the rain Xq led K'b to the interior courtyard, into which the cedar walls bloated like sails. The roof enclosed so severely it might well have been glazed over to create a large indoor atrium, but no matter: it was dark. Even with the shade and birch thicket the grass was still sunbleached. They ignored the Adirondack chairs and sat among the parched tufts, watching the rain move.

K'b, singing arrhythmically and below the breath, plucked eight or ten dry blades and floured them, aerating the powder back to the cracked soil before peeling off an orange jumper to reveal a heavy shirt of magnets and ETFE.

Xq said, *You never spent a minute here before cutting up the building.*

Cutting it up is the best way to learn about anything, said K'b. *Maybe it's an autopsy.*

It's called surgery when you're still living.

99

Who's living?

Before coming here I had only worked in academic libraries, at which everything was a high-security ritual, said Xq. *I just thought it was a great thing, to attend any of the talks or courses, to know culture could shape you as much as a conscious lack of money, or your family, or religion. Knowledge didn't need to be the prerogative of the privileged.*

Wise of the designer to make the courtyard too small for suicides. Your people are dying. Very slowly and all at once the way all Americans want it.

It's just a library.

The way your monsoons are a mist.

These people you speak of are not dying any more than you or me or anyone who was or wasn't born here. I refuse to entertain the idea that anyone is more mortal than any other.

That's ridiculous, said K'b.

Everyone who comes here gets a sturdy desk and a heavy lamp and shelves. They can find almost literally any book they want. It has the mission of any great public library.

Like the British Library. Thatcherism at its peak.

That was a very long project. There must have been five prime ministers.

They demolished much of Bloomsbury for nothing.

What, was Martin Chuzzlewit upset? Xq shouted.

Probably. Martin Chuzzlewit was an architect. K'b guzzled the last of the tendon water.

Xq looked up at Hameçon with its glowering sign, with a smaller version above the douanes' offices; English-speaking schoolchildren were taught the town name's meaning with the hook of the cedilla and the giraffe-necked cranes. There were ten elevators, the slowest of which traveled at one meter per second, the fastest fifty in a kind of capillary vacuum. Many—unwilling to adapt to the prevailing mores of the corpulent, enjoyed a leisurely climb up the stairs, and for the bold in rucksacks there were ice picks attached to ropes, hurled a great distance between platforms, with art deco arcuations designed in praise of the automobile by an American president after firing all the architects, banned in Distrait and physically impossible to bring into Hameçon. The banlieue ballooned outward like a mushroom. No one had air rights.

When a magnet dinged Xq on the head it was clear K'b had left the courtyard, perhaps to the studio, or to balance on the sloped roof, scraping green and bronze dust from boot soles or to bash open the glass so as to coat the Rig Veda in ramp foam, but that wasn't what happened. Instead the sky melted into a last cataract gush; the climber silhouettes in the distance wrapped themselves around the ropes with cheeks Xq knew were bloated, breathing through the ears.

The copper hollow of the roof popped and rose and K'b's silhouette was distinguishable from the raccoons, who were increasingly large but unlikely to spend much time in treetops, and after tugging the hair of the pearly ghosts in the birch thicket it had reached the court, all Doric, at the base of the city, bubbling upward in twentieth-century sugar cubes. Xq tried to call out but was deaf even to the ears on either side of the skull that instead felt the rush of drainage underground and realized it had knocked everything flat throughout the courtyard.

A police officer rushed in, shouting, *The alarms were delayed, what had happened? Was this Xq's doing? Whose? Why was anyone there so late?*

There was an incident, said Xq. *I've got no details.*

People who live in glass houses shouldn't change clothes, said the police officer.

The clock on the nearest tower—Gothic and Venetian, also in tribute to the Minor Orient—clanged eleven. The sky had burst open. Xq thought the constellation Kṛttikā read clearly but it was soon blunted by K'b's face hanging over, red and taut as Mars. Perhaps five or six police officers were inspecting the grounds and terraces, glowing—glowering too—in the fire of the glass terracing. K'b gestured to them. The police rushed in to identify Cassiopeia and asked K'b if Xq had really been the perpetrator. When K'b claimed responsibility they all heaved with relief; they said they had been waiting for someone to cut holes in an emblem of civic hatred and divisiveness; the destruction of the library would be as momentous an event as Alexandria. Everyone would again say the names of Caesar and Aurelian and Pope Theophilus; men would get their names back; men would be men again. It would be beautiful.

Two Poems
Robert Kelly

INCLUSIONS

The amber in chamber
glows against the wall
opposed to the window.

Sit where I can see you.
Your hair. The chair
painted yellow
(like that van Gogh
empty bedroom)
long ago looks
golden now. You now.

You now. You know
how things have turned
into shadows of us,
thousands of years to
take on our shapes.
I love this room,
it understands my eyes.

Robert Kelly

FOR STEVEN HOLL

The architect is everywhere.
So many solutions
to no problem, like poetry.

Imagine a house, walk in.
Your shadow leads the way
mornings. That sort of house.

Tilt the floor a little
away from the moon,
you're man enough for house

woods highway storm cloud
churchbell in the dining room
the sea-sunken bed.

Sometimes number theory
is an agony,
five miles in another's shoes,

your shadow scrapes the floor
you know it knows things
you'll never tell

no critic knows—
the way a shadow breaks
at the first stair step

a simple bird
bounces off a window
stunned flies away.

This is what a house must be
the rule of three
divided by eternity

we have to know it
to let it go,
a house too is stunned

by where it stands,
wake it
with revelry and prose,

hibiscus, spandex,
the swimming pool
must have no shape

but water alone,
you have it all now,
have her in your arms,

the form of water
wakes up the mind.
You build of light—

footsteps follow.

Architecture for Monsters
Mary South

BROKEN RIB CAGE RISES ABOVE the desert of Abu Dhabi like the mirage of a satanic cathedral. The condominium tower is ninety-one stories of bleached-bone concrete curving from a central sternum. This skeletal structure, however, has not the dancer's aplomb of a Calatrava. Halfway up, steel beams suddenly wrench apart the facade, offering a glimpse into a courtyard that's so fecund, it's visceral. Critics have proclaimed it a magnum opus of feral genius, while others have mocked the aesthetic as "roadkill architecture." It is the most famous of the Damaged Organ buildings by Helen Dannenforth, an iconic, if controversial, doyenne in the field. She has repeatedly been lambasted for possessing a sensibility that is viciously carnal, if not outright bloodthirsty. "I was watching videos of surgeries," she said of her design. "As I saw doctors crack a man's chest and force a window to his heart, I was compelled to sketch."

It has been a good year for Dannenforth. A MacArthur Fellowship was followed by a successful bid for the renovated Bilbao-Abando high-speed train station. The Met is putting on a retrospective of her work, a rarity for a living practitioner. Early access to the exhibition was like peering inside a cabinet of wonders. Here stood the presentation for her Memory of Skin pavilion at the Serpentine, a series of porous mesh panels rigged as the masts of a galleon upon which a plush, synthetic coral would grow via photocells. The artificial tissue would retain every indentation, every cicatrix incurred on its surface before being removed at the end of the summer. There lay her drawings done in brush pen with flourishes of watercolor, the details wrought with the precision of a miniaturist. Whispers are circulating she's the front-runner for the coveted Pritzker Prize. None of these accolades affect the woman herself, who in a few weeks will be feted by friends and family in celebration of her fifty-fifth birthday.

I met Helen Dannenforth for our interview on Long Island, a few hours from the firm she founded in Soho. Her Cumulus House ripples in contrast to silhouettes of the surrounding stolid manors. East Hampton commonly conjures visuals of rustic shingles salted by

105

ocean winds, gambrel roofs, wraparound verandas, shuttered bay-window seats. While she retained many of these elements—white trim, transomed doors—the classic cedar shakes have been changed to aluminum. As the pitched roof slopes into frothy formlessness, it's as cells replicating in a petri dish or the transition of rutted terrain to sky, those eponymous cumulus witnessed from the belly of a passenger jet. The floating median marking this bifurcation, a kind of cream shiver, is a poured translucent acrylic meant to evoke clean linen. The house is a regression to precognition, its genesis from lying in her Michigan backyard as a child and staring up at sheets breezy on the line. It is an homage to laundry, weeds, naming clouds after the animals they resemble, power lines, suburbia, reverie.

"It's supposed to feel as if the house has become atmosphere," she explained. "I've been trying to tinker with softer constructions. Earlier in my career, my proposals were for buildings that had violence done to them. I was wary of the perception that I was merely feminine, too airy."

To labor under her has been likened more to taking holy orders than a job opportunity. The lucky are plucked from courses Dannenforth has taught at Harvard, Yale, and the Architectural Association in London. Acolytes rendering are attired in monastic black or gray—de rigueur, but also required at Studio Forth by strict dress code. They muff their ears in huge headphones and don't speak unless necessary, as if sworn to vows of silence. Helen accoutres a wardrobe that is part nun, part drag queen. A closet of monochromes surprises with the random attack of pigment. Gaudy statement jewelry scaffolds her knuckles and collarbone. She styles the opulence of her matriarch-white hair between her shoulder blades in a low chignon like a large bellows. "They say people deface Rothko and Barnett Newman canvases because of their intense swaths of color," she told me, holding a cocktail ensemble red as a spanking to my figure. "Wear something like this to both entice and threaten a man."

Not a single person in the community has heard her raise her voice, yet there is a pervasive fear of rousing her wrath. In general, she is unreadable, sibylline. "She shits ice cubes," said a former employee. It is rumored that she dismissed an assistant for expressing an opinion while in Zurich for a conference. The two were reclining in a sauna at Therme Vals, and the assistant stated that Russian suprematism was "paint-by-numbers for the blind." Helen shot back that she should pack her bags and return to the States. When, of course, this little fit wasn't taken seriously and the unconscionably witty assistant had the temerity to show her face at dinner, the table was made to wait to eat until she had been checked out of the hotel. Then again, to be a Dannenforth favorite is to acquire a second mother who is better than a mother. Those chosen few have spent holidays at her side. They have been armchair counseled on their portfolios, their love lives, their childhoods. They have occupied rent free the guest suite in her loft apartment in the city. Oblivious, she has had conversations about current projects as her protégé du jour is nakedly lounging postcoitus with a paramour.

Romance isn't something that concerns Helen on a personal level, though she does have a daughter by an estranged ex-husband. Lily, sweet sixteen, came crashing in with keys, boots, and weekender bag during our chat over tea. It would have been easy to mistake her for the pubescent doppelgänger of her mother if not for the bits of leaves in her tangled hair, the wabi-sabi scratches and insect bites on her shins. She had gone on a camping trip with her boyfriend and unpacked by tossing makeup, snacks, tabloids, dirty clothes around the room like so much flotsam, the shipwreckage of a girl. "A girl becomes a woman when she learns everything has its place," Dannenforth aphoristically observed. On my official introduction, when I wasn't distracted by this charming chaos, Lily's sunburned cheeks reminiscent of hammocks and pitchers of lemonade and sneaked cigarettes, the effortless peasant blouse I'm certain cost hundreds of dollars, did I discern the asymmetry in her features that urged me to both look away and to peer more closely at her countenance in reverie of its peculiarity.

The jaw was excruciatingly small and pulled to one side, as if she were frozen in an expression of trying to make up her mind about something or other. The mouth, despite its full lips with their pinup appeal, was similarly torqued. Helen, noticing my staring but trying not to stare, swept the hair from her daughter's face and said, "You might as well see it all." An ear was pierced several times with studs; the opposite ear was proportionally sized but its ridges softened, as if it were sand on the beach washed over and flattened by the tides. Lily had been born with craniofacial microsomia and classified as "severe," using the grading scale known as OMENS. She had needed assistance even to survive, as her breathing was obstructed. When she was old enough, a rib had been taken from her to supplement the absent bone of the jaw. Cartilage from that rib went to crafting her ear. The surgeons had been the best in the world and they had done their best. I could tell she would have been conventionally beautiful had she not

107

suffered this anomaly in the womb and she still was attractive, though mostly because she was compellingly unusual.

When the daughter went to use the shower, I dared to ask if Lily's condition had had any influence in Helen's notoriously ravaging style, her mangling of anatomy. The rib, the surgeries, how could it not? "That's offensive," she replied. "I'm asked that because of my sex. If one of Frank Gehry's sons were disabled, would you inquire if that had affected his concept development? My interest in the body began before I became a parent. It is primal. I don't need to use Lily for creative fodder. Remember what Juhani Pallasmaa wrote: 'The origin of our understanding of space lies in the cavern of the mouth.' Picture the crocheted, hoodoo majesty of the spine. I'm not the main practitioner with a corporeal bent, yet I get the nickname 'Mrs. Biomorphosis.' I am the one who is labeled a sociopath, a predator."

I never knew my mother. An obsessive-compulsive lab tech who experienced paranoid delusions assaulted her and stashed the remains in a cable chase of the Genetics Department at Berkeley. She was a molecular biologist studying strawberries, specifically strains that were drought resistant versus those that were not. My father had a nervous breakdown after her death, so at twenty months old I was sent to live with my maternal grandparents. I cultivated my mother's passion for structure, but my pursuits turned to architecture in lieu of science. Dannenforth was my heroine, a beacon of powerful estrogen in a profession hostile to female influence. The coincidences in our biographies also helped the flourishing of my worship, I admit. When Helen came to give a lecture at Rice University in Houston, where I was pursuing a master's, I waited my turn to speak with her until I was the last student in the auditorium. As she addressed me, I muttered some phrase of thanks and fled, too filled with anxiety to permit her to become real.

Soon afterward, I dropped out of my graduate program. My grandmother was diagnosed with Alzheimer's, and I returned to sell the house and set her up in an assisted-living facility. I was the sum total of extant kin. Choosing to remarry and start over, my dad didn't reclaim custody. Boxes of knickknacks and mementos were the raw materials from which I constructed the aleatory model of my mother. Gardens were her refuge, as were birds. She kept nests. Pads of paper were filled with graphite nests, their twiggy tessellation like the still life of a tornado. It occurred to me that a nest is the epitome of dwellings, a safe haven between firmament and roots. There was a metaphysical warmth to the belongings I sorted through, as if I sensed spirits lingering under afghans, doing dishes, slamming the screen door the way she did as a child and later the way I did as a child. They say the haunted house symbolizes the border between the natural and the artificial—or is it the artificial being overtaken by the natural?

At any rate, I freelanced laser-cut shelving and patio extensions. I also wrote articles. Finally, that fortuitous day arrived when I was commissioned for a profile piece by the seminal *Inhabit*. Helen failed to recognize me, which wasn't demoralizing, but what vexed me was succumbing to incoherence despite the years in between our introduction. Too cowardly to mention I was simpatico with her motherlessness, the abandonment by a father, I segued into her research on family estates with the aim that she would reveal her past. "I lift from Gothic novels," she said. "There's something about the entropic vision of an ancient manor that's both creepy and welcoming. We treat architecture how we treat our physical selves, as doomed to oblivion. No effort is spared in restoring the Sistine Chapel ceiling to pristine éclat. A Matisse won't go to waste. Take a Mies van der Rohe, though, and it's given the care of a crypt. Preservation's a Sisyphean task in this craft. 'That's all that's left of the voice of Enrico Caruso / from all that's left of an opera-house somewhere in Matto Grosso,' a poet wrote."

She waxed melancholy about the replicas of Japanese and German villages fabricated from scratch in the 1940s to test the incendiary capacity of napalm. Hollywood set decorators outfitted each domicile down to the details of toiletries and authentic newspapers. "Extraordinary amounts of effort for the simulacra of ghost towns that were then blown up," Helen lamented. "Sounds about right." Discussing books rekindled the embers of her monologue. In her office, Ernst Neufert's handbook on ergonomic principles rests alongside *The Castle of Otranto*, *The Woman in White*, and *Jane Eyre* with its crazy wife in the attic. Recondite chambers and whimsical, old-timey chicanery are her fetish. "Any shelter should also expose ourselves. I'm a fan of that genre of literature because passages of prose describe passages through ramparts, hedge mazes, and servants' quarters. The plot hinges on a secret in a secret room. It makes visible how the brain harbors a secret."

Helen has her own cache of secrets. Upstate New York, on acres of rolling hills, woods, and manicured demesne is an institution ominously titled "the Retreat." Mustering a mosquitoed tenacity, I managed to schedule a visit with a patient there, Hannah Dannenforth, her half sister. The drive in a rental without a working radio was spent feeling sorry for myself. My interview had bombed. I was in the doldrums. A woman who looked like everybody's aunt sat down across from me in the rec center. Where Helen was lissome, Hannah was corpulent; where Helen's hair was loosely elegant, Hannah's was tightly cropped and turfing every which way, like a lawn in severe need of mowing; where Helen entertained in haute couture, Hannah hid in stained secondhand. "Do you know why I'm stuck here with a bunch of junkies and schizophrenics and Adirondack chairs?" she asked. I said that I didn't—sleuthing out her contact information itself had been a test of will. "I'm here," she replied, "because I'm Lily's real mother."

Of course, there is another reason for her being committed. She kidnapped Lily, twelve years old when the incident occurred. In a postmodern imitation of manifest destiny, the two began heading west, except in a Honda instead of a covered wagon. Hannah agreed to a plea deal: five years of probation on a suspended sentence provided that she voluntarily check into a psychiatric hospital. "There's buildings devoted to locking up people like me for good," she said. "I bet you don't hear my sister talk about the architecture of the prison, of the sanitarium, do you?" Cupping her palms in a beseeching gesture, she went on, "Helen blames me for Lily. When she looks at her, she sees her biggest failure that she has to live with every day. I was constantly afraid while I was pregnant that I would birth one of those babies with microcephaly or spina bifida or their intestines spilling out of the body. But after I saw her, those feelings seemed so trivial. When I look at that girl, I feel proud. I made her, I think. She's mine."

According to Hannah, Lily was in on the abduction. Surreptitious emails and phone calls were exchanged. A lot of kids want to run away, I argued. That doesn't mean you take them up on the offer. "This wasn't about hating your mother because she grounded you during spring vacation," she retorted. This was about the sanctity of the shared meal, report cards pinned on the refrigerator and pinwheels in flowerpots, coercing the dog into a costume for funny snaps, an abode that wasn't relegated to a spread in a magazine. Yes, disappearing had been drastic, but Helen's forsaking her was also drastic. Helen was indifferent as an oyster when she was laid off, when medical bills piled up, when her property was foreclosed. She was living out of her car like a secular mendicant—"the Wandering Spinster"—

bereft of wisdom to dispense. Visits with Lily were forbidden. Plus, legal recourse wasn't available to her because she had signed away her rights. I found myself confiding in her how I had wanted to confide with her sister. "I know how it feels," she said, her voice wistful-intimate, "to have lost all that you cherish."

America is an idea that there is more space where nobody is than where anybody is. Gertrude Stein uttered that statement, herself a nurturer of great talent under her tent of personality. "There are vast tracts in this nation that are beyond vacant space, they're degraded space, zombie space. It's the pastoral of the forlorn mini mall," Helen pontificated. We were on the topic of the factory she'd built in North Carolina for HUSK, the high-end furniture manufacturer. Redolent of palafitte, the warehouse takes pilotis to the nth degree. It is caterpillarean, raised up on disembodied legs, looking to crawl away over the terrain at an instant. When the company went out of business, it was converted into a museum of artifacts endemic to the United States: slot machines based on horror films, the face of our savior inscribed on toast and sundry pastries, toilet-seat mosaics. "A region that has been populated and then forgotten triggers sentimentality, which is why we have a predilection for kitsch. It's funny how everything has to prove that it is what it is."

Any geographic location can be the end of a journey. Hannah was incantatory as an oracle as she described their route past pine-tree nurseries, fields knuckled with gourds, billboards blistered on blue vistas, factories weathered as newspaper with their collection of faces crumpled as yesterday's headlines. Here was the alleged heartland. To my mind, this prompted the performance of Francis Alÿs and five hundred volunteers with shovels moving a dune but ten centimeters outside of Lima. It's acknowledged that something has happened, but there's no evidence for what that might be. Novelty, for me, was always accompanied by the orchestra of longing. When I saw the Duomo in Florence, when I went on an elementary-class trip to gaze upon the pharaohs in their bandage robes supine in sarcophagi, wonder harmonized with the wonder of why an anonymous man murdered my mother. So I didn't dare cross-examine the story of a reunion of the sort I had fantasized about and would forever be denied.

"I forgot the appetite the world has for girls," Hannah said. At a McDonald's in Ohio, they had hunkered down with their banal origami of boxes to enjoy the heat-lamp potpourri of starch and ketchup packets and antiseptic, the nonpareil crumpling of oiled wrappers, when a bus unloaded a bunch of misfits into the parking lot. Immediately, Lily was surrounded by backpacks. They played with her hair, caressed her ear, asked her to smile and giggled at her lopsided grin. Someone produced a temporary tattoo of a butterfly. There were cries of "Put it on her face!" She contorted head over shoulder in the bathroom to scrutinize the result, planted just below her jaw. "It's ugly," she decided. Soaping thoroughly, she scrubbed until it was bits of torn wings and her neck was red. That children were casually cruel was one matter, but the attention of grown men was another. In the desert, they stopped for gas. A wind sock flopped on top of the shop, desolate as the horizon. The station was the spot for the stroll of a sole tumbleweed. It was a parody of itself, trusty rusty pumps flipping analog digits with current prices. When Lily went in search of Twizzlers and Slim Jims, truckers were mesmerized by her ass. "Girl," they hollered, as if they were this moment catching on to the names for things. "Girl, girl."

A girl, a woman, can be a slut or a tragedy, but not both—that was Hannah's theory. When a member of our sex falters and endures unwarranted punishment, she is told she summoned her own disaster. It's how in the aftermath of a tsunami or seismic event victims are reprimanded for putting down flooring where they are vulnerable to some tantrum of earth. "I have to work alone," Helen said. "Women are cheated in the partnerships of our industry. Eileen Gray and the E-1027 villa is the foremost instance. Le Corbusier saw it and was smitten, so without asking for permission, he painted murals on the immaculate walls. She was furious. It was a violation. This architectural pissing act caused the press to erroneously credit it as his. I suppose there's justice that he had this restless fascination with the machinery of aviation—the sculptural contrapposto of us against solar systems, galaxies—but did not die aloft. Swimming his laps by that villa, he drowned."

As their flight continued, Hannah worried more about her daughter's safety and less about being apprehended. Winded from the switchbacks of the Rockies, they rented a room that led out to a pool with clinical depression. The soullessness of these suites was an uncanny source of comfort—the oily genital smears on the mirrors, the matching TVs, duvets. Helen Dannenforth too has a fondness for the contradiction inherent to hubs of transit, which is why that train station in Spain will branch like dissected capillaries and arteries to dramatize the purpose and many pathways of travel. In the morning, Lily was missing, her twin bed a maelstrom of blankets. She wasn't gormandizing gummy pancakes at the buffet. She wasn't off taking the car for a joyride. Back in their uncaring accommodations, her sad, middle-aged would-be-felon mom assumed the traditional pose of defeat, cradling her head. Track blinds cut slices of shade and of sunshine swarming with dust motes, and she thought, "Someone has died on this mattress, to that neatly divided light." Then the baritone hum of the air conditioner switched off, and she heard the glass-dulled laughter.

"I got water up my nose!" resounded a flirtatious, high-pitched protest. Lily was at the center of a group of teens goofing around by the "out of order" diving platform. Their ease had the quality of established friendships, though Hannah knew those were but the tenuous bonds of Coppertone and chlorine. A boy dipped below the surface and burst forth as a flume with Lily on his shoulders. Not pausing to deliberate, an opposing couple did the same. Both boys strutted, enjoying the ruffled crotches against their necks, the spandex cleavage grazing their buzz cuts. They waded nearer and nearer until the girls began to grapple the air like trees come to life in a nightmarish forest, if trees could also be girls at the height of their fertility. Her competitors hubristically concluded that Lily would be shy and weak and that they would topple her no problem, but she fought viciously and below the belt—yanking braids, shoulder ramming, lunging for bikini tops. She bested team after team until the last girl fell, the thunk of an elbow to the skull and the subsequent splash the signaling bell of defeat.

"She won because she's a freak," the loser declared, climbing up the ladder. A scratch crosshatched a string tie of her suit and blurred with moisture. "Look, I'm bleeding." Runoff swished on the deck to the rhythm of her hips like a fluid hula skirt. The rest of the girls joined her, hiving into a clique on reclining chairs and scrunching their fairy-tale hair dry. "Is that it?" Lily challenged. "Come and get me, bitches!" The boys, unwilling to upset the girls, drifted toward the shallow end. "Lily saw our relationship differently after that," Hannah said. "The future had shifted, if imperceptibly." Waving grandly for her daughter's attention and to subvert their ostracism, she yelled, "Lily! Lily!" This gesture, however, was met with an expression of deer-in-the-headlights mortification. Whenever Helen showed up, she had recontextualized Lily's features as sexy or mysterious. A mother with a paisley nightgown tucked into her jeans and pressure socks would make her simply a mistake of biology.

Now Lily had questions. What was my mother like growing up?

"She was mean. Helen's ten years my senior," Hannah said, "so

113

while in charge of babysitting, she raided the liquor and poured alcohol down my throat. Sometimes she kicked, pinched, hit, or bit me where the adults wouldn't spy the injuries. When I defied her once, she gave me a shiner."

But was she pretty? Was she popular?

"She was out of control. The verdict was unanimous to enroll her at a boarding school in New England for her participation in the arson of a derelict cabin. The unspoken reason was the fear she would get pregnant out of wedlock like her real mother."

Why does she hate you?

"I was a usurper. Back then, if a girl accidentally got knocked up, the option that was available to her was seeking refuge in the Upper Peninsula and clandestinely having it. That's how Helen was born, from such a liaison. When our father was let in on her existence, he initiated contact. He didn't intend to fall in love with her stepsister— my mother—it sort of happened. Can't you imagine her lying awake in her dormitory and resenting me?"

Am I like her?

"I told Lily she shouldn't desire to be like her. Helen was battling a lot of demons—I know that today, though I didn't then. She was packed up and moved between our house and the house of her adopted parents like baggage. The positive is that out of necessity she philosophized about the meaning of rooms and became a visionary of this century."

This apologia was gratifying to Lily, who confessed she had already been tried in skipping class, smoking pot, allowing herself to be fondled by boys. "I was nauseous with jealousy, that Lily was fascinated by my narcissistic half sister but not me," that she aspired to toss her innocence away in imitation. Helen was the chosen mother because she was distant, unknowable, though in a sense wasn't everyone? In a study of unknowability, Studio Forth was commissioned for a church in France at the base of the Jura Mountains. It is a dome of obscure dimensions, a cocoon of mist sourced from Lake Bourget. Inside, a plexiglass column extends to an oculus through which water is poured and frozen, then the plexiglass removed. The notion was Cartesian. If the soul was like a wax, recognizable as a paraffin taper or a melted padella, God could be understood as hydrogen—as vapor, as solid, and as liquid after a chilling encounter. The column has to be continually replaced, since it is suspended in an endless process of wearing away from a patina of fingerprints.

Utah brought a bed-and-breakfast run by Mormons, a matron with a forehead smooth from her devotions carrying towels up Victorian stairs. "I'm not sure about you," she said, "but I don't feel like I've arrived somewhere until I've had a wash." Upon waking, a kitchen with a bona fide family greeted them, cool scrambled eggs in a warm majolica bowl, bacon scalloped like a petticoat on a porcelain plate, toast with honey, toast with butter, toast with marmalade. The father drank coffee in a fatherly way. It was a rare lay indulgence for a man who followed religious rules. A couple girls around Lily's age laid out place settings, methodically circling like the hands of a clock. As for Lily, she had draped a gossamer wrap around her head, sweating in defiance of the heat. Taking pains to hide her face was not like her. Usually, she flaunted her deformity like a new haircut. Reading comics, the calm in the middle of this endearing storm of preparations, was why: a boy, tall, blond, fresh as a seraphim in a fresco, his awareness limited to the nimbus of his own importance.

"When are you due on the road?" the father asked. The salt-of-the-earth wife chimed in that she suggested a detour to the salt flats, if they weren't in a hurry. It was possible for them to spare the afternoon and be tour guides, pack a lunch, et cetera. With the family involved—that is, the son—it was obvious Lily was keen on the scheme, so Hannah consented, repeating a mantra that these acts of concession, like daily prayers, would win over her daughter. A soporific minivan spun to where the landscape blanched. Wasn't the Dead Sea also a saline promise? It was inevitable then that a tribe of faithful would settle there, by God's blankness. The divine liked to woo with nectar, but wed with salt. In Gnosticism, the divine is discovered through this absence, dubbed apophasis. The trunk was unloaded, gingham spread against the white, along with tinfoiled wedges of tuna and wheat, grapes, seltzer, plastic utensils shiny and pure as if by baptism. There was a scooping of chips into an avocado, then it was a ripe reminder.

Benjamin, the boy, bounced a tennis ball off a racket while his greyhound watched in anticipation, sleek and solid as the handle of a water pump. He got around to throwing the ball for the dog—leaving divots with a puff puff puff of crust. Too long at that game and they would wear those paws raw. Lily paid attention to Benjamin by way of the dog. "What a wholesome family you are," Hannah mused. "We try to raise our kids with proper values, to say 'please' and 'thank you,' to listen to their elders, to treat the body as a temple," the father replied. "I thought that people preached that the body is a temple to prevent girls from living in theirs," Hannah countered.

"Female or not," he said, "if they don't respect themselves, then who will?" The sisters screamed, "Benji! Lunch! Lunch! Benji!" until he jogged in their direction. Dutifully, Lily accompanied him, a shadow of his shadow, but as she closed in, the wind kited her careful wrap into the air with that inanimate grace of the graveyard. She didn't move, under the spell that if she didn't move, no one would notice.

There was a struggle against tears, then the tears. The wrap had landed on the crepitant grate of the van, so Benjamin went to the rescue, mumbling to her, "Here you go," as he offered it up, crudely folded. "That fabric is so pretty," the older girl said. "Where did you buy it?" the younger asked. They sat her down, untangled the fringe, and rearranged the wrap around her neck. The boy scarfed his food and was off, but Lily let him go solo. He adventured so far with the grey-hound, the pale dog in alto-relievo over the pale dust was some spirit of salt. When he tired, he returned to lean on his elbows, eyes only for ozone. His dreaminess was an aphrodisiac. Not that it was per-fect—on the ride back, the sisters quarreled and the mother warned that she would confiscate their cell phones, meanwhile Benjamin irritatingly rebelled by thrusting his knees into the seats. During departure, the girls hugged tentatively how girls do, avoiding press-ing breasts yet expressing genuine affection. Lily blatantly ignored the boy as he said goodbye.

The family was like a faded daguerreotype as they waved in the headlights. Passing through Vegas, Lily relinquished the silence she had been fattening to say, "This is the brightest city astronauts can locate in orbit." There was the replica of the Eiffel Tower, the pyra-mid of the Luxor with its fake sphinx, the Doric-columned Caesars Palace, green-felted card tables a mise en abyme of Astroturfed casino golf courses. The Strip was a name that was emblematic of a situation women find themselves in, not theirs, but troubling nonetheless—an odalisque spreading her lips on a chaise or, more appropriately, a des-perate single mother of flesh and blood draped on a pole, a verb co-erced into a noun. Miles out, where lodging was cheap, they checked into "Motel Apocalypse," a science-fiction vision of the future from the past. Murals depicted Asimovian hover cars and robots but no ethnic diversity or women in roles besides housewives. Imitation too is a kind of character. Imagination is circumscribed by our circum-stances. Cheesy theme motels were no exception.

The apocalypse they picked was a virus-ravaged colony on the moon, a lunar Roanoke, though the Rapture was debated. "This is stupid," Lily complained, throwing herself on the bed in their room-as-geodesic-dome the way girls who yet throw their limbs too hard at objects do too, before they're told not to. Watching her, her daughter seemed the personification of sun through a winter window, apricot delicate. As Hannah knelt before her to offer comfort, pressing a cheek against her cheek, she felt shaky, sacrilegious. It was the first time they had touched since setting out, and while she knew they had time, nothing but time, it was like the end of the world. She had the same feeling when holding her in the hospital for the first time. "No one will ever love me," Lily moaned into her pillow. Kissing her on the slope of her nape, Hannah said, "Not true." Later that night, police escorted her from Motel Apocalypse, their strobes revolving in the lobby like it was a junior-high dance.

That her daughter was missing turned out to be a revelation to Helen. She was overseas in Beijing, supervising the foundation pour for her labyrinthine concert hall, cochlear like an ear ("too literal an interpretation," said its detractors) with a tympanic, abalone outer shell. What must Lily have made of such a design? If she saw it as a rebuke, she had reason to rebel. Those mandated with her care had been strategically confused as to the girl's whereabouts: the house-keeper believed her to be staying with a friend, her driver that she was off with family, which in a weird way was accurate. When Lily phoned from Nevada, complaining that Hannah had kidnapped her and how much it sucked, Helen alerted law enforcement and didn't bother to buy a plane ticket. She was needed at the site. "What Lily did was a betrayal," Hannah said, but if life is occasionally interest-ing in anecdote, it's not in the actual living, and she was worn down by forgiveness. Lily was a child, after all, and children are still sub-ject to the whims of their boredoms. "Why do we have children? I kept asking myself that question. We can't protect them—not with our infrastructures, our technology, our culture. They're going to die. They're also going to intentionally and unintentionally hurt each other. It's selfish to have children."

Strangulation as indicated by a fractured hyoid was the cause of my mother's death. She had been raped. The coroner folded open her skin like a map, emptied the cadaver—or, rather, the body of evi-dence that was my mother—of parts, and stitched her shut with a sailmaker's needle, while painstakingly recording the bruises, the cuts and abrasions, the vaginal swelling into a microphone. I related to what Hannah was saying, though what were those of us who were here to do? "Love," she said. "Love as much as you can. Lily may not feel my love yet, but she will. I even love Helen." No doubt she sounded oversaturated in therapy. Platitudes were for pharmacies and embroidery. Still, the truth is that love doesn't vanish. Love is our legacy. When you love, she postulated, it stays with those beloved for life, passes into whom they love, and unspools through the universe, expanding with it into eternity.

I wanted to love. I wanted to believe my mother had loved me and would have continued loving me, but I didn't feel her love. If I searched for it enough, perhaps I would find that emotional inheritance, hidden somewhere inside myself like an appendix, an organ I didn't know was there or why I needed it until it ruptured and potentially annihilated me. Is that the reason, during my drive back to the city in the saddest rental car on earth, I fantasized about every tiny detail of that miserable Hannah-Lily odyssey? I wasn't sure what I was writing anymore, as certainly my editors at the glossy, coffee-table magazine wouldn't publish this mess of an article and piss off a star-chitect like Dannenforth, one of the most powerful among the elite set of that portmanteau. The interview would have to serve as another bit of paper I crumpled up or tore apart and added to the model of my mother—perhaps, after this piece, that nest would finally be complete and I could curl up inside of it and be nurtured.

The fifty-fifth birthday party for Helen Dannenforth was held at Cumulus House. Clusters of blown glass that collected radiant energy became glowing globules. Helen was right—these fey environs did indicate the evolution of a tender ideology. A recent installation of hers at the Tate Modern was similar in tone. Suspended alveolar sacs gave visitors the chance to climb inside the knitted webbing and sway, read, or nap for whatever duration they wished. A faint pulse beat was also broadcast throughout Turbine Hall, imparting less a sensation of nestling within a pair of lungs than the womb's secure embrace. "I was charmed that tourists and commuters, away from their cubicles on lunch, would let down their guard in a public space the same as a private one," she had said. The ambiance was somehow oddly sterile. In search of her, I navigated a bespoke obstacle course of bankers, effete photographers with their gallerina companions, architects in glasses thick like a second pair of eyebrows layered over their eyebrows and lazy cognoscenti.

They talked about art that has inspired architecture, architecture

118

that has inspired film, literature that has inspired architecture, architecture that has inspired literature, musicians who have inspired artists who have inspired architects, arcane illustrations of vivisectionists and botanists that have inspired architecture, how psychoanalysis has influenced architecture and how architecture influences psychology, architecture during war and architecture during peace, the architecture of fashion, the architecture of cuisine, the architecture of children's toys. They talked about the obsolescence of libraries, movie theaters, and journalism. They talked about curators and what would happen to a curatorial vocation in the digital era. They talked about innovation—thermal metals that breathe like a rubbery shark pelt, printing customizable chairs with fungi, neon electronic tattoos that would blush with a touch. They talked about the weather. They talked about the parties they had been to and how annoying those parties were and the parties they planned on attending and how annoying those parties would be.

I observed Helen as she clung to her latest darling. As they mingled together with each group of guests, he ensured she was well lubricated with wine, he smiled benignly but not enough to be ingratiating, he mentioned a story he had heard on public radio during a pause. She was gracious, but she was also intimidating as per normal in a backless Chanel dress, Hermès bangles, and Louboutin heels. Despite his ministrations, he was inadequate to stop her increasing unsteadiness on those heels. They dug into a patch of sod and she stepped out of them. Their two red soles stranded in the grass looked lewd and yet not lewd, like the undersides of tongues. Conversations drifted onto the topic of the hostess, on whether she was sleeping with that attractive man she was mentoring ("They're very cozy"), whether or not she had slept with past mentees ("They tend to be male"), whether she was sleeping with her ex-husband ("No, he's investigating the tribal beats of Balinese rain-drum music in Indonesia"), whether she had slept with a Saudi prince when she was in the Middle East ("He gifted her with Lorraine Schwartz earrings worth one mil"). They just had to gossip.

Ensconced in a corner by the alfresco bar were Lily and her boyfriend, a reedy, bland kid in an awkward blazer who attended Horace Mann. She didn't budge from her position or speak unless addressed point-blank, though he frequently sallied forth in order to bring back heaping portions of artisanal junk food—burgers, chicken strips, fish sandwiches—with "deconstructed" aiolis, as if they were bougie hunter-gatherers. "She's drunk," Lily said, implicating her mother

119

with a glance, and she ushered him into the house. At an unsuspicious distance, I tailed them—I had something to give her, for her and no one else. They evaded me behind a closed door upstairs, so instead of interrupting, I snooped. Alas, it was as expected—the medications, the thread count—though in an underwear drawer I did find a gleaming chrome dildo. The dildo was less of a dildo than a Brâncuși or a parametric mock-up of a bridge or a spaceship. Perhaps I perceived it so because of whose dildo it was. Briefly, I contemplated stealing the dildo. For the rest of my life, I'd display it and pronounce, "This dildo used to pleasure Helen Dannenforth."

A voice accused, "I understand you met with Hannah." The feet of one of the few women renowned for her talents these days were muddy and her chignon was straggly so that the yin-yang roles were reversed and she was the fully grown, sophisticated doppelgänger of her daughter returned from a camping trip. "I did," I replied. Unfortunately, that meant she or a member of her staff would have to sign off on what I had written before it went to print, she informed me. Demanding that was unethical and a bit insulting, I communicated without thinking, simultaneously taken aback by my impromptu lackadaisical attitude. I could have told her I no longer planned to publish. Perhaps she or a member of her staff preferred to pen the entire article? I was slightly light-headed during this confrontation, like it was like a high. At least I now would be "seen" by her, albeit negatively. The sentiments expressed by her sister, I said, might strike her as a very welcome volte-face.

"I'm guessing she told you she has ultimately overcome the wounding at the core of her identity or guileless id or what have you to walk a healing path of forgiveness," she replied, buoyed by rage. "She also said that the meaning of life is love, am I correct? This isn't some unsung epiphany. She's a pathological liar." Who pays for her indefinite stay at "the Retreat," essentially a spa with papier-mâché-type activities where she can whine about how wronged she feels? Helen pays, though she doesn't have to, and Hannah was deemed just fine, perfectly sane, although, she added, definitely crazy, posthaste. Who spent that "road trip" with Lily insinuating Helen had been abusive toward Hannah when they were growing up and so on? The worst, however, is the reminiscing about her pregnancy and manipulating newcomers like me into believing Hannah is Lily's "real" mother and that Helen maliciously hinders them from having a relationship par excellence.

"My Lily is my Lily." Helen Dannenforth was emphatic so as to be absolutely clear. Lily was her genetic daughter. Hannah had been the surrogate, after recourses of IVF, acupuncture, herbal steam baths, pro-uterine diets, and pretty much every snake-oil remedy under the sun had failed. She supported her half sister on account of vestigial gratitude. "How you cope with loneliness determines whether you are strong or weak, particularly if you are a woman," she said. "Hannah isn't equipped to cope." Sad as that was, Helen wasn't about to let Hannah turn her daughter against her. I stood at a loss. When I interviewed Helen, it felt fake, rehearsed. There was no vulnerability, no spontaneous insight. Hannah was scrupulously candid, exposed as a stumbled-upon ramshackle widowed of its human owners in the wilderness. "My responses were premeditated," was her justification, "in that I'm dedicated to meditating upon what responses I would give to questions. Don't blame the subject for your poor skill."

She could tell I was intelligent, but I hadn't been educated as to the drollness of my conventional views or yet shed the nacreous snake-skin of my naïveté. "There isn't one blueprint for how to build a life. Character and family are also constructions." This advice of hers wasn't new either. Architecture hierarchizes us, and not the reverse, from medieval thatched cottages where they slept communally on a straw dais and if there were extramarital shenanigans, well, it had to have been that roguish incubus, to our contemporary thrall to individualism borne out in individualistic enclosures like the capsule pods for rent in Tokyo, daintily segmented as a bento box, or the micro apartments in Manhattan. All individuals require their own tiny niche, their own luminous screen to satellites, social media. "We have separated ourselves out," Helen has said in previous interviews, "as the home was separated out in the Industrial Revolution. What was the source of work, play, sex, the gamut, has been butchered and sold as chops and steaks."

Neither I nor society at large—strangers—had the privilege to judge how she raised her daughter—it was evil—or how she demonstrated her love. "Thoroughly fact-check your piece before it appears in *Inhabit*. Oh, and if you were scouring my house for a souvenir, feel free to select whatever you fancy from my stuff."

After my preceding tête-à-tête with Helen, I had a disturbing dream—please pardon me. A woman went through an excruciating metamorphosis. Her sinews stretched, her bones elongated into a suprascaffolding, her joints a joinery, like some kind of hellish transformer. She towered in agony. I roamed her muscular corridors, investigating the warp and thrum of a high-rise circulating with lymph, hemoglobin, nerves, hormones. It was a monstrous architecture, an architecture for monsters. We take for granted that our mothers accept whatever risks to bear us, that they would die for us, or that they otherwise gladly sacrifice for us their quotidian hours, days, and weeks, but this is a fallacy. If children are born or become cruel and reproducing is a vice, as Hannah Dannenforth posited, perhaps it is not because it is in our nature, but because we too easily forget the unique identity of our mothers.

Hannah had composed a letter I said I would pass along to Lily. I tore the envelope and convinced myself that I was ostensibly reading it to ascertain that she wasn't trying to abscond with her again or malign her real "real" mother as a monster, but I was reading it as a cipher for myself. Was there some clue as to whether my brilliant, dead mother would have loved me or resented me, or if I would have loved her?

I slipped it under Lily's door after reading these words:

"Did you know, my dearest daughter, that in sanatoriums and prisons there are classes in designing your ideal house? We request catalogs, tiles, and swatches from area stores. I've been at leisure to ruminate on it, and the house I would build for you would be a miracle of staircases and country stars. Great fires burn in a stone hearth. It will be sprawling, but not so sprawling that if you shout, there's a danger of not receiving an answer. Nooks and crannies are scattered around for when dinner is served but you're not ready yet. An attic holds trunks with crystal globes of your memories. You'll be able to list all the plants that spike like cuneiform in the garden. Perhaps it's along the coast of the sea—or, no, in the mountains— or its own island, or poised above a city like Siena or Buenos Aires or Istanbul. You can't reach the house unless it's by boat or dirigible. The forecast reflects your mood—rainy when you want it to rain, sunny when you want sun, in the midst of a blizzard when you want to feel your sanctuary as a sanctuary. Within brisk walk or bicycle, there will be a quaint grocery and anything you seek—a salon, an arcade, a scary orchard—and a Benjamin who adores you. There's more, but what I hope you intuit is that we would be happy."

Terlingua
Brandon Hobson

THE PHONE I BREATHED in was the old rotary kind. In my room at the El Cortez Motel, I dialed random numbers until someone with a voice I liked answered. Mostly I breathed into the phone. I listened for their reaction, which I found pleasing. It would always take a few minutes before people hung up.

Once, a man asked, "Is it you?"

Another time, a woman threatened to call the police. "I can have the police trace this call," she said. "It happens all the time."

"I love you," I said.

The room was the center of nothing, dim and warm despite the air conditioner blowing. The room felt like an isolated presence welcoming me. I liked the room dark—no light entered from the drawn curtains, which were green. The lamp threw a jagged and intimidating shadow across the pale wall, and the carpet was the color of dark blood. This was room 121, my first time in this room, though I had spent nights in other rooms. I'm certain the motel clerk had recognized me. He chewed on a toothpick and wore a patch over one eye. His hands looked like my father's, dry and cracked with stubby fingers. I don't remember much about my father, but I do remember his hands. Behind the front desk, the sign on the door read: MAN GER. The motel's VACANCY sign flashed pink out front, a blur of color in a darkening sky. All the motel doors opened to the empty parking lot. Nearby, a desolate highway stretched west through the plains.

"The door says manger," I said. "Away in a manger."

The clerk handed me the key but never looked at me.

In the room I sat on the edge of the bed, looking up at the ceiling. Something in my head was expanding, I felt, trying to force its way out. My skull felt heavy when I kept my head tilted back, looking up. This was always how it was—first the head, then the stomach. The beard I'd grown was full and itchy, and when I saw my reflection in the mirror across the room I wondered whether the people I called imagined me looking differently.

I drank a bottle of water and felt hungry. My bag contained my

clothes and some food, my chess pieces and board, a carton of ciga-
rettes, cash hidden in a sock. I kept my turquoise snakeskin lighter
and magazines underneath everything. The lighter was a gift from
Rae. I imagined her here with me before she overdosed, Rae in her
jacket and boots. All those bracelets. Rae, who slept in the homes of
strange men and addicts. She developed a speech impediment before
she died, the result of having a stroke at thirty. I thought of her watching me play chess in the park, with her snowshoe cat in her lap, daring
me to lose. She kept me on edge, a dominant and unpredictable force,
now gone.

I missed her terribly.

I ate a burrito with rooster sauce and turned on the TV. A movie
showed a man walking through the desert. I stared into the TV while
I ate. The man was walking and walking, going nowhere. Where was
he going, I wondered. A drifter, a wanderer, in search of something
important. This must be real life, I thought. Searching for something,
trying to move forward. Looking for meaning or happiness. The commercials were all in Spanish.

When I finished the burrito, I looked under the bed to make sure
nothing was there. I checked the dresser drawers and found only a
small green Gideon Bible. I touched the walls, running my hands over
them, then checked the bathroom, the shower. The room seemed
OK for now. I pulled the bedspread from the bed and looked at the
sheets. It was exactly seven paces from the bed to the front door,
where I peeked out the peephole and saw the parking lot outside. I
could see dark storm clouds in the sky. I could see dust blowing
around in the wind. I found I was still exceedingly hungry.

I looked back up at the ceiling. Roadside motel rooms were all
designed to look the same, to give the impression of transparency,
isolation. This was the way I saw it. I felt a sense of longing, a damp-
ening of the soul. I found I craved something but couldn't place what
it was. I looked at the dim walls, their paleness, and found myself
thinking about an equation specific to the room and its design. An
equation of some deeper meaning for my life. In one sense the room
was threatening, an enclosure of space. On the other hand, I found
its silence calming. The room smelled like all the other motel rooms,
a mixture of bathroom cleaner and cigarette smoke. Above the bed
hung a framed watercolor of a farmhouse painted in browns and reds.
A field surrounding the farmhouse was dull green with nothing else
around, only empty pasture. The farmhouse looked vacant too, with
a broken-down pickup truck beside it. No sign of life anywhere. I

wondered who lived there and then who painted it, and for what purpose. On a different wall, the only other picture in the room, also a watercolor, was a painting of an old wooden fence with barbed wire. A dreary sky in the background. A barbed-wire fence seemingly in the middle of nowhere. I wondered why a fence, such a lifeless and dull thing. A fence, used to enclose territory. The two pictures hanging in the room held both little and great value. What did it mean for me?

The room darkened as I sat in silence. This was how I liked to spend late afternoons, it occurred to me, sitting in a room as it darkened. Letting the darkness spill over me and the room. I kept with me a pocket tape recorder I spoke into. For a while I played the tape and listened to my voice. I heard myself say, "I looked for God today." I heard myself laugh through my teeth. Here's what I wanted to hear: someone else's voice, by circumstance, unfiltered and cautious. To listen for a response, how long it took to hang up, how curious they were. The element of surprise was what I liked, even if people quickly hung up. I called a random number and a woman answered. "Hello?" she kept saying.

I told her I liked her voice.

The next person I called hung up when he heard me breathe.

The next number I called rang and rang and nobody answered.

The next number was a business. The guy who answered said, "Maintenance."

"I miss you," I said.

"What the fuck?"

I called a number that registered a busy signal. I found it strange and rhythmic, an alert of sorts. The sound put me at ease, helped me feel better. I became aware of my surrounding, of the dim motel room with the green curtains and pale walls. Maybe there were no colors in the room. In my mind I see black and white, something out of a French film. I liked watching the room dim on its own, listening to the hum of the air conditioner blowing.

I called my friend Byrd, an old friend I hadn't spoken to in several months. He'd crashed his Harley on a highway just outside of Albuquerque and managed to survive with a concussion and stitches in his tongue. "I grew my hair out," he told me. "Now everyone thinks I'm Neil Young. The guy at the diner keeps asking me what happened to Crazy Horse. What happened to the Stray Gators, he says. Sing 'Yonder Stands the Sinner.' Sing 'Cinnamon Girl.' Where are you?"

"In the middle of nowhere."

"The park misses you, chief. We all do."

"I quit. I need to find a hospital or someplace to go."

"You quit chess?"

"Everything."

"Come back to the park," he said. "The Greasers are playing early Elvis at the shop, those rockabilly motherfuckers. Someone found a wrench under Rowdy's bed and now he's gone too, probably off to the boondocks for a while. You guys trip in unusual ways. By the way, people said they saw you buying radiator fluid at the Auto-Zone on Tenth. Is that true? Someone else said you were walking around downtown, pulling a little red wagon."

"Wasn't me."

"Right now Lucille's calling me to the kitchen, but you need somewhere to stay? You can stay with us, chief. I got an extra mattress in the basement. I got Rubber Soul on vinyl."

"Maybe I need a nurse," I said. "I need a bed to stay in all day. Someone to check on me every hour. Will you talk to me?"

"Lucille's sister's in from El Reno for the tribe thing tomorrow night. You've seen the Chickasaw commercials. Try to lay off the pills, brother. We're here for you."

He hung up and I found myself waiting for someone to pick back up. The line went dead. I turned on the lamp, opened the phone book, and flipped through pages. I saw an ad for Claire's Party Supplies. The woman who answered said, "Claire's, this is Janice," but then hung up when I asked if she liked motel rooms.

I called Camille's Salon and asked what Camille looked like.

"There's no Camille here," the woman said.

"What's your name?" I breathed.

She hung up.

When I called Sharee, a girl Rae and I knew from the park, some guy answered.

"I miss Sharee," I told him.

"Who is this?" he said.

I hesitated a moment, and this time I hung up first.

The next call sounded like an elderly woman. "I need to tell you this isn't a prank," I said into the phone. "I need to tell you everything has to do with loneliness. I mean everything that's happened. I mean the sadness. Nothing feels right anymore, if that makes sense. If you could just talk to me about yourself, anything really, it would be nice. Actually it's not just about the sadness but something way deeper and more personal than I ever thought about before until recently. I'm not kidding, don't hang up. If you could just talk. If you could just talk about what you like, what makes you happy, those kinds of things. Tell me about your husband. Tell me about your son or your daughter. Your grandchildren if you have any. I'm in a ghost town far away."

I could hear her breathing, so I knew she hadn't hung up. There was a pause, then I breathed back. I didn't want to say anything else. I wanted to hear her. She never responded, yet never hung up. I knew she was there. Maybe she was waiting for me to go on. Maybe she desired the same as me, a voice to listen to, an anonymous presence on the other end of the line. Maybe we both found ourselves waiting. This went on for twenty minutes, the silence between us. I'm not sure who hung up first, but afterward I rested the phone in my lap and put my face in my hands.

Then I called my aunt Ariana, who had been on a spiritual retreat with a group of people from the Osage. "We swam and meditated," she told me. "We sat outside in groups. We explored each other's faces. Where are you?"

I told her I liked the way she said "explored."

"Stop, stop, stop," she said. "Listen, they said you disappeared? They said you left for good?"

"Maybe, I don't know yet."

"Why don't you come back home?"

"I don't know," I said. "It's late and I have to go."

"Listen, all these people are asking about you. Where are you?"

"Nowhere. Somewhere."

"Listen to me," she kept saying.

I said, "I'm sorry, Ariana."

After I hung up I didn't feel like calling anyone else. I needed to find someone like Rae, someone I could talk to. I needed someone to help. I needed to communicate with someone whose life was like mine, whose body and voice responded to the words I spoke. Rae and I could heal each other through language. We could say words and reach an understanding. We could touch each other's face and say one organic word. Sometimes we never spoke. We once spent an entire afternoon embracing in the park.

Darkness spread around me. I found it soothing and lifeless and free. After a long while I got out of bed and went into the bathroom, where I filled the tub with warm water. I stepped into the tub with my clothes on, hoping time would transpire. I wanted time in isolation, quiet. There was laughter coming from the next room, voices talking. My body felt warm and heavy in the water. The heaviness was an abstraction, I felt, a part of some equation convoluted by the presence of the room. Be aware of your surroundings, Rae used to say. Be aware, cautious, observant of time and place. The universe aligns for a reason, but what reason. I reclined in the tub, thinking of the times she and I splashed around in the tub in a different motel bathroom, maybe at the Route 66 Motel or the Knights Inn, a mirrored image of this room. A bathroom with the same tile full of squares, part of the equation to entrap me in something. Motel bathrooms all look the same, I told myself. I thought of Rae, of us splashing around one hot July afternoon during a dust storm that sanded over the windows. We listened to the Mexican radio station and drank Mexican beer. We paid the housekeeping to stay away, immersing ourselves in our own bodies, in each other, for three days.

In the tub I counted the tiles from ceiling to floor, around the room. I lost track and started over, counting vertically by row, then horizontally, eight, fifteen, then twenty, thirty-four. I kept losing track from the room's dim lighting. The tiles over the sink were smaller and of different color—pink rather than light blue. Pink, the color of skin and flesh, the color of body parts, tongue. I counted over a hundred square tiles, not counting the partial tiles that stopped at the edge of the tub. They were not half tiles, maybe a quarter of a tile. The numbers were confusing and I couldn't figure out the pattern. I was suspicious that there might not have been a pattern in this room, but rather the tiles were there to throw me off and keep my mind focused on counting rather than on something else. An equation. I had a strange and intense vision of being stuck in an elevator as a child, gripping my mother's hand. The jar of something breaking, maybe a cable or faulty electrical circuit. A woman crying out. A loud ringing from somewhere, an alarm. I felt the loss of air, no oxygen, the room shrinking. Everyone staring at the numbers. Closing my eyes, gripping my mother's hand. My mother bringing me closer against her. The doors finally opening.

In the tub I let myself slide down into the water until my head was underwater and I was staring directly up at the trembling ceiling. I blinked underwater. I felt my eyes come out of their sockets, fill with water, and I saw only blurred whiteness above, everything shaking. I saw myself falling backward. I realized then I was drowning, being held underwater by some force beneath me. The heaviness of my body, my clothes, made it difficult to sit up, but I managed to gain enough strength to lean forward and gasp as I came out of the water like some horrific beast, sputtering as I steadied myself in the tub. I leaned forward to pull the plug and drain the water, which made a sucking noise. Slowly, I got out of the tub and stood to watch the water drain, all of it. Once I knew everything was safe, I went to get my bag to change into dry clothes. I saw my reflection in the darkened mirror, thin and pale. In my bag I found my turquoise snakeskin lighter, picked it up, and lit a cigarette. The room felt much dimmer than before. I looked to the curtain and saw part of it trembling from the blowing air conditioner. On TV, an old movie showed a crippled boy taking his first steps. I sat on the edge of the bed and watched. The boy's mother fell to her knees. A crowd of people surrounded the boy. There was no sound. I changed the channel with the remote and saw a movie with De Niro, the young, tough De Niro, sitting in a dingy apartment, writing in a notebook. De Niro, talking to himself, strapping a gun to his arm and ankle. Pointing a pistol at his reflection in the mirror.

I spoke into the tape recorder. I said, "Because I didn't mean to hurt anyone." I said, "Because I love you." I said, "Because I'm never able to talk about anything." I said words like "checkmate" and "pills" and "God." I said "Rae." I said, "I'm going to die in Terlingua."

By sunrise I had spoken thousands of words into the recorder. I went to the window beside the door, peeked out the curtains, and looked up at the morning sky. Something flashed and I thought it was God. I could see the open land past the parking lot, dust swirling in the wind. I could see the motel sign, the pink VACANCY flashing. Then I went to my bag and took out the pill bottle, tilting the last of the pills into my hand, and swallowed them with a cup of warm water.

I put on Rae's broken sunglasses, which I'd doctored with tape, and lay down in bed. A surge of pain went right to my head. I saw myself projected forward into the darkness, an eccentric and intense dream, my body heavy with the strange weight of years. I saw people walking backward. I saw the rain lifting from earth to sky. At some point I heard a voice and rolled over and vomited. I wasn't asleep for long. When I woke, the sunglasses were on the floor, the curtains were open, and it was bright in the room. I remember hearing two housekeepers talking to me in Spanish. "Close the drapes," I managed to say.

129

Blue: a chair is a very difficult object
Lance Olsen

Somewhere, someone still remembers.
Somewhere else, someone forgets.

—Ellen Hinsey, "Eastern Apocrypha"

WALKING, MIES VAN DER ROHE
concludes as he watches the oily
Spree slide by his cab, is—

I never—

That is a building.

I never walk.

Look at the building.

(The efforts of the mystics remain
episodes.)

We must have—

There is a man.

There is a building.

Look at the man.

That building is—

Order.

One could say Berlin is a captive of
the nineteenth century.

The broad boulevards.

Massive stone facades.

That poor man.

Those neo-Grecian pillars.

Look at his face.

One could say I always take—

(Every How is carried by a What.)

We must have order.

It can be no other—

What was wrong with his face?

Because the word *rectilinearity* exists.

I always take taxis back and—

There is a building.

Perpendicular.

(Every force evolves a form.)

Because a taxi is—

And so I rarely see a city.

What is there to see in a city?

Is that a—

Berlin, an imperial hallucination.

(One should never forget a square is also a rectangle.)

In the end the war being a failure of German architecture.

A taxi being a moving room.

Because red is money.

Because we can.

Have order.

Because civilizations must.

Who said—

A motorcycle bombinating past.

The clean line: like time travel.

I miss my wife.

Bombinating.

All this moving.

Otherwise we would be something else.

I love her but I cannot live with her.

Because less is—

Blue.

I can live with Lilly but I cannot live with Ada.

We must know that life—

I can live with Lilly now but I could
not live with Ada then.

Her chairs.

This sky: that blue.

But later it will rain.

They say.

Because red is money and yellow is
also money.

Because what would it feel like to
know your son's name?

His uncluttered substantive.

What would it feel like to—

All this moving.

Lilly's chairs untaught me so much.

There is a building.

If there is a god, he is—

I changed my own.

Name.

The sound of *Mies* stretching into
the sound of—

There is a—

Thank you, Lilly.

133

Lance Olsen

There is another.

The sound of *Mies van der Rohe*.

Will they ever stop?

When in doubt, deploy the Dutch.

Just a suggestion of the aristocratic.

If not, perhaps, the substance.

Because my father carved stone.

Because when in doubt check the streetcars in Berlin.

(Every human being has the right to pure color.)

Because the important thing in any crisis is whether the streetcars are running.

Because the Kingdom of Prussia.

Because if the streetcars are running then life is bearable.

Lilly's furniture hurts, its lines so impeccable.

Because the phrase *industrial steel* exists.

Plate glass.

(Because every architect has been or will be a refugee.)

(This is a self-evident truth.)

(Because 1927.)

We become exiles inside our own
countries.

Because my father carved stone and
I carve space.

We become exiles inside our own
countries.

The efficiency of skin.

Bone.

My son carves—

(That man's face.)

Specialists are people who repeat
the same errors over and—

Martin used to say.

I hear you, my father's last words,
deathbedding, *but I haven't crossed
over yet.*

Just a moment.

Just a—

Then the elated smile spreading
over the mask he used to be.

New York, a beautiful catastrophe.

Berlin doomed like Pompeii.

The will of an epoch translated into three dimensions.

Is the definition of architecture.

We must know life cannot be changed by us.

(A chair is a very difficult object.)

Light and—

A house a machine for living in.

Said Le Corbusier.

His name eleven letters and one lack.

Mine fourteen and three.

It should be pointed out.

And so life will be changed.

And they came to me and said: *Design a memorial for them.*

Gimpy Rosa Luxemburg.

Scrawny Karl Liebknecht.

And so life will be changed, but not by us.

To her: *Kindly stand still while we beat you with our rifle butts and shoot you in the head.*

Lilly's chairs designed in wind tunnels.

Because less is—

To him: *Kindly step out of this moving car while we shoot you in the back.*

Ada.

Because the space between buildings is—

They execute people in front of brick walls.

Because the space between buildings is as important as the buildings themselves.

So I built a brick-wall monument.

Cantilevered slabs.

Steel-and-concrete frame.

Bricks jagged.

Grout unsanded.

Because one could say—

All this moving.

Because one could say the clean line represents a choreography for living.

One could say a way of maneuvering through the present.

If there is a god, he is—

Architecture starts when—

Lance Olsen

Architecture will always be the real
battleground of the spirit.

—he is in the details.

Speechlessness sans silence.

Because architecture starts when you
carefully put together two bricks.

And so they asked me: *What do you
talk about when you're with a client?*

And I told them: *Never talk to him
about architecture.*

That's the most crucial thing.

Talk to him about his children.

About his dog.

*Talk to him about his rust-red and
dark-chocolate snakeskin Italian
loafers.*

Talk to him about those.

Talk to him about—

About—

The Weekend Salvage Unit
Susan Daitch

WE WERE AN OPTICIAN, a seventh-grade teacher, a man who called himself a paracoroner, an entomologist, a professional gardener who had trained in Brussels, and a semiretired loan officer. The group's director, a former contractor who had lost his license for reasons that were never entirely clear to me, would locate a building about to be demolished and obtain permission for us to gain access and remove anything we were able to extricate: a marble statue of Hermes, red tin Coca-Cola signs like giant buttons, oak railings, spindles and banisters from the birthplace of Winston Churchill's mother, marble fireplaces, ball-and-claw bathtubs big enough to bathe a pony. Our group always appeared on-site one step ahead of the wrecking ball. Small things: faceted-glass doorknobs, Bauhaus-era tiling, Victorian faucets and spigots, these one could take home. Larger pieces we stored in a warehouse located off an industrial canal. A few gargantuan objects would eventually be sold on eBay or elsewhere to defray our operating costs, though the goal of the group was essentially to preserve these treasures as best we could. Over time the warehouse began to look like a miniature metropolis, as if the city were turning itself inside out. There was no end of buildings about to be demolished. The city could have sustained many groups like ours, easy.

I first met the group one afternoon when walking over the Union Street bridge, where I spied a small cluster of people unloading what looked like body bags. The bodies would have to have been extremely heavy, because several people were required to carry each one into the warehouse. They weren't really bodies, of course, but marble caryatids from a bathhouse whose time of origin lay in the era of robber barons, Catalonian anarchists, and films viewed via a kinetoscope. The next van to pull up contained balconies from an old movie theater. They were rolled out like gilt chariots and, standing in a meridian of skunk cabbage and dried-out stalks of Queen Anne's lace, I was reminded of the night P. T. Barnum paraded elephants through the Holland Tunnel at three in the morning because that's the only time they could get into the city—it was like that—the oddity of

139

watching these behemoths carried into a cinder-block depot was nearly as strange as seeing tropical wild animals loose in northern city streets. My curiosity got the better of my reticence, and I struck up a conversation with the professional gardener, tattoos of choking vines circling her arms, legs, and neck, who told me she dreamed of designing grounds around the mythological creatures, the Poseidons, Persephones, the satyrs, and sphinxes they'd found in the past year alone. Then Alan, the ex-contractor, introduced himself to me. Interested in being part of our little crew? How could I resist? He gave me the emergency contact and medical forms, and I was in.

My husband had departed months earlier for the topmost edge of the Greenland ice sheet, and from there he was to travel to points unknown in search of the semisolid North Pole. His journey, in truth, had begun even earlier, and there was no talk of freezing your butt off on an ice floe. It began with cleaning our apartment, but then the removal of objects accelerated to the disposal of books, photographs, dishes, clothing, until only an empty box remained.

"Will I be next to go?" I asked.

"No, not you," he said as he prepared to exit, though he packed no bag. In his quest for emptiness, to be rid of all possessions, he planned to travel to the Arctic. I pointed out that in such a climate there would be things he would need for survival. He knew this. He had been there before. His job was to drill through glacial ice, to pull up long cylinders that emerged like clear frost teeming with invisible microbial life. There were viruses, bacteria, pathogens in a variety of forms, shaped like hair combs, soccer balls, sea anemones, the letter Y, all in suspended animation, slumbering in their frozen shelters for nearly a million years. Then, presto, a metal drill, hollow and determined, separates them from their neighbors. They're flown to a lab where their shelter will be thawed, and they wiggle back to life.

"So these microbes, liberated from their chambers, can now screw their brains out.

"They divide and subdivide. Their dormant genomes will now reproduce."

That sounded alarming. Who knew what diseases could be unleashed? Hand on the doorknob, he reassured me, he and his colleagues weren't intent on launching new and fatal epidemics. The ice cores, the diameter of an orange-juice can, are memory banks, Pleistocene hard drives. They will, he said, tell us everything about early life, but also how to survive in extreme conditions, the kind that will be found on the moon, on Mars, and beyond. If you, a microbe that looks like a piece of vacuum hose, can survive for a million years in a house of ice, then the lunar Sea of Tranquility will be a piece of cake. He was seduced by the sheer absence of any markers, the intoxicating glow of light on ice, the idea of extreme cold, all this sent him into raptures. Last communication: a photograph taken from inside an igloo: bright light sliced through a grid of cracks, the space between blocks of ice. A sight rarely seen when you think about it. Most igloos are photographed from the outside.

When he left, I began taking long walks, and this is how I first met the Weekend Salvage Unit. After joining I could actually trespass in some of those apartments I'd walked past in envy, thinking other people's rooms swarmed with life, only to find the lights were deceptive, a power-company fluke most likely. In many cases the residents themselves had long since departed.

On Saturday mornings we donned bright-yellow construction helmets, packed toolboxes, flashlights jangling from our belts, lunches, water bottles, and thermoses, and we were on our way. Once in a while we arrived at a building that still had occupants, not many, but a few. They shouted at us: Tools of the capitalist hydra, get the fuck out and on and on about eminent domain. We're on your side, Sol the optician would shout, but you're going down, there's nothing we can do about it. We just want to preserve what we can. Residents tend to want to ostrich it out. This never works.

On my first weekend, heavy crowbar in hand, I felt powerful in a way I never had before, like I could take whatever I wanted to from any edifice. I pried loose a marble threshold slab and found a bundle of pornographic postcards, edges moldy and eaten away. The images of Korean War–era pinups barely dressed in nurses' uniforms, as maids, or in other predictable costumes smelled like penicillin. Each was more or less in the same pose, bent over slightly. Their mouths were shaped in an O of eternal surprise. The cards crumbled in my hands. An old woman came out of her apartment holding a blue plastic colander that dripped water onto the floor, a floor that would never be washed again. A tang of burnt mustard hung in the air, and piles of Christmas icicles blocked one of the doors. She was the only occupant left on the floor, I think, and didn't say a word to me, only looked through big glasses that gave her eyes an owl-like and startled appearance. I dropped the cards, turned on my heel, and left. As I became more determined, I learned to ignore the squatters and old-time denizens clinging to whatever walls, gabled ceilings, and windows remained to them.

141

There are dangers involved in what we do. Rooftops can no longer be depended upon to stay parallel and horizontal to the earth. Crumbling water towers, pigeon coops, even a few hives belonging to long-gone urban beekeepers have been known to fall in on scavengers as we make our way through lobbies and corridors. Sol the optician brings goggles and sometimes masks if there's a lot of dust in the air. He collects these after every job, counting to be sure he has all of them. Also, I never take the elevators in these buildings, a Russian roulette–like experience at best, but there are those who do without a moment's hesitation. Who would want to take such a chance? I'll tell you. Alejandro Ocampo, the paracoroner, that's who. As an assistant to the coroner he sees all kinds of death every day, but the possibility of his own doesn't stop him. In fact, just the opposite. An unoiled cable snaps, boom, you're dead, he says, fast and easy, that's the ideal way to go, believe me. Lingering residents often pirate electricity from lampposts outside on the street. Current goes off, fine, you take a snooze until rescue comes, he mimes sleep as he hops into a dented old Otis. You could die of a heart attack going up stairs that collapse under your feet. Alejandro points at me as the doors close. Someone has to take the loot downstairs in the freight elevators. Ocampo is the chosen one for this task. It's as if he thinks he has superpowers, from being around death so much, he's developed immunity.

Alan had worked on nondescript towers—the kind, he would be the first to admit, no future salvage crew would consider. No longer practicing, because once, or maybe more than once, he made a deal with someone who watered down the concrete, because he didn't think it would make that much difference, structurally speaking, and it was a good way to keep costs low. Alan was fond of balancing abstract concepts in one hand and then the other. Time (we only have, at most, three hours of daylight left) versus potential gain (Rodchenko-like mosaics on the ground floor near the mailboxes). The hands would move up and down, weighing alternatives, which should we choose, then he would turn to the loan officer or whoever was in the passenger seat and say, "OK, let's go for it," in a voice like a reality-TV majordomo. Yet I liked Alan. He inspired confidence that the structure at hand still resisted the force of gravity.

I was nervous about the location we were headed to. It was beginning to rain in torrents, and I was afraid of collapsing roofs. I slumped in the seat so my feet were up on the seat in front of me, grazing Ocampo's legs. Warmth radiated from the side of his body. Despite

Susan Daitch

my anxiety, I could fall asleep here, as if the ride to an unknown site, though under discussion as if it actually existed, would go on forever and I too would end up near the North Pole.

Then I became distracted when the entomologist undid his pony-tail and ran his hands through his hair, and I stopped thinking about the euphoria of trekking to the edge of Baffin Bay. In seriously de-cayed buildings he had found a variety of ants and termites, and even a couple of flaming-red harlequin stinkbugs, rarely found north of Texas. From him I learned that ants, in their subterranean colonies, practiced a kind of slavery; they stole larvae from other insects and raised them to be servants to masters who were as cruel as they were relentless. He showed us their tunnels and storehouses, miniature metropolises riddling walls and under floorboards.

Ocampo didn't talk about his work much. Discussions of cadavers upset the gardener, who retained her accent from years spent in Brussels. She grew misty-eyed when the entomologist spoke about enslaved bugs. Though she sat behind me in the van, she smelled of salt and lavender. The gardener seemed like someone who had gotten lost in the wrong century, and though she had a history of drug abuse, you could imagine it was the green fairy, laudanum, or opium that she had abused, not a drug with a modern pharmaceutical name. The entomologist stroked the leafy tattoos inside her wrist where blades and tendrils tangled with blue veins.

Seventeen Van Hayden Street had, in grander days, been a residen-tial hotel with a ballroom, a bar, a coat check, and a barbershop in the lobby. Though it ought to have been condemned long ago, Alan warned us, a few inhabitants might still be clinging to their rooms, or perhaps they had never heard the news that the building had been bought by Valhalla Equities. No joke. According to the posters slapped on the blue plywood surrounding the site, it was to be leveled to make way for some kind of missile-shaped tower that would include its own gym, Olympic-size pool, movie theater, convenience store, and chain drugstore. You would never have to step outside, or hardly ever. From the boarded-up windows, chunks of brick missing from its facade, and deeply eroded foundation, the present structure, listing and creaking, appeared to be in such bad shape that I wondered how Alan had gotten permission for us to enter it, or perhaps he hadn't. The site of the future Van Hayden or Valhalla Towers, he insisted, offered great treasures. We ducked under the scaffolding surrounding the old hotel and met at the main entrance. The loan officer clipped the padlocked chain that held two heavy coffered front doors together.

143

"This way, folks," he said, as he held the door open.

Rain poured through the spaces where roofs and ceilings used to be, and we went off in different directions to find what we could. Ocampo's practice was to take the elevator to the top floor and work his way down. I had no intention of accompanying him on his route. I only joined up with him in small buildings where you could walk up the stairs, and this was not one of those. The entomologist and the professional gardener went off together in search of rare species, beginning with the marble sinks, old barbering tools, and autographed pictures of Frank Sinatra and Tony Bennett they expected to find in the defunct barber's. Alan and Sol the optician paired and, debating the merits of copper versus brass pipe, said they were going into the basement to see if they could find ladders capable of reaching the ballroom's chandeliers. I was left to wander around by myself. Opening a door behind a bank of elevators I climbed back stairs to the third floor.

The hall would be lit as long as it was daytime, though because of the storm the corridor was fairly dim. I could still make out gold-flocked wallpaper, buckled from water damage, while ocher carpeting patterned with maps of mold stifled the sound of my boots. Some doors were locked, others were open. Under each door a glossy prospectus from Valhalla Towers had been slipped, just in case any current residents wanted to buy into the complex, provided they could trundle up to the developers' Midtown offices with wheelbarrows full of cash.

In the first room a cut-glass decanter and used glasses remained set up on a tray, residue of an amber liquid dried in crescents on their bottoms. The floor was littered with old programs from plays and concerts. Drugstore plastic bags clustered in corners as if having private conferences. Apparently the same kind of garbage turns up from Spitsbergen to Siberia, demonstrating the kinship of global detritus, even here in this abandoned building. Someone had drawn a winking smiley face on a dust-coated window. Apart from the bottle and glasses, the room contained only the usual hotel-room signposts from souvenir ashtrays to the stripped bed with stained mattress. Further doors led to more bare rooms. Some of the suites were apartments, however, where people had lived for varying lengths of time before they were forced out. I didn't see anything architecturally special, though one suite of rooms looked as if the last tenants had left suddenly in the wake of a disaster or emergency. The alarm was sounded, and they'd just run out the door. Remains of a half-eaten breakfast lay on a table covered with dust, finally abandoned even by mice and bugs. In a closet I found an assortment of costumes: a gorilla suit complete with head, two halves of a horse costume (front and back), a devil suit, a long silver sequined dress with train and head-dress. When I picked up the gorilla head, moths flew out. There was nothing worth taking here. Even the costumes, some in dry-cleaner bags, were well-worn. Whether they'd seen great parties in the ball-room below or had memories of walking blocks in the cold with no money for cab or subway, they weren't saying. I set down my helmet, put on the gorilla head, and continued to look around. As a gorilla, I lost all inhibition, as if drunk. I hummed "East of the Sun (and West of the Moon)" and thought about how I would scare the pants off Ocampo, maybe even the entomologist too.

After further fruitless exploration I was near the end of the hall and had found no evidence of why Alan had thought the Van Hayden site would be a gold mine. Perhaps the fourth floor would yield Russian constructivist spandrels and Gaudian joists. As Ocampo preferred to operate from the top down, and I worked up from near the bottom, we often met somewhere in the middle, and then we would excavate, and prize out finds together. I liked listening to him talk about how he'd wanted to go to medical school, how his boss who was incompetent had a thing for "lady stiffs," how he didn't get along with the medical examiner, and what the fuck was up with the bug guy and trippy vegetation queen? "They're prob-ably doing it on some stinky bed while we speak, talking about spiders and photosynthesis, and whatnot." Sometimes I remembered his stories and would laugh while staring into space on a crowded train.

"So one day we get a pair of arms, hands attached, so you think, OK, we got a nice set of prints here we can identify the guy, except it's a woman's arms and hands. The nails were perfect: those artifi-cial glue-on nails like an inch long. Each one had a decal on it of a palm tree and a sunset. With each nail the sun set a little more, but never all the way off a finger so you could say the sun never set on this lady's hands. My boss goes on and on about her nails, how they were one of a kind and could be traced. Well, maybe, but what about the damn prints? Needless to say we never ID'd her."

After our salvage missions Alejandro would go out clubbing until early Sunday morning. I went with him once to a place not far from the group's warehouse. Ocampo told me you should always know where the exits are, a piece of advice he gave me as if I would need

145

it on a regular basis. Fire, he said, can do some nasty things. And if there is a fire here, never jump in the canal. It's full of live gonorrhea strains. Why get it that way? He winked.

I opened the door to the last room. This one resembled an archive with old newspapers and magazines stacked from floor to ceiling. A firetrap within a firetrap, it was laid out as a series of rooms off a short hallway. The kitchen and bedrooms looked barely used because of the towers of paper. I took a brittle, yellowed newspaper from the top of one pile; the headline screamed about the Bay of Pigs, April 17, 1961. The paper underneath was from January 28, 1986, the day the *Challenger* spacecraft exploded. Next came October 31, 1938, Radio Listeners in Panic, Taking War Drama as Fact, referring to the broadcast about a Martian landing in Grovers Mill, New Jersey. The papers didn't appear to be in any particular order, chronological or otherwise. The funny papers were archived in the bathroom. Aleta lured Prince Valiant. Modesty Blaise put her fighting know-how and expertise on the subject of the London underworld at the service of some MI5-like entity as far as I could tell. Squash-faced social-climbing Maggie chased Jiggs with a rolling pin. At the end of the hall was a small living room. There, sitting in a swivel chair facing bay windows, was a man wearing a suit and top hat.

"Sir?"

No answer.

"Sir?"

I walked over and touched the man's shoulder. The chair spun around. It was just like the scene in *Psycho*, except that a monocle was still wedged in the corpse's eye. He was new dead but past the bad-smell stage. Under one of his hands was the prospectus, turned to a shiny photograph of a couple looking out at the skyline, drinks in hand. On the other side of the fold was a woman in a Jacuzzi. Perhaps the corpse had been studying it, considering making a bid on a condo. I didn't scream but ran to the elevator bank, yelled for Alejandro, who was able to hear me, and began the descent in the lift. Yellow light appeared under the transom as the car made it to the third floor. The doors made cranky sounds, resisted opening, but finally Ocampo stepped out.

"What the f?"

I removed the gorilla head and tucked it under my arm. Ocampo followed me into the room, snapping on plastic gloves as we entered. We always brought pairs of these, though rarely used them.

The man was still sitting in the swivel chair.

146

"Who've we got here, Mr. Peanut?" Alejandro looked at the body like a pro, I could tell.

"It was bound to happen sooner or later in this business," he said. "You can't break into city buildings on a regular basis and not expect to find a stiff or two. I'm surprised it's taken this long."

We assessed the man's clothing. He was wearing a charcoal-gray suit and black vest shot through with purple silk. A monogrammed handkerchief and a tightly whorled rose wilted in a buttonhole.

"I'm not sure how that monocle has stayed in place so long," Ocampo said. "The guy's been dead several months, at least, and has no motor control to speak of."

"Glue?" I suggested.

"I've seen it."

In the course of his work Alejandro had seen everything. He removed the man's gold cuff links set with opals. "You don't want these," he said as he pocketed them. "You have to be careful with opals. They bring bad luck."

One by one or in pairs, the others arrived in the suite.

Sol and Alan had tried to remove two chandeliers, but many prisms had fallen off in the process, so they only gathered these up and abandoned the main lighting fixtures as unsalvageable. Sol had put the loose prisms in a bag; they sounded like straitjacketed wind chimes as he walked, so he put them on top of a radiator while he examined the man in the chair.

Next, the entomologist and the gardener floated into the room. They were still looking through the rosy lenses of their fresh relationship. Everything appeared beautiful to them. The gardener plunged her hand into the bag of prisms, held one up to the light, then handed it to me before taking another one for herself. She didn't even notice the body sitting in the swivel chair. Even if, like a fly, the entomologist had thousands of eyes, he only had eyes for her. The gardener promised him an Eden of earthly delights. He pulled her to him, and they leaned into a tower of newspapers, which promptly shifted and collapsed. This seemed to wake the entomologist from his reverie.

"Is your cell phone getting a signal?" the bug man asked. "We should call the police. He had finally noticed that the room had an occupant who was not part of the original Weekend Salvage Unit.

"Wait a minute," Alan said. "I'm not so sure that's a good idea."

"What are you talking about, man?" Ocampo feigned a shocked look. In reality he probably didn't care one way or another about Mr. Peanut, but he knew we needed to report the body. "The weekend

147

shift coroner is going to have a busier than average Saturday night." Alejandro was looking forward to seeing the expressions on their faces when the man in the top hat was wheeled into the morgue, or so he said.

"Well, you know we're not really here legally." Alan, the ex-contractor, stroked his beard, and I believe he was completely serious.

"We need to report this body."

"The Van Hayden isn't very sound, structurally speaking," Alan said matter-of-factly as if we all knew this, since risks were part of our weekend thrills, it was a given, no one should make a fuss. He tossed a prism up in the air; a ray of light hit the spinning glass before he caught it while waiting for someone to say something.

"What other kind of speaking is there?" Ocampo asked. "I mean when you're talking about buildings?"

"You know, but we really shouldn't be here. What's left of the roof's not going to fall in, but worse, technically, we're trespassing, and the police, once they're called in, could arrest us for that alone. You, Ocampo, are a state employee. You could lose your job."

"We can't just leave the body here," Ocampo said.

Alan was afraid Ocampo would rat on him. Some of the scavenging expeditions had been legit, with permits and passes signed by whomever, but others certainly were not. If Ocampo decided to turn him in, there wasn't much he could do about it. Serving time just for salvaging a gargoyle here, a statue of Mercury there, all because of a body found by accident would be a kind of terrible revenge, a final insult on the part of the profession that had ousted him. He had been in jail, and he didn't want to go back.

The corpse's face had a chiseled, starved look. Apart from his clothing, his face reminded me of the deflated Goering in the box at Nuremberg. Perhaps he was a fugitive from Serbia or Argentina, I volunteered.

"Don't be ridiculous," Alan said.

The optician handed me another prism from the ballroom's chandelier, a booby prize for invoking Alan's disdain, the bitter aftertaste of Sol's weekends.

"We have to do something about this poor guy." The gardener spoke in a little-girl voice, momentarily distracted from the entomologist, who had clearly come to believe every small thing she did or said was spellbinding. Attracting his attention had taken her a while, but keeping him magnetized was easier than she had imagined. She wanted him to think of her as a selfless, caring kind of person.

Her voice reminded the entomologist of Marilyn Monroe's voice, which was exactly what she had intended. He'd seen *Some Like It Hot* for a college film class and remembered Marilyn Monroe waving gloved fingers one at a time at the camera. He didn't want to risk getting arrested over a dead man either. He wondered if the gardener had a green card and, if not, would she marry him to get one, then ditch him as soon as the ink was dry. Was that her plan from the beginning? He didn't really suspect her of ulterior motives, but it was a thought that crept up on him.

"What are we talking about here?" Alan sputtered. "He's nobody. Who cares? He's only dead and getting deader."

"No one else is going to find him. In a few weeks the building will be torn down, and this fellow will be buried under piles of rubble. No one will ever know." Sol was trying to bolster Alan's position, but the ex-contractor's face turned into a wad of mashed wood putty.

"Shut up, Sol."

"You've buried bodies before," Ocampo began, referring to the watered-down concrete.

"If you want to get arrested, then by all means, call whoever it is you want to call." Alan stormed out, followed meekly by Sol.

The bug man's fingers traced petioles of ivy circling the gardener's neck while she said in her high voice, "Maybe he's happy where he is, where he's lived his life out. Let him be." She had changed her tune, but no one particularly noticed.

"I don't think Alan's right about getting arrested," I said. "I don't think the city would bother." But in pairs everyone left the room until only Ocampo and I remained.

"Sorry, son," Alejandro said to Mr. Peanut. "Maybe you deserve a decent burial, maybe here where you sit is just fine. Maybe someone's desperate for news of you. Maybe nobody gives a shit and hasn't for a long time." He shrugged. "My nephew was in the police academy. One night his buddies persuaded him to go to an after-hours club and guess what?"

Mr. Peanut, the body in #17, had no idea.

"It got raided on just that night when he decided he would step out. No more police academy for him. Once you're out, you're out. That's what happens when you work for the city."

We left the Van Hayden quickly in order to catch up with the others. Our salvage unit drove back to the warehouse in silence. Alan didn't offer to stop for food, and once he parked he didn't even propose that final customary act of kindness, dropping people off at their subway

149

stops. It was night and the blocks around the warehouses were deserted. In our director's silence I feared lay the termination of our unit. The optician counted his goggles and mentioned buying special respirator masks with filters for environments with high levels of particulate matter if everyone would chip in to cover costs. We said our good byes, Alan promised he would find a better site next time, and everyone melted into the air.

When the hotel on Van Hayden Street was torn down, there was nothing in the paper about it at all. You'd think if they'd found a body it would have been in the news, so it's probably safe to assume when the walls came crashing down everything was carted away unexamined. I even walked by the site from time to time, but no, nothing. The body was never found or identified. It could happen to anyone, I suppose, getting swept away with no identity to speak of, no one to claim you or remember who you were. It was as if the man had never existed. The Weekend Salvage Unit didn't meet much during the winter. The optician joked that all worthwhile buildings had been torn down, there was nothing left to salvage, and then the group seemed to peter out.

A postcard arrived from Ellesmere Island. Cores had been drilled and sent back. Had he made it to the North Pole? No, but he was not far from it. There is no pure north, he had decided. No pure sublime moment. Eventually you get grabbed by the lapels and slammed against a wall whether the wall is made of brick or compacted snow. There were stories of people who became lost, snow-blind, delirious, took off all their clothes and ran naked into the tundra night abandoning huskies, anorak, freeze-dried camping food. In a place where your spit freezes into an amoeboid glob way before it hits the ground, the fragile don't last long. He stayed indoors.

The following winter I saw Alan working as a volunteer guide at the seaport dressed as an old salt. He was giving a speech about the real pirates of the Caribbean and looked at me sharply, as if to say, This is no time for a reunion, I'm working. Another time I saw the loan officer behind the plate-glass window of a bank explaining what appeared to be unpleasant business to a couple in down jackets. He patted one stack of papers, then another, indicating, because of this circumstance, we have this situation. The man looked angry, and the woman actually stared in my direction uncomfortably, so I quickly moved on. Sol's office was part of a medical pavilion that was not easy to get into unless you had an appointment. Security guards stopped you at the desk. The entomologist wrote to tell me the gardener had left him to do a course on Mexican botanicals, which, he could see now, had more to do with plant products than botany. I meant to write back to him, but never did.

Once I saw Ocampo in the subway on the other side of the platform, but he didn't see me. I was in a hurry to catch my train, so didn't run upstairs across the mezzanine, then downstairs to the uptown side, and later felt bad about it. The following week I waited on the same platform at the same time, hoping to see him again. I did this as often as my job would allow, which wasn't much, but I tried.

One last postcard arrived, this time from the Arctic, or so I thought. It was of a cartoon polar bear holding a martini. The bear looked happy. Then it occurred to me, Where do you mail a postcard when the nearest mailbox is a thousand miles away? I looked at it under a magnifying glass. Though the postmark was smeared, if you looked closely, the letters around the circular stamp read: Lake Placid. Cold in the winter, but not the site of glaciers and permafrost.

Nobody wants to end up like Mr. Peanut, doomed to be a collection of microbes in some future ice core, but it's more easily accomplished than you might think. I had one of the prisms in my jacket pocket and rubbed it like a rabbit's foot or some other talisman that could retrieve the cracked from the brink, revive the tired, and in very extenuating circumstances (or so I liked to believe as the ghosts of the Van Hayden flew over the city), possibly even nudge the delirious back to earth.

No Mothers, Only Ghosts
Ryan Call

THE FLOATING SKYLAND ON WHICH we had roughly set down in order to escape the roaring storm—some great and violent thunderstorm that had surprised us, suddenly driving our flying machine dangerously through wind and rain—remained shrouded in a thick, blue-gray fog for what became the first of the many days we stayed upon that floating grounds within its caretaker's labyrinthine mansion high up in the atmosphere of the *second sky*.

In the rain and fog that fateful morning, my hapless cargo of lost children—all of whom I hoped to one day deliver to their families even as I searched out my own missing daughter—grew quite anxious, and understandably so, for they had become used to the clear air of the *second sky* over the course of our flight. Here in the grounded flying machine they again found themselves overwhelmed by poor weather, by impenetrable mist, by unusual dreariness—all of these unending curtains of heavy rain and thick fog that hid from them the scary figments of their imaginations: snarling beasts, shadowy ghosts, stalking giants, enormous terror birds, mobs of hideous gremlins, whatever nightmare creatures they dreamed might populate this new and shrouded skyland into which we had nearly crashed. The settled fog reminded them of *the beneath*—that stagnant, dead land far below from which we had finally escaped—and of their immense fear of the unknown, of the plummet, of the out-of-control fall, of their confused wanderings as they sought to return home, and so, thoroughly terrified now, they huddled together in their sleeping quarters, peeking occasionally out into the fog through the portholes. Some whimpered in their nests of blankets, others cried in the bunk beds, still others hid by themselves below deck far in the darkness of the cargo holds, or near the ballast tanks, or among the links of the massive anchor lines fore and aft, all alone by their snuffling selves, and I took much time to coax them back to the living quarters of the airship, that massive ark we had taken up into the air.

As the older children comforted the others, I took stock of our equipment and discovered that the instruments aboard our airship—

our magnetic compass in particular—seemed out of alignment: the compass needle spun lazily around its casing and the chronometer advanced by varying degrees, at times quickly and at times profoundly slowly, as if some inconstant fault had suddenly appeared in its mechanism. I wondered if the power of the storm, the shuddering turbulence our airship had suffered, perhaps the striking of St. Elmo's fire upon the masts, might have upset their calibrations. Really, what might have caused these errors and inaccuracies, I could not truly know—I only knew that we needed to find another source of instrumentation in order to correct them and regain our way. And therein you might understand the cause of my own anxiety, for I had not once ever experienced such drastic error in my instrumentation, fog or no fog.

We were lost.

Still the fog persisted even as the rain ceased, and morning passed to afternoon.

The fog so encircled us that various parts of the flying machine's structure—the wings, the masts and sails, the empennage—seemed at once to disappear into the blankness beyond our sight. What little we could see of the grassy ground beneath the landing gear appeared well manicured, and the few bushes—those that the machine had not crushed during our landing—we could see clipped neatly into shapes, though what shapes exactly we could not know from our position above them. We could only see fog, and beyond that, we could know nothing at all of the skyland. As an aviator, I had long experienced the feeling of advancing into the nothingness, of journeying off into that which I could not know or understand, and I had spent much time with the children in the unknown of *the beneath* and had even survived to escape it, but even this fog here upon the skyland gave me great worry as it behaved unlike any other fog I had heretofore encountered. This terrible fog throughout the day pulsed about us, expanded its parts on occasion to reveal to us a glimpse of the blue *second sky* above, contracted in other ways about the flying machine so that wisps and tendrils of it seeped through the portholes, down the hatches, into the flight deck and living quarters, up through the landing-gear wells, the cargo bays.

I wished to depart as soon as possible.

Because the children believed the fog held terrors unimaginable, none volunteered to accompany me on a quick expedition around the

153

skyland so that I might better assess our situation and come to understand the fog and all it hid from our view. Perhaps, I wondered aloud to them, I might even discover a new method of escape, though secretly I wanted to find somewhere upon the skyland a clue as to our location, any detail that might help us reorient ourselves and continue on our way. Yet even the larger boys who had joyfully escorted me through the craggy landscapes of the many other skylands we had encountered during our journey, even these boys denied my entreaties to group themselves into a touring party, so I announced that I would go out by myself. This message the children greeted with even greater consternation, for they could not bear to be left alone without an adult present in this creeping fog. They begged me to remain with them, and instead suggested that the older children draw lots—a method they had often used to resolve conflicts aboard the ship—to determine which of them would go out in my place.

I insisted still that I should go, even rose unsteadily from my hammock to gather some equipment, when one of the largest boys, my handler, came forward and pushed me down. In my weakened state, for the stress of the long journey with the children had taken a toll on my body, I could not resist his strength, and sighed dramatically instead. While the children seemed to have flourished as we had tramped through *the beneath* and made our escape to soar through the *second sky*, I had grown weaker and had finally resigned myself to a certain physical helplessness in the presence of these children. I could do nothing but pilot the airship, and so while they tolerated me and controlled me in many ways, they also needed me, for I was the sole crew member capable of flying them toward home.

Meanwhile, the older children organized themselves into a circle, and a young boy passed by turns from one child to the next, his tattered hat held out before him, and the children one after another withdrew from his hat the sorting stones, the small polished stones they had carried with them throughout the journey, a kind of charm set they believed, some small tools the children hoped might create order in their chaotic lives. After the voices and excitement ceased, the smallest of this group of older children rose, and I recognized the standing child to be the girl with the withered arm, a girl whose very figure reminded me on occasion of my own daughter, the one I had lost long ago on a skyland such as this.

I saw that she held aloft in her good hand the single white stone of the lot.

I again rose from my hammock and made to intervene, though I doubted I could change the outcome of the stones. The children would not abide it. They did not fear me, had not ever feared me since the beginning of our journey.

She can't go, I said.

The others too stood from their circle, arranging themselves between me and the girl so that I could not come to her aid.

My handler-child pushed me back down and I relented.

She goes, one of the older boys said.

Her arm, I said.

She drew just as well as any one of us, he said.

She's one of the oldest here, said another.

I have to go, she said.

I cannot help it, she said.

She shrugged away from the group and gathered a few supplies—a hammer, a coil of rope, a twist of twine, a lantern, and her watch, which she wound to track how long she might be gone—before stepping out of the flying machine and dropping easily to the soft, mossy ground of this mysterious skyland.

We watched as she slowly disappeared into the mist.

The children and I waited there in the safety of the flying machine, and soon afternoon gave way to evening—we could tell by the changing shades of fog as it ranged from a soft dove white to a purple bruise of color—and still she had not returned to us. As the time passed, I worried: had I now lost yet another child even as I hoped to discover the whereabouts of my missing firstborn? Should I have gone in the girl's stead to face whatever terror she had certainly faced in the fog beyond us?

If only the children had not forbidden me!

If only the children had demonstrated some compassion for the girl!

As dusk came I worried about what might have befallen her: some ferocious and wild animal nesting secretively in the fog of this skyland; a collapse of the ground at its center, giving way to a hole and the unavoidable drop-off into *the beneath*, into near certain death; or perhaps she had unknowingly stepped over the final edge of the skyland in the deep fog; or maybe a band of sky pirates had taken her prisoner. As I worried, the children grew bolder, and soon some of the older boys had left the confines of the airship to forage for the rare bits of dead wood at the edges of the fog. They returned quickly, and soon we had all of us crept out of the ship and into the lush grass of the meadow, a tiny pocket of grass clear of the fog around us where one of the older boys had lit for us a watch fire against the coming darkness. There we sat—I in my hammock and the children on their small cushions—in the shadow of the flying machine, just as we had some time not so long ago in the landscape of *the beneath*, and together we awaited sleep. The children held on to their fear, nervously yammered into the night about this and that, finally begged me to tell them a bedtime story, which I did, a fantastic story about a young girl who had fallen, but in her long, interminable fall had learned to fly so that she might fly away into the evening just as the stars came out above her, and soon one after another the children fell into sleep, leaving me awake to wait for the girl with the withered arm.

Her absence rekindled in me the old horror, the buried despair at my having lost my daughter, and these feelings again plagued my rest once I too fell asleep, sending me into a nightmarish realm, an ironically beautiful, pleasant skyland, that same skyland that in my past had wrecked my fate, and there I again relived my tiny daughter's fateful plunge of long ago: she toddling out of the meadow toward the skyland's crumbling edge, I reaching out for her, my wife waking to my screams. I sat up then, the dream leaving me suddenly, and looked about me frantically. The children had all of them snuggled one against another, covered each other with the blankets from the flying machine. The fire had burned down to a fistful of embers in the midst of us, and the sun had just begun its dramatic rise, its rays spreading out above us to reveal that the fog had slowly begun to recede.

Beyond the edge of the firelight, I saw the ember of a boy's pipe briefly flare.

The girl with the withered arm still had not returned.

I sat there wrapped in my blanket and watched over the course of the hour as the sun's rays descended upon the skyland, and slowly the children too awoke, and together we witnessed the sun burn away the fog to reveal to us the true nature of the skyland. We had crash-landed in a small meadow, yes, perhaps what one might call a garden or a green, a lush hillside that revealed itself above us as the fog withdrew in the morning sunlight, and the once terrifying forest all about us now gave way to a clean stand of tall, well-organized trees, fruiting healthily, planted in rows, with ferns and bushes carefully arranged about them to form a lush undergrowth beneath the vibrant canopy. We saw trails too, pebbled walking paths that snaked in and out of the trees around us, all converging in our little clearing, making a circle here, an oval there, and other geometric figures upon the ground that pedestrians might wish to follow in their meanderings.

Unfortunately, our machine had crushed some great bush there in the middle of the meadow, and as I examined it, the children began to laugh gleefully, for scattered throughout the meadow were countless more bushes, each shaped into a kind of animal: here a pig rooting in the grass, there a rabbit standing on hind legs to tower over the children, farther a dog at point, nearby a lion rearing upon its hind legs, over there an ostrich with its head tucked hilariously down between its legs, and closer an extravagant peacock, and here finally a gigantic octopus with eight topiary arms expertly cultured and trimmed into a whirling, turbulent mass of boxwood. The children scrambled around the gardens, some climbed aboard the topiaries and carefully pretended to ride them about, others played tag at their feet and shouted to one another. The fog burned away quickly beyond us, quietly, and as it rose up the bright green hillside, there appeared a gigantic mansion, countless stories tall, brightly lit, white and pearlescent in the morning sun, its windows gleaming as it overlooked the massive gardens of this skyland.

Had I known then that we might remain trapped in that mansion, and had I known then how long our stay there might delay our journey home, and had I known then what sort of emotional distress a single bedroom in that wicked mansion might cause me, I would quickly have ushered the children back into the flying machine, locked its entrances from without, and set out on my own to gather the girl with the withered arm, to rescue her from that mansion, all so we might escape.

But how could I know what deception lay within that house?

How could I know the enticements of memory contained within its rooms?

I simply could not. Instead, I can only warn you now, those of you who might chance to read this flight journal, that somewhere upon a skyland in the *second sky*, there floats a mansion from which escape is nigh impossible, a mansion in which one encounters the past, can live for however long in reminiscence, can reside in memory, all while time dangerously passes by outside its walls.

As the children played around me, I raised my eyes to the rooftop, and there, atop it, a solitary figure, a silhouette, a dark shadow, stood upright behind the railing of the widow's walk. The children too soon sensed this figure, and they paused, awestruck in their play, and watched the fog lift, stared respectfully at the mansion, and suddenly the figure vanished into the house, and the fog completely receded to reveal to us the rocky, darkened landscape behind the mansion. We could see now the skyland in its entirety, with its landscape bounded on nearly all sides by a carefully constructed fencing that disappeared into the base of the rocky cliffs behind the mansion. We saw through the woods a stable, a large rolling meadow upon which a flock of sheep lounged peacefully, then a sparkling rivulet of water cascading down the slopes of the bluffs, past the mansion, and into the forest where it gathered into a large turtle pond, dammed up and carefully bounded by flagstones and mossy boulders, only to again trickle out of the depths of the pond and creak its way into the woods, past the topiary garden beneath wooden footbridges here and there, and then to end, plummeting off the side of the skyland just beyond our flying machine.

The children dispersed then, quickly, excitedly, so that they might discover as much of the skyland as possible floating there within the realm of the fog. Groups of children rushed toward the edge of the pond; others ran off to the meadows to play with the sheep; while still others traced the pathway of the creek, carefully climbing boulders and fallen logs to reach, at some point or another, the spring in the small rockslide just above the mansion. I carefully followed a footpath, exited the topiary garden, and weakly walked along the crushed seashells and pea gravel up toward the mansion atop the hill. I reached its front door, a massive oaken affair two stories tall, and there upon it greeted me a great bronze knocker, an eagle's head affixed to the center door panel, and so I knocked, once, twice.

I listened as the knock echoed throughout the interior of the mansion.

The door eased itself open.

Hello, I called out.

Nothing.

The house seemed empty upon my first entering its enormous foyer, but then I heard, echoing neatly down its many corridors, a feminine voice calling to me, beckoning me to go farther into the mazelike hallways and stairways.

Come in, child, it said.

I cast myself forward into the house—a few children had by this time followed just behind me, curious as to my purpose here—and together we made our way throughout, following after the voice, climbing stairs, exploring sitting rooms, traversing crooked hallways and long corridors, passing by enormous bay windows that fronted the house and revealed the terrific landscape of the skyland beyond, across which the figures of the other children scattered in the grass. Great swaths of sunlight shone through these windows, and in these rays we could see particles of dust dancing in the air, slowly, peacefully. The house seemed still and undisturbed, as if no one had lived here for countless years.

And yet, still, we heard that voice, this woman's voice.

I found her too familiar, as though perhaps my own mother, whom I had known to be long dead, had returned to take up residence in this odd place. Soon too the children spoke of recognizing the voice. One claimed it was the voice of her mother, while yet another claimed that, *no*, the voice was that of *his* mother, and still a third claimed the voice certainly belonged to *his mother too*, until each of the children, all of whom had listened intently and anxiously to the voice, began to hear in the voice the voice of his or her mother, and the crowd of children became delighted despite their confusion. For, after all of this time, after their plummeting out of the *second sky* and surviving whatever air disaster had befallen them long ago to separate them from their mothers, these children now believed they had finally arrived home, that I had taken them there.

Oh, thank you, they said to me, each hugging me about my legs.

You promised to deliver us to our mothers, they said.

And you have done so, they said.

Joyously, they bolted away from me before I could warn them, their voices too now trailing up and down the hallways, voices of happiness and curiosity and delight wavering in the air all around me, joined now by the sound of doors creaking open, doors slamming shut, footsteps pounding up and down the lengthy hallways and wooden staircases, and still the voices of their mothers clamoring for their attention, and soon I found that only I remained, for even the large boy who always seemed to shadow me had run off in search of his mother.

Cautiously, I crept down the hallway, having muffled my ears with a bit of cotton against the voice still beckoning me as though it might fool me into believing my long-dead mother walked these halls, and in my dullness I investigated the rooms. The voices of the children had quieted somewhat too, and whatever shrieks of joy and peals of laughter had previously filled the air had transformed into the quiet babblings of children at play, of children content in their surroundings, of children lost in the tiny worlds of their childhood rooms, for my journey led me to find that many of the children—these, my lost and flightless charges—had discovered behind the doors that lined the labyrinthine corridors their very own childhood rooms, the rooms they had left intact back home, wherever home might have been for each of them, before they had embarked on whatever fateful travels had led to their air disasters, to their crashing into the unknown of *the beneath*. I traversed back and forth these corridors, opening doors here and there, especially when a doorknob or certain pattern of wood or decorative molding about the doorframe attracted my attention. In one room, I opened the door to discover two children—twins I recognized—splayed out upon the carpet of their room, a game of marbles before them, their reading lamp brightly lit above them as the sun set in the window. Another door revealed to me a child, a young boy really, sitting astride a rocking horse, calmly moving to and fro as he gazed at a flickering oil lamp ensconced on the wall across from his bed. A third door I had to push rather force-fully open to discover one child singing little songs to herself in a blanket fort, which she had constructed from the many pillows and comforters she had stripped from her bed. Other rooms revealed sim-ilar scenes: these children at home in bedrooms that exactly recreated their own childhood rooms at home, wherever home might have been for them long before they were lost from their various flights across the *second sky*.

Lastly, I discovered the girl with the withered arm. She had found her room too and had fallen asleep beneath the covers of her little bed, a small stuffed animal in the shape of a bunny tucked in next to her and a picture frame clutched against her chest, the photograph within a depiction of her mother and father holding her up between them and smiling toward the camera. I leaned down and gave her a quick kiss good night and drew the curtains over the window, casting the room in darkness.

But, of course, none of these rooms contained their mothers, only ghosts.

I wondered what sort of creature might create such a home. I thought of that mournful figure we had seen upon the widow's walk, and as I did so, I entered the last room I'd ever see within that house, the room in which I suffered my loss, the room in which I fainted, in which I awoke to a bleak, cold, dreary day perhaps many days later, the room in which I found only traces of my gone and fallen daughter, the daughter I had sought throughout the blustery atmosphere of the *second sky*, the daughter who had fallen years ago beyond my clutches, who had tumbled from the edge of the skyland and away from her father forever.

You see, in my desire to check on all of the children I cared for, I had unknowingly turned the knob to a replica of my lost daughter's room. The door swung open and there immediately I paused, struck by its exactness: the six illustrations of baby animals hanging on the wall above her crib, the linens my wife and I had purchased and in which I had often swaddled my daughter in her earliest days alive, the single twin bed against the other wall in which I had often spent the night so that I might easily carry her to my wife for the feedings, the rocking chair in the corner in which I had rocked her to sleep, at its feet the woven basket of stuffed animals she had collected, then to my left the changing table I had converted into a dresser—on it a lamp, a series of decorative nesting boxes my wife particularly admired, my daughter's night light. I hesitated to grasp the drawer pull, for I feared what I might find within the chest, and yet I knew I must look.

And so I did. There, just where they should have been, in that top left drawer, I found an assortment of tiny socks, some decorated with cats, others with birds, still others spotted like little ladybugs. The cat socks she had liked best, and I felt suddenly a great heaviness overcome me, blocking out my vision to dullness and clogging my mouth with rancid spit. My weakness returned then, a dizzying spell that overtook me, sending me into blackness.

I awoke—how long I slept I do not know—to the frantic sounding of voices, the distant moaning of children in the throes of their waning sleep, for the children had begun to awaken throughout the house, and in their new surroundings they had begun to call out fearfully from their bedchambers, their couches, their nests of blankets, wherever they had finally fallen asleep as they waited for their mothers to tuck them in, to sing them bedtime songs and whisper to them nursery rhymes and chatter to them nonsense love sounds, mothers whom the children did not understand would never come in this damned house.

In that horrible room, I discovered I had managed to crawl into the twin bed after my episode. Throwing off the covers, I staggered into the hallway, my body aching with disuse and pain, a sudden wind whistling now throughout the corridors, as if some great hole had opened deep within the house, blowing about dust, debris, fabric, bits of insects that had died and curled up along the floorboards. I made my way through the mazelike corridors, first opening one door, then another, and another, and another, all so that I might gather up the children, shouting as I went that they ought to wake up, wake the others, clasp hands together, and follow me into the grand hall-way at the base of the massive staircase, and soon they all emerged, each surprisingly taller than I last recalled, their clothing ill fitting, their hair much longer, their faces leaner and more mature, their mouths wider, their noses stronger. Even their eyes appeared differ-ent, seemed no longer bright and clear. They stood in the swirling dust of the foyer, and as I opened the heavy door to reveal the sky-land before us in the gray light of that morning, the children gasped behind me.

Stretched out beyond the mansion the landscape of the skyland appeared old, dead, some altogether bleak and unremarkable thing on which we had landed. In the distance the meadows looked dull and devoid of life, the creek dried up, the topiary garden now barren, the grass there brown and burnt, the forest suddenly lifeless, the koi pond sludgy and overgrown. We stepped out onto the front lawn and turned to behold the mansion, which had itself become listless, no longer shiny and attractive. The windows did not sparkle in the sun any longer. Its whitewashing had dulled, the paint cracked and splin-tered, a pane of glass here and there shattered, the stone walkway overgrown with moss, weeds, mud, and dirt.

The children began to cry then. Some wished to return to the house, to lock themselves back in their bedrooms, but I knew we could not risk such a false escape, as it would spell disaster for our little crew. We had to flee this eternal place before it was too late for us. Already, I knew we had lost valuable time to those splendid, memory-filled rooms.

I urged the children to link hands together.

They did so, and I began to make my way from the house toward the airship.

A certain tugging began, and our line stopped.

I turned around to find the girl with the withered arm at the end of the line.

We have to go back, she said. My parents are in that house.

No, they are not, I said.

But my father, he kissed me good night just as I fell asleep.

That wasn't your father, I said. That was me.

If I wait in my room tonight, he'll be there again to say good night, she said.

The other children began to stir as hope took hold of them too.

The girl sensed their hope and, tears mounting now in her eyes, pleaded with them.

If you too believe, if you too wait in your room tonight, your parents will finally come, she said to the others. If you too can manage to stay up a little while longer, you will see them, she said. You will hug them and kiss them and never let go of them ever again.

She had worked herself into a fit now, and I did my best to calm her down.

I'm sorry, but your parents are not in that house, I said.

I will take you to them, I promise, I said.

No, you won't, she said. You're trying to keep us from them!

Crying now, frantic, she began to tug on the line of children to draw them back into the house. She tugged roughly on the girl's arm that had linked to hers, and this girl then tugged on the child's arm now linked to hers, and this child in turn tugged again, and the next arm tugged, and the next arm tugged again, and all movement of the line ceased despite my best efforts, and then the movement shifted, and I found myself in my weakened state dragged slowly back toward that great mansion, the house of the lost childhoods, and though I resisted I could not arrest the movement of the desperate children.

And so I write now in this journal from the bedroom of my lost daughter.

I spend my days wandering this maze of a house. I check in on the rooms of my grounded children. As the days pass, I watch as their bodies change further, as they outgrow their clothes, as their limbs lengthen and their faces become drawn and thin, even as their minds remain trapped in the past, for these large children still clutch at the remnants of their childhood: the toys that populate their rooms, the blankets they knew long ago, the stuffed animals they snuggled with back when they were little, the pictures of their parents and siblings from their past lives. I can do nothing for them. I realize I should have one night tried to quietly sneak each of them into my arms and carried them all down to the airship, but those days are gone now and not a moment passes when I do not regret attempting to save them. For had I done so, we might yet have survived our journey to return to their real homes, to return to their real families, to return to their real lives. And had I done so, we might yet have discovered somewhere in the *second sky* my lost daughter.

For now, I'm fated to remain in my daughter's old room in this wicked house. Still I resist that motherly voice and its daily pleadings. I am the last remaining occupant yet to succumb to her advances. She beckons me now to search out my own childhood room.

Son, she calls me, come see me.

I know I do not have the strength to resist her forever. One day I will give in. I fear what I shall confront in that bedroom.

Song of the Andoumboulou: 181
Nathaniel Mackey

Once again we sat in a taqueria watching soccer. "Heads were coming off
daily," Ahdja found herself saying, "when
        Lay-
la heard her Majnoun sing." Brother B
had been wondering out loud about the
perch he looked out from, inwardly what
          to
  make of the meaty lips her mouth proffered, sweet-meat inducement to what
he sat wondering, meaty lips it maybe
only seemed her mouth proffered, death
           ever
  the backdrop she might or might not
  have been saying, lost heads meant so
much else... Sweet meat's tarjuman the
          perch
made him, many a lost head's interpre-
ter, would-be tarjuman, he made it seem she
made it seem to say. "The world's on fire,"
          she
  came out and said, "the ice cap's melting. You hang on every twitch of my mouth,
you dote and you ogle. Perch or no perch,
          you
make me blush." Brother B's head rolled
or might as well have rolled as the rest of
us watched, tarjuman of aught but embarrassment, he too made to blush, nothing if not
          Ah-
dja's toy, his head a soccer ball of sorts...
It seemed we heard a high keening sound. Ahdja's rebuke went on echoing, arctic water
          beat

on the taqueria door. Planetary gas trap,
planetary sweat, world at risk, Ahdja's alarm

si-

rening
yet

•

Eighty-fourth minute, still no score, we
chewed our tacos. News of a new bombing interrupted the match, we kept eating.

World

in our faces world at bay as we wrapped
up our food stop, soon to be gone again...
In my thoughts a broken voice that no

long-

er signified serenaded us, notes learned
by rote from day one. My mind drifted
back to Low Forest. Deer stood like

sta-

tues beside the road... Drizzle native
to North Lone Coast came down, mist
heard as missed riffed on as mystic, yth-
mic dismay. Ahdja braced for loss I could

see.

She mourned abandonment long beforehand I could see. Her bones glowed under
her skin... Ahdja's mouth glued on Brother

B's

face, adjunct prophecy, his pasted on hers
I could see. Hers was a game of playing his
I could see, his playing hers I saw. All I saw

was

alarm lit them
up

•

(chant)

Brother B looked in on the world, all
aspect interdicted under threat of
house arrest, comeliness whose midriff
                      drew
him in. Ahdja's blank body absorbing
his own blank body, late lady of the chur-
chical girth no arms could get around,
                      all
   its amnesiac allure... Not bounty but
a beyond beyond bounty, bodily wonder, broad unembraceable thought's mor-
phic thrum, thought-song's day begun.
                      He
dreamt her wide, he dreamt her flat the
way the world once was, conferred
with by crows blown off their perch the
                      same
   as he'd be from his, theirs the rings a-
round Saturn... Implicate girth he got
   next to in dreams, an implied surrogacy,
                      so-
nority's reconnoiter, sonority's recondite
compass, funk too strong a word for it,
                      so-
nority's hermetic
whiff

———————————

(*invoice*)

Ahdja and Brother B stared off into
    space, looked out the taqueria's wall
  that was all window, the alarmed
                        lovers
    or the would-be lovers they were
notwithstanding, alarmed or in love all
  the more. Some unlikely regard's
                        white
    fire they were not to tell they all
  the same dwelt on, bodily welter's wry
  dissolve, some essential sadness...
Caught up in spirit we called it, biting
                        into
  our quesadillas looking on, his and her
    blank bodies a screen for the world
  outside, a masque if they could, a ritual, a
                        rite
      they'd remake it
      with

                •

(*chorus*)

Brother B blushed and missed a beat
    but said in reply, "Not since his and
  her turned heads fell off have they
                        stopped
    rolling." It was polis compounded
  of eros again. "Why," he topped it
    off, "think not?" It was eros construed
  as polis, again our eternal wont... We
                        felt

sorry for them, we felt sorry for ourselves, burnt-out buildings tattooed on
their skin, skin like it was newsprint,
> world

so with them they shrank, Andoum-
boulou again, refugee dead on their skin...
If not shadow play shamanic dance. His
> and

her platonic exchange. Black Ellie leaned
and whispered in my ear, "I wanted
wontons," a fight that might've broken
> out

suppressed... If not shadow play cha-
rade of the dead, tarjuman of tally, toll.
Itamar paid B and Ahdja no mind, alarm
no mind, lost to the savor of asada dashed
> with

lime, spark's or spat's ignition no mind...
We were taking our time, the screen had
gone back to the match, no score yet, Brother B and Ahdja's exchange by the wayside,
> ver-

bal tick's verge on skirmish done. The tri-
butes to the dead posted on their skin
made them shiver. If not shadow play the
> tim-

bre of lust I was thinking. Huff mock-
sang, semisang, as everyone laughed, "I'm
in love with a dicty woman, I just can't
keep from crying"... If not shadow play the
> sway

of the floor I was thinking, the table's way
with gravity as well. I was thinking no
Dogon made the Middle Passage but here
they were, I was thinking all sorts of things. I
> was

thinking the at-some-point-to-be-abandoned
girl heard the song of herself, if not shadow
play the way she'd always heard love would
> find.

169

If not shadow play a run of suns I thought...
No Dogon swam the Atlantic or crossed the
Rockies but here they were at Taqueria Vallar-
ta, we the migrating they all over again, each
           in
our awkwardness desirous even more, salsa
  spilled on our soccer shorts, chorus, carousel,
crew... Caroling, carousing, chorusing, heads
          com-
  ing off, Ahdja pointed out again, when Layla
heard Majnoun sing. Black Ellie mock-sang
  seconding it, all of us on our way out the door
as if out of a tej bar, bellies full but wondering
          what
  did we see, why did we
  stop

Once out the door we walked in a ring.
Chorus. Crew. Carousel. Planetary gas
up and gone but not gone. Another bomb
          gone
off somewhere no matter what... What had
  it all been getting at we wanted to ask,
too caught up to ask. Mummers we might
          well
have been, love with its way of moving on
  and we in its wake, all that might accrue to
it a more viable body, a footnote or a perch
          note,
  Brother B's
  reset

Nave

Ann Lauterbach

1.

Or, such incentives as a golden
hook dangling from the neck
of a swan. Glint of moon.
Circumference
of a pond and the
incessant vibration of wings.
A song off in the distance,
song, or chant. Above
a yellow willow
the feminine
drift of clouds
gauzy and unpredictable
secrets intact. And
the devotional
sun ruptures its coil
and leaks through,
long fingers
of tarnished light
touching a bowl.
Pews, aisles,
heads bowed

to stone. Above

the willow, clouds

assemble a congregation

of weeping girls,

heads wrapped

in bandages,

feet muddied.

None of this can be seen.

So the dream

sutures images

onto pale drawings:

here will be the bed,

here the gown,

here will be the drain

for the new sink, here

the table, candle, spoon.

And these? Stairs

folded out from air

and stars, made

to lean against a broken

stump. Up, up, down, down

counting the steps

as the river disappears

behind a looming scaffold.

This would have a name

but it is mute as weather

and the thin poles

are transparent

to the sound of bells

heaving their toll.

Havoc? Is this havoc?

In the dream, we

climbed like children,

counting *one two three*

up the ancient

ladder with its scent of pine.

A man played a cello.

A woman lay

prone on a deck, turning

into the stench

of salt and tobacco, her

hair flooding

across the hull. I guess

a band played

to keep the ritual intact

but the sea

and the sails

and the moving clouds

heard nothing of the repeated

drum pulse. The woman drowned.

Molecular and luminous

she assembled in front of a cave

where hands had touched rock

and rock became bird.

2.

The anchor's chain rains down

link by link, in a clatter of

hardened soot.

Have we been here before?

The interior doubles its enclosure.

A circus forms. A mountain

is a bruise on the horizon

but the sky, hidden again,

continues to harbor

the girls' undistributed lament.

Pale light, virtue in long

rags pulls across

a blind little passage.

Were we ever inside?

And yet the glass

broke into glittery shards

and the freed bloods

crossed the floor, the gravel,

the fields. And water?

Yes, water

fell for the architect

and for the carnival jester

and for the improbable swan.

Memory's fraudulent

desire strips

rapture onto fable.
Soldier standing in front
of a statue. Woman
in floral robe.
Bricks of the missing house.
Turn down that street
sit on that porch
watch those roof cats
scatter for their prey.
Is murky now, and the dark
contracts its allegory
into testaments of faith.
We are waiting
for a crumpled assonance
to undo the cries
for mercy, or make
from artifice an actual tool.
The dump contracts our purview.
We count blue bottles
thrown from the sea, we
toss gray pebbles
at empty jars. Choice
is consequence.
Were we
wearing hoods that day?
Which day? The day
the clown

climbed all the way

to the top and stared down.

3.

Neither extended nor reached.

Habit's insatiable laps

roving in orbits,

their bright slogans

drawn into icons of intent.

What shall we do? What do?

The bridge hangs over

the river, a diadem of light.

And the unbuilt globe

traverses the amphitheater

from above, unblinking

dry eye on the rubble lot.

The clown scowls

through his mute mask, unable

to know how many, how

much. He spins

the toy top, he

pinches the mean air.

There are constellations

sieving the night,

equations

distorting the aperture

—this does not

equal this. Into the aporia

floats the sum of disbelief

as the parable

calls its miraculous

lyric—*was blind but now*—.

—*For Dan Beachy-Quick*

Euphoria
Can Xue

—Translated from Chinese by Karen Gernant and Chen Zeping

Ms. WEN SAT IN A DARK ROOM pondering the structure of the universe. Then she stood and opened the window, whereupon all kinds of obscure shadows wandered in. The room turned half light, half dim. Poo, poo, poo . . . came the noises from the shadows. Ms. Wen felt herself sinking; the ceiling and four walls were scattering in all directions. Ms. Wen wasn't suspended in the air, however. Rather, she stood firmly on Mother Earth, all kinds of things clustered tightly around her. She didn't feel she was tied up, though; instead, she felt pleasantly free.

"You're on the second floor facing southwest. It's the room with an apple on the windowsill. It's a medium-sized room with simple furniture and a typewriter." The voice came from a tape recorder.

"Thank you for telling me where I am. But who are you?" Ms. Wen was puzzled.

"I'm your friend. You don't have to know my name because we're in touch with each other only inside this building. This has nothing to do with the outside world."

These words must have been recorded in advance. How odd! Now she was going to do some deep-breathing exercises. Each time she inhaled, the shadows also rapidly flew into her nostrils, and her body sank continuously and slowly. During this process, Ms. Wen always wanted to know where she was—where was she in this "cosmic building"? Was she facing west? But the recorder wouldn't respond to her questions very often. So she was puzzled most of the time. It was OK to be puzzled, but she did long to be oriented. The answer would come from the recorder sooner or later. When it came, it always happened unexpectedly, and it made her feel fantastic. She loved what was going on inside "the cosmic building." The walls and ceiling had scattered—wasn't that true? The voice from the recorder made it clear that she was in a "medium-sized room" located "on the second floor" "in the southwest part of the building." These descriptions couldn't indicate any place outdoors. But she also kept

178

sinking; she couldn't remain inside a room. It was really hard to decide where she was. How wonderful to be in this delicate uncertain state! Maybe she was simultaneously in both the south and the north, but the announcement was always clear, making her feel that she could depend upon this reality.

Years earlier, Ms. Wen had looked forward to this kind of exercise. She had looked forward to being in a large building of uncertain design and groping her way into a strange room. But this had come about only in her old age. She had now done this many times. The more she exercised, the more the building expanded—that is, there were more and more strange rooms and floors. It was almost impossible to figure out which room or floor one was in, or where the corridor led, or where the entrance could be found. Once, she had groped her way to the end of a corridor. As she hesitated to take the next step for fear of stepping into emptiness and falling, the corridor turned again. And so she involuntarily entered a windowless room that was terribly small—only one square meter. The moment someone closed the door behind her, it was unbearably stuffy. She wanted to leave, but the more she struggled, the smaller the room became. The four walls pressed in on her, and she dozed off in terror. She slept standing. Finally, at dawn, she heard the voice from the tape recorder say, "This room is in the southwest corner of the seventh floor. It's a storeroom." Just then, Ms. Wen discovered that she was standing in the corridor; on her right was the staircase going down.

There was no elevator in this building; Ms. Wen found it exciting to climb the stairs late at night. Once, she recalled that she had alternately climbed and rested until at last she had climbed twenty-five stories. The twenty-fifth was apparently the top floor; the corridor extended in all directions. It was like a gigantic tower. The faint light glimmering above seemed about to be extinguished. When she steeled herself to open the door to the roof garden so that she could go outside and look around, she found that there was no roof garden. Instead, there was a staircase continuing to go up. A little afraid, she closed the door and turned around, intending to go down the stairs. But she couldn't find the down staircase. No matter which direction she took, when she reached the end of the corridor, she came to the up staircase, as though being forced to continue to climb up. Ms. Wen sat down on the wooden bench in the corridor to nap for a while. A noise awakened her: someone was coming down the stairs with slow, heavy steps. It was an old man, wearing a tartan duck-bill cap. He walked over to her, and—looking into her eyes—he said, "It's

179

always heartwarming to run into old friends in foreign countries." She knew she had answered him, but she didn't remember what she had said. They walked to the end of the corridor, and as they rounded a corner, they exited the building. Ms. Wen looked back. The only thing behind her was an average-sized six-story concrete building. The roof was slanted and covered with ornamental tiles. The old man left in a taxi. Ms. Wen wanted to go back inside and look around, but someone had closed the main door and was locking it from the inside.

That building was on the same street as her home: it was a place for senior citizens' activities. But not many elderly people went there for recreation. After Ms. Wen retired, she had asked her neighbors about this. They had told her, "It's really stuffy inside, not suitable for elderly people." But after going there just once, Ms. Wen was captivated by this building—especially the room for chess and card playing. That spacious room had an unusually high ceiling. Usually, only two or three people were playing chess. By afternoon, no one was there. And so Ms. Wen made a habit of going there in the evening. It was a few months later that the metamorphosis of this building occurred. A wall and ceiling disappeared. When Ms. Wen looked up, the stars were visible. There was a design in the starry sky. She heard a deceased cousin laughing beside her: "This pastime belongs to you alone." These words gave her goose bumps all over, but they also heightened her curiosity. From then on, she went to the senior citizens' recreation center every few days. Later, this became stranger and stranger. The oddest thing was the time this six-story building turned into a bungalow shaped like an octopus. In the center was an immense hall, surrounded by numerous endless walkways. On either side of the walkways were rooms that looked like offices. Ms. Wen experimented: each walkway tempted her to take an infinitude of walks, but after walking for a while, Ms. Wen became afraid. Then she returned to the hall in the center. A transformed building was so dangerous and yet so alluring! The most interesting thing was: when she walked on the concrete walkway, she could hear a shadow play being staged somewhere. It was just like those she had seen as a child—striking the gongs, beating the drums, acting and singing. It was so exciting. Still, Ms. Wen didn't like to walk straight down without looking back. This was not only because she was afraid, but also because she thought doing this was beneficial.

A former colleague ran into Ms. Wen coming back in the evening, and began talking with her.

"Ms. Wen, you enjoy exploring by yourself," she said.

"Um. What do you think of this structure?" Ms. Wen felt cold sweat running down her back.

"I can't evaluate it. That's too risky. You're really a brave explorer. I admire you! Wasn't this senior citizens' recreation center constructed just for you?" The colleague's tone was enigmatic.

"But in the daytime, other people also go in," Ms. Wen argued.

"Others? They don't count. They just go in, chat for a while, and then withdraw."

After they parted, Ms. Wen was astonished to realize that this colleague really understood the situation. Maybe she was also paying attention to the same thing? If so, could one say that this senior citizens' center had been built for this colleague too? This ordinary six-story gray structure attracted no attention at all on this street. Every morning, a janitor opened the main door and cleaned all the rooms, as well as the corridor and staircase. Because this building had only one staircase and twelve apartments, the janitor wrapped up her work by noon. The main door stood open. The female janitor, wearing a rat-gray uniform, always waited until late at night to lock up. The next day she reopened it at dawn. Ms. Wen wondered why she would rush over here late each night to lock up. Ever since her colleague had pointed out that this building had probably been constructed for her—Ms. Wen—Ms. Wen had grown more suspicious. Could the janitor be leaving the door unlocked for her? This thought horrified her.

In the last few years, Ms. Wen had become more and more composed. She thanked the sinking exercise for this. That was because as soon as her body sank downward, her thoughts rose—as free as a bird flying in the sky. At such times, her misgivings about the janitor also disappeared, even though she had met her once late at night and been subjected to her questioning. The more she performed the sinking exercise, the more adept she was—almost reaching the point that she could sink or rise just by thinking about it. At the beginning, she had done this by herself, and the exercise had also been restricted to the room she was in—usually the one for chess. Later, after all the walls and ceilings had scattered, when she came and went and whirled freely in midair, it seemed the whole building became transparent and was an extension of her body. She carried this intangible building everywhere she went. In other words, the very existence of this building depended upon her. When she wasn't thinking about it, the building disappeared, and when she gave it all of her attention, the structure once again appeared clearly. This pastime was great fun. One time, she even ran into her son Feng in the corridor. Her son was wearing mountaineering clothes, as if he were going far away. "Feng, were you looking for me?" "Yes. They said that you were climbing up. I too want to enjoy the scenery up there, and so I came here. But how high is it? I can't see it." "Who can see it all of a sudden? You can experience it only while you're climbing. Let's turn to the right. There must be a roof garden in front of us. Oh, this side is the left, this side the right." "In this kind of place, Mama is still hanging on to her senses. That's really impressive." Before she realized it, Ms. Wen had walked out the main door with her son. That's all Ms. Wen could remember. Later, her son admitted to her that he had been terrified by the height of this transformative building, and had wanted to give up. Then he took hold of Ms. Wen's arm as they went down. After this, Feng didn't bring up this incident again. Maybe he thought it better not to speak of it.

The senior citizens' recreation center was Ms. Wen's secret, but it also seemed to her that everyone knew this secret. Besides her two sons, some retired colleagues—affecting a casual manner—also asked her about it. Ms. Wen thought a certain kind of structure is closely related to everyone's life, and that structure always had to be embodied in some real objects—buildings, for example; otherwise, there would be no way to see it or visualize it. Had she discovered the structure of the senior citizens' recreation center, or rather had the structure kept sending her messages, luring her to be part of it? Perhaps once this kind of thing happened to someone, he or she would naturally draw people's attention. And so Ms. Wen now sensed that she was enthusiastically surrounded by people. Everyone seemed to expect something of her. Even the vegetable vendors in the market were talking about her. "She transformed an ordinary building into a thing resembling fate." "People say that if a building went through infinite changes, this must have been caused by someone's physical force." Ms. Wen just happened to hear these comments. These two people were purposely talking loudly; obviously, they meant for her to overhear them. The vegetable vendors' feedback heartened Ms. Wen. New hopes kept surging from her heart. If the structure was revealed in everything in the world, she could speak from it at any time to anyone she wanted. Yes, she had to continue with this, because it was connected with happiness. Ever since last month, as soon as she stepped into the starry sky, a roof appeared above her. She felt perfect. She wanted to transmit the profound mystery of euphoria to other people. That is, one could enter into different things and become the thing itself. Of course, this involved having some skills; she would be happy to pass these skills on to others. She would share her experiences: how to discern directions by touching the walls, the doorknobs, the staircases, and so forth. And how to determine the scope of her movements according to the height of the ceilings and the length of the corridors.

Going to the senior citizens' recreation center to meditate had become Ms. Wen's privilege. This began as a casual visit to the building after she retired. One day, after eating dinner and tidying up the kitchen, she went out for a walk. She remembered that she had run into a retired school principal. He had said that she "looked healthy." Then she had passed the senior citizens' recreation center and noticed that the door was open. The lights were still on in several rooms. Curious, she walked in. She went first to the ping-pong room; the two ping-pong tables stood quietly under the light. No one was likely to come here. And so she withdrew and walked into the chess room. On the chess table was a drawing of a person's head. The drawing was blurred; perhaps it wasn't a picture of a person, but the contours of a granite cliff. Ms. Wen sat down and looked at it, and wondered which old person would paint like this. As she kept looking, she went into a sort of trance. In her trance, she felt faintly excited. She heard a tiny disturbance on the ceiling; it came in fits and starts—sometimes vehement, sometimes quieting down. What kind of animal was making this noise? Ms. Wen climbed up on the table, intending to find out what this was. She had no sooner stood on the table than someone opened the door. Zhong Zhidong, a retired electrician, stood at the door. Embarrassed, Ms. Wen got down from the table.

"I came to have a look because the lights were still on," Zhong Zhidong explained.

"Apparently I'm not the only one concerned about the senior citizens' recreation center," Ms. Wen said.

"Naturally. We're always concerned about this center," Zhong Zhidong said firmly.

Zhong Zhidong left soon. Ms. Wen sat down at the table again. The noise coming from the ceiling had stopped. Ms. Wen looked again at the drawing. This time, she saw that it was a drawing of a building. The method of drawing was quite distinctive: looked at from various angles, the structure of the building was quite different from the number of its stories. At first, she thought it was a drawing of the senior citizens' center, and then she thought it was a drawing of the building where she had taught. Finally, she saw that the structure drawn on this piece of paper had thirty-three stories; it was much like an office building in the city center. Her interest aroused, Ms. Wen didn't want to leave anytime soon. Inside herself, she began feeling almost as energetic as she had when she was young. She wanted to engage in activities in this building. Of course, just then she had no idea exactly what activity she would engage in. For a while, she went upstairs, and then came downstairs, then went up again, then down again. While she was walking up and down stairs, she found that the entire building was pressed to her heart, making it exquisitely private. It was as though someone were asking her amiably, "Turn left or right? How about going to the room on the south side of the eighth floor . . ." She certainly heard the voice of the person making the inquiry, and she responded casually. She felt comfortable both physically and mentally. Then came the metamorphosis. How many exciting scenes had she experienced? Ms. Wen asked this inner question out loud.

Late at night, Ms. Wen walked out of the senior citizens' recreation center with great satisfaction. On a night like this, the transformation of the starry sky and the city depended upon her will and her passion. She stopped next to a newspaper kiosk, gazed at a dark shadow approaching slowly, and said distinctly, "Once more."

A Brief History of
the Colonial Map in India—
or, the Map as Architecture of Mind
Matt Reeck

1.

NOT JUST A MAP, but the authority of a map.

The silliness of all the bad maps at the beginning of academic books.

Gulliver's maps. Gilligan's maps.

Where does the authority of a map come from? Why am I obsessed with maps? Why, if there has been one sort of collection I have always wanted to have, has it been a collection of maps? Who does a map move? What does a map move? A population scientist? A dreamer? A general? Does a map move land? What does a place feel like without a map? What is unmappable ground? Merely the remote? No, there is no more remote in the world. The sacred? Is it sacrilege to map sacred ground?

When we reflect upon maps, the statements we can make seem too self-evident to risk making. Maps and mobility are connected, synergistically. Maps are a dynamic part of a process of settlement and commerce. The advent of good maps is the advent of control over the land, and the end—or beginning?—of our romance with wilderness.

Maps are said to use scientific measures of distance, rather than the unscientific, like landmarks, or time as a physical embodiment—"two days' steady walk." Maps mean to make standard, to standardize the physical; they mean to place places outside of time. For instance, Lucknow will always be 556.2 kilometers from Delhi, along a certain road. Though, of course, Delhi is growing toward Lucknow, and Lucknow toward Patna.

Legend.

As a moral is to a story, so a legend is to a map.

Legend.

As the map grows, the legend spreads.

2.

Map as architecture. Architecture of mind.

The map builds the mind, the constitution of matter, a material unfolding. The map marks the levels, the stories, of power. Ground, then up.

Ground down. The native skill, a figment of the imagination, a pigment coloring the lens. When I asked him why they didn't have maps, he said, "Only people who aren't from here need maps."

Strangers. Maps estrange the land. Taking away history. Taking away the spirit. But taking them where?

Terrain. Country. Overseas.

To tax the land, there must be owners. Titles. Tithes to those who come with the power of maps to fix, to fixate, upon the written mark. *First come, first served? First written, first served.*

Legend.

Each time a new man came, the map grew by one inch. By the time the army came, the map, they said, proved the land was theirs to keep.

3.

The founding (grounding) of the geographical & human-geographical sciences.

Trace the locations on a map:

1784. Asiatic Society of Bengal.
1822. Société Asiatique de Paris.
1824. Asiatic Society in London.
1830. Royal Geographic Society.
1831. Royal Geographic Society of Bombay.
1839. Société ethnologique de Paris.

Legend.

A Descriptive Ethnology of Bengal *includes extensive vocabularies and forty lithographs based largely upon the photographs of Sir Benjamin Simpson, one of the best-known colonial photographers whose accolades include a gold medal for his collection of eighty photographs entitled* Racial Types of Northern India *at the Great London Exhibition of 1862. In the preface, Edward Tuite Dalton acknowledges that ethnology is the by-product of an abandoned plan for a "great" Ethnological Congress in Calcutta meant "to bring together [. . .] typical examples of the races of the Old World, to be made the subject of scientific study when so collected."*

Legend.

To be a world, you must first have people in it.

Legend.

To study their craniums, a natural science?

Legend.

They wrote the misspelled names of the natives upon the map, all that was left, a smudge on the back of the mind.

187

Matt Reeck

Legend.

In their imaginations, there was a map of the world with them at the center of it.

4.

Connection between war and maps. Route and military surveys. Ethos of heroism.

Ground equals law. Map equals might. A map of the sea? A map of outer space? A map of the mind? All would look different. Why, when we think of maps, do we think of maps of land?

Heroes and compatriots in the scientific community, colleagues of self-congratulations.

E. O. Wheeler, surveyor general of India, writes from Dehradun, June 1945, in the preface to R. H. Phillimore's *Historical Records of the Survey of India*, "The research work has been immense; the records have come from a multitude of places; many have been rescued from oblivion; they have been studied, sorted, and compiled into an admirable history that is at once instructive and entertaining."

These men thought that they were heroes of science.

Phillimore: "A large part of this volume is taken up by biographical notes, in spite of a warning given to me that the work is always more important than the man."

No, he says, the man is important. The man is a hero.

Legend.

Each time I traveled the road, it looked different to my eyes—buildings replacing buildings, faces replacing faces— though it was the same road on the map. I experienced a sensation, like the sensation of speaking a foreign language for the first time, of my mind being adjusted to a new pole.

188

Legend.

Meant to reveal the land, set to a mean, it acquired the thumbprint of the industry of mapmakers. All hail the map-maker, the builder of the arc of our mind's eye!

5.

Density equals knowledge. Density is power and control. Making visible. The thrill of the power to make visible, a godlike power. Phillimore: "It is interesting to note the natural triumph of every surveyor able to correct by actual survey the map of some earlier worker who never had the opportunities!"

Collegiality. But competition.

Foucault's natural history: "Natural history is nothing but naming the visible."

Naming the visible. The map's value increases as its density of information increases. Is there a limit to the world rendered visible? Does the world forced into verisimilitude retreat into pronouns—*that one, this one, there, here, there*?

Legend.

The coordinates of the visible, the scope of what can be known.

Legend.

Arranged as such.

Legend.

The map limits horizon. A frustration of the imaginable.

189

6.

Imperial Europe allowed any European country access to lands in which other European countries had established mercantile and military inroads.

Inroads. Roads going in. Into the middle country, the heartland, the hinterland. Hinterland. Far inside. The heart of the beast.

For "business purposes."

"Thanks to the French!" the British imperialist cartographers say. Thanks to d'Anville, Du Perron, thanks to Claude Martin working with Rennell.

The Anglo-French imperial formation?

"One part of my idea of an imperial formation is that it is dialogical or dialectical. The agents in it, the imperial leaders and the interrelated scholars, not only compete with one another, they also shape each other. Each appropriates features from the other." (Ron Inden)

> *Legend.*

> *One thing you can say about imperialism, one map, two maps, three maps, four. Five maps, six maps, seven maps, ore.*

> *Legend.*

> *I awoke from my ~~nap~~. I awoke from my map. There I saw ahead of me the country as though for the first time. ~~Déjà~~ vu. No, "vu." Eyes shorn of blinders. A synapse fires, each detail allotted its place in my mind.*

7.

Mercantile and military competition.

Harbors to be kept secret: "The Directors were anxious to keep these surveys of their harbours secret" (Phillimore).

Safe harbor. Safe haven. Harbor a secret. Harbor a criminal.

The ships in the Opium Wars set off from harbors.

Legend.

The map was laid across the table, stones set on its corners to hold it against the breeze. Here, here, and here, he said, pointing to names, dots on a map. But what did it mean to his audience, when the air in their lungs then was a different air than anything they would experience there?

8.

Seas and rivers.

Changeling | nature | surveys | dreg | constructing | rule.

"Rennell's surveys of the Bengal rivers will always be of interest for the study of changes of details along their courses" (Phillimore).

Rivers as part of natural history, rivers as part of spiritual inheritance.

Rivers dredged are narrow lakes.

What would a mythological map of rivers look like? Why don't maps represent the mythological or spiritual dimensions of land and rivers?

Rivers, in the wild, aren't steady things. They're seasonal. Their courses change. They're hard to navigate. Being hard to navigate, they're not good means of commerce.

Matt Reeck

To make rivers the conduits for a commercial society, there has to be management. They have to be dredged, diked, bridged, deadened.

Chart a river's course. Sound its depths. Dredge a river. Open it to commerce. Run a railroad along its side. Build a bridge.

Walking by the river, a map in hand. Trash accumulates on riverbanks.

Legend.

Did you see her in Devi *disappear into the river grass at the film's end? Did you see the wedding party arrive on the barge in* The World of Apu? *Did you see the way that a river and a railroad speak of different lines, lineages, and architectures of mind? The river's inconsistency meting one type of humanity, the railroad's consistency fit for the factory?*

9.

How cartography is a first process in the secondary mapping of humanity: ethnography, city planning, and social science. The key word emerges—population.

Two quotes:

The era of geographical and topographical surveying also ushered in numerous other surveys on the botany, geology, forests, and other natural resources as well as on the antiquities and archaeology. Though population was not the object of concern in these surveys, it has been noted that right from the early surveys of Colin Mackenzie, population and its characteristics figured in the statistical surveys to some extent. By the mid-nineteenth century, population became an explicit object of concern, and this moment of surveying and mapping was extended to the population as well. From surveying and mapping territories, the epistemological concerns and administrative requirements shifted to mapping populations. (U. Kalpagam)

Lastly, population is the point around which is organized what in the sixteenth-century texts came to be called the patience of the sovereign, in the sense that the population is the object that the government

192

must take into account in all its observations and *savoir*, in order to be able to govern effectively in a rational and conscious manner. The constitution of a *savoir* of government is absolutely inseparable from that of a knowledge of all the processes related to population in its larger sense: that is to say, what we now call the economy. (Foucault, "Governmentality," 1968)

Legend.

People transformed into population.

Legend.

It took months before they updated the maps, and that in a busy city. We kept looking for what we knew existed, but the maps denied us the satisfaction of seeing our world represented to us in the authority of a map. Then the advertisements started appearing for a place in our town, a neighborhood with a name that none of us knew. Shifting ground with bulldozers and backhoes, were the city planners and developers renaming or not naming, as whim might move them? We started to think that if they could change the map so easily, when would reality follow? Or had it already? Leaving us with an image in our minds of a place we used to know.

10.

To talk about maps, the way that maps "talk" to us, represent us and our designs on the world, the way we can't see the world without first seeing a map. We, modern humans, we, the populations of nations, inscribed in an architecture, populated through maps.

As a child grows to inhabit the body, the adult inhabits the map.

Legend.

He set the legend, he modeled the scale to reasonable proportions. Blank space balances the mind, a sensation of beauty. The semblance of order. One white lie, then another.

193

11.

Not just a map, but the authority of a map.

Where does the authority of a map come from? Why am I obsessed with maps? Why, if there has been one sort of collection I have always wanted to have, has it been a collection of maps? Who does a map move? What does a map move? A population scientist? A dreamer? A general? Does a map move land? What does a place feel like without a map? What is unmappable ground?

Legend.

Texture, architecture. What relief then! The map's ambiguous sheen—like the moon, reflecting what you choose to see.

Legend.

The pull of uphill, the old man looking at the full moon, bemoaning, "When will we get there!" The night spent at the temple, wrapped in a mattress alone in a back room, the pain in the knees going down, the way that perspective shifts with each footfall. On the map, Girnar.

Legend.

The feelings that place instills in breath, lapse, breath, lapse, being.

Legend.

Texture, architecture. Whose rough estimate, the map organizes the mind.

A Tiny Haunting
Lisa Horiuchi

A WAXING MOON HANGS ITSELF in the sky over Scottsdale, its silver face dampened by a passing cloud. Anna, Jock, and I greet each other in its sensual glow, commenting on the autumn chill and admiring the lush details of Anna's garden. The yard is ringed in mature olive trees and white-bloomed shrubs—gladioli, mums, and cabbage roses; in a dark corner a full-bodied elm tree rises from a mound of mulch while sweet alyssum creeps around a stone path across the lawn, the grass showing a vivid shade of green under the lattice of moonlight. It's an impressive plot of land, if entirely outsized for the house it's meant to showcase. While stylish and clean lined, Anna's home is no bigger than a shipping crate, hovering a full foot off the ground on hidden skids. It was prefab and assembled on site, Anna tells us, a product of the tiny house movement . . . surely we've heard of it?

I assure her we have, but Jock only lowers his chin in a partial nod. He's taking to Anna so silently and so subtly that he doesn't even seem to be aware of his desire. It is a virile, autonomic thing. He stands between us, macho and stoic, his legs rooted firmly in the grass and hands tucked inside the pockets of his Cardinals hoodie, but it's clear to me—he's magnetized. His body inclines toward Anna in breathless increments, and in response she fakes disdain with a coquettish lowering of the eyes—that trope of a gesture, a mating feint, an ugly dance. I'm no more blind to Jock's romantic lapses than he is to my occasional bouts of envy, but having been business partners for the better part of two years, we've learned to tolerate each other's petty offenses. It's the pathology of brotherhood, the common abuses of a too-familiar friendship.

Anna Chalmers is also a familiar element, of sorts. Jock and I once shared a homeroom with her back at Saganitso STEM Academy in Flagstaff, where she sat attentively in the front row wearing pin-striped men's shirts and ballet flats decorated with silver horse bits, her sand-colored ponytail slicked back and resting high on her crown. Though our acquaintance was brief—she was gone before summer— the five-year gap between then and now has made the idea of Anna, a specter from our past, lavishly mystifying. She is a woman now; moreover, a different sort of woman than anyone would have predicted. As she leads us into her home, Jock takes mental note of her physiognomy: her face, faintly anguished; dyed black hair and kohl-smudged eyes; the pallid, tattooed forearms, St. Peter on one and Hellboy on the other, masterful in black ink, the Sistine Chapel in line art. I find the grownup version of Anna Chalmers mildly repulsive. Jock, on the other hand, is cultivating the possibilities. There is a danger in their contrasts—a scorching, sexual danger—and he is wondering what it might feel like to break her open.

To communicate the obvious: the timing isn't ideal.

Anna's reached out to Jock and me—the Northern Arizona Paranormal Society—not for erotic theater but for support. She is desperate to rid herself of a ghost.

Anna flicks a wall switch and a family of scattered sconces and recessed overheads comes on, revealing a small but tasteful interior. The entirety of the house is viewable from the entryway, and while hardly capacious, the high ceilings and maple walls somehow create a mood of comfort rather than claustrophobia. This is the essence of southwest living—not in the way of cowboys or New Age but of nesting and contentment, in the sense of a womb in a body, a central park inside a metropolis. Everything Anna could possibly need is within a convenient, thirty-foot reach. There's a kitchen and what looks like a closed-off bathroom on one end of the house and on the other she's set up a loveseat and a minimalist home-office vignette: a plain, flat desk with a gooseneck lamp, an ergonomic chair. Above the office is a pull-down ladder leading to a shallow sleeping loft where clerestory windows offer narrow views of the sky. The house smells like breakfast muffins and wood.

"Well, this is a first," Jock says, "the smallest investigation ever." The boundaries of the house are tight—in a single step one is suddenly consumed by all things Anna—and Jock is glued to the welcome mat as if he's not quite ready for such a commitment.

"How'd you hear about us?" I ask, as gently as possible, but it's a miscalculation; Anna is in no mood for special handling.

"Google search," she says.

The odds of Anna finding us, a couple of old high-school acquaintances, are slim. The Northern Arizona Paranormal Society is only twenty months old, with a negligible advertising budget and, until

196

now, largely relegated to the icy highways and honky-tonks of Coconino County, well outside the glamorous perimeter of Phoenix metro. I take it as a sign. This isn't just an accidental client call, it's a pilgrimage, an audition for the main stage. I spent a good chunk of the three-hour ride down to Scottsdale in a daydream state, energized by the changing scenery from pine forests to concrete, the presence of my best friend at the wheel, the blank slate of our partnership. I'll even admit to entertaining visions of our own reality show—*The Spirited Southwest*, starring the paranormal team of Jock Morgan and Mitch Pacey—bedding down in antebellum mansions and strutting through the swampy hallways of abandoned asylums, Jock flexing his good looks and biceps while I play the cool scientist, demonstrating our Mel Meters and Faraday cages and scrutinizing the EMF readouts with my exacting eye.

"Earth to Pacey," Anna says.

"I'm listening," I say.

I suggest we settle into her couch for the preinterview while Jock heads back to the car to unload our gear. Anna starts in immediately with questions of her own, mostly regarding the provenance of her haunting; the house is too new, too impersonal, too neutral, and too modern to birth a ghost. "Too, too, too," she says, the tempo of her anxieties rising. "Why this house? Why me?"

I explain that she's right in a sense; haunted houses are supposed to breathe the energy of the past. But time is a mutable thing, and ghosts can attach themselves not only to homes but to unconventional structures, empty land parcels, even people. The phenomena appear to have been triggered not by Anna's moving into her new home but out of her old one. About a month ago, her mother had been called back to New York by a former employer, and her father, having never left the big city, gifted the home to his daughter to ease the sting of her forced independence. The irony of her long-divorced parents living again in the same city of her childhood has left Anna feeling dizzy and unmoored, and unable to focus on her studies at ASU.

"It makes sense," I say. "The perfect storm of drama and trauma."

"So I'm a nut job, is what you're saying."

"Tell me about the haunting. What happens? Where? How?"

Anna leans back in her couch, stretching her legs and tapping the toes of her low-top Chucks against each other with a rubber thwack-thwack. She chews the tips of her black fingernails and glances nervously at the front door at the sounds of Jock moving in the night, zip-tying motion detectors to the awning outside. "I never would've put the two of you together," she says. "Not in a million years. And ghost busters? You can't make this shit up. Don't you need a third? They come in threes, I thought."

"Who's 'they'?" I say.

"Ghost busters, wise men. Stooges. You know, the trinity."

"Are there three ghosts here with us now?"

She sits up, leaning forward and resting her hands on the faded denim of her knees, suddenly engaged. "Just one, I think," she says. "One too many. Shouldn't we be burning sage or something?"

To put Anna at ease I tell her about the long tradition of haunted houses, and that she's neither the first nor the last but one of a great many generations of people fortunate enough to be touched by spirits. In communing with the dead, one communes with life, and Anna should consider herself blessed, chosen even, despite the terrors she may be experiencing in the moment. There are four major classifications of hauntings—Demonic, Poltergeist, Residual, and Intelligent—and each is extraordinary in its own way. In demonic possessions, malevolent spirits seize the physical bodies of the pious; poltergeists hurl skillets and table lamps across rooms and down stairs; in residual hauntings, scenes from the past replay themselves like a movie with no end; and in an intelligent haunting, a person as real as Jock or Anna or me dies and refuses to move on, glomming on to a familiar site or a beloved body.

"Where do you think your situation might fall?" I ask.

"I don't know," Anna says, "but it's real, anyhow. I hear it creeping in the night. It starts over there, near the kitchen, a sort of scratching, like little fingers on a wall. That's how it tells me it's here. I had an exterminator come. He says the place is clean."

"So we can rule vermin out," I say.

"It scrapes and claws its way back to this end of the house and it goes up the ladder." She gestures to the loft. "Where I sleep."

I realize Jock's turned off the porch lamp and I imagine him walking the dark arbor of Anna's immaculate garden, peering through the warm, illuminated windows of her tiny house to see Anna and me leaning into each other in an intimate gesture of nascent friendship.

"And then?" I ask.

She shrugs, as if what the ghost does next is inevitable. "It climbs under the covers, and it cries. Like the world's ending. Like it can't get a grip on its sorrow."

The ghost is sentient, but only barely; based on its behavior, Anna believes it's a baby. It tugs at the hem of her jeans when she's at the kitchen sink and flushes the toilet when she's in the bathroom. Sometimes it strokes her cheek at her desk as she studies, and at other times, she hears it crawling around the floor of her closet, bumping into storage boxes and shoes. It never speaks. Its only willful attempt at communication is its habit of lying next to her in the dark of the loft and wailing, full voiced, like an infant desperate for its mother's touch.

With baseline sweep completed, it's seventy-three degrees indoors, EMF is at .1 milligauss, and my sixth sense is on high alert. I'm stationed at base camp, which we've set up in the home office, while Jock and Anna prepare for an EVP session on the other side of the house.

There are, of course, any number of natural explanations for a so-called "crying baby" haunting. Foxes, mockingbirds, and bobcats in heat all vocalize like infants, and under the cover of darkness, their cries can be frightening. But there are no easy answers for Anna herself. Though my memory of her is vague—we weren't well acquainted during her single year at Sag—she fell squarely into a conspicuous category back then. Saucy, urban transfer, a fair-haired dispenser of double-edged snark, doing time in Flagstaff grudgingly while counting down the days to Act Two of her life as a genteel coed at Dartmouth, Wellesley, or Yale.

But the person with us now is not that person.

I'm trying to concentrate on the IR video monitor in front of me but it's not easy with the three of us investigating this small, open space. On the other side, Jock and Anna are sitting together on the linoleum floor of her kitchen. He's showing Anna his digital audio recorder, turning it over in his hands like an artifact, and advising that her haunting is probably intelligent, meaning the ghost was a living, functioning person once, a person who's been, in his words, blindsided by death, sacked at the line, refusing to believe the play's over.

"Luckily," he's saying, "there's a ton of ways to help them cross. Electronic Voice Phenomena is the most basic. EVPs. We ask them questions. They answer."

"But my ghost is a baby," Anna says.

"Souls are, like, universal when they die," Jock says. Then, with more conviction, "In the afterlife, you're transformed. You can move without legs. You can solve physics equations and feel colors and . . . taste emotions. Like every part of you is part of something bigger. You see everything, you know everything. You grow wings."

Anna responds in a small voice, with something that sounds like *That's poetic*, but I'm not getting a read on her sincerity level.

We spend the next half minute or so, the three of us, without speaking, surrounded by the buzz of silence. Just as I'm about to break the spell, Jock gives Anna an aggressive command to shut down the lights. "We're going dark," he says.

Anna produces a miniremote from her jeans pocket and presses some buttons. It's a theatrical affair, the overhead cans and sconces dimming by degrees until we're sitting in total blackness, the unseen room suddenly powerful in its invisibility, encroaching on us. In the dark our machines are king: the steady red blink of Jock's audio recorder; the amber flicker of a REM pod on the couch; the green, underwater glow of my base-camp monitor showing a grid of six infrared feeds placed strategically throughout the home. All this technology is meant to shed light on the unknowable, to deliver revelatory, physical evidence we're incapable of acquiring on our own, but so far it feels like we're just three kids in a trailer, waiting in the dark for a jump scare or a romantic grope or some other excuse to believe that things aren't exactly as they are.

After a few seconds of meditative silence, Jock fills the room with his voice, intoning slow, deliberate questions into the recorder and leaving the three to five textbook seconds in between for the ghost to respond, if it's so inclined.

Are you the baby who's haunting Anna?

Would you like to give her a message?

We're here, we're listening. We want to help.

What is your name?

Is there something you want to tell us?

He does a quick playback to check for unexplained voices we might not have heard. Nothing.

"Just one more," he says.

Can we help you get to the other side so the living may carry on in peace?

This is more than a small misstep: most ghosts don't even know they're dead, and such blunt allusions could send them spinning into a cyclone of confusion and sadness. This is a question to work up to, and treat with delicacy and respect. For a moment I feel pity. Not for Anna, but for her ghost.

"Kitchen's clear," Jock announces.

They're on Camera One on my IR monitor, huddled next to each other like doomed characters in a teenage slasher flick. She mumbles something about feeling sick to her stomach and Jock places a hand on her tattooed arm.

"You're not alone," he says.

It's midnight and a shard of moonlight filters in through the blinds of Anna's office window. It occurs to me that it's brighter out there than it is in here, but this is no different than any other haunting: a small, vibrant moon in the sky, a quiet home, and Jock and me, calling out to spirits in the dark. Maybe it's the size of the house that has me on edge, or maybe it's the client herself, who is both a known and an unknown; the more I think I've pegged her to something, the quicker my idea of her slips away.

Anna is leading Jock to an alcove near the kitchen, to a closet where she hides her clutter and where the ghost occasionally makes an appearance. When they slide the door closed behind them, my chest thumps, once, hard, a warning strike. There is every reason for the two of them to investigate the closet; there is, even, every reason to shut themselves in, but sometimes the body knows things before the REM pods and Mel Meters do, and it's my job to keep my partner safe and the investigation aboveboard.

I grab my phone and text him, trusting Jock to keep the message to himself despite the close quarters.

Be careful, I write. *Something odd re this haunting just saying.*

There's a muffled chime from the other side of the house as Jock receives my message. He mumbles something to Anna and in a moment a text lights up my phone.

What do u mean?

Just be careful, can't put finger on it.

OK, Mom, he writes back.

Before I can overthink it, my thumbs are keying in a last, perhaps recklessly brash message.

Keep little poltergeist in pants.

It's a joke, mostly, a playful attempt to remind him of our mission, but in any case, Jock's phone dings and it's dead quiet on the other end of the house. I stare at my own phone as a tickle of casual remorse grows into full-blown dread. After an excruciating minute, I get his text: *Not funny.*

201

Across the way the closet door slides open and Jock's shadow appears, looming and cocksure, it seems, with the advantage of the moral upper hand. Anna's shape, black on black, sinks into the space behind him.

"We're going to the loft," he says.

The red light of Jock's audio recorder bounces as they navigate their way toward me on uncertain footing, their bodies bumping things in the dark. Anna appears to be pressing into Jock, maybe clutching his arm, I'm not sure, and I'm struck by how their two figures have molded into one in the passageway, how monstrous they are without the benefit of light, how anything and everything can be made to appear frightening or innocuous given the flip of a switch, a shift in perspective. Their shadows draw forward and lighten in the gentle blush of my monitor, and they manifest in front of me, the faces of Jock and Anna of the single torso, the accidental high-school chimera, and yes, they are holding hands. I know instantly the loft session, though a high point of our investigation, isn't meant to include me.

"Hey, guys," I say, mustering up a generous serving of tonal contrition, "not enough room for the three of us up there. I'll hold down the fort."

Jock ignores me and mounts the ladder ahead of Anna, the softwood rungs creaking behind me as they climb to the loft. I keep my eyes focused on the monitor. So far, there's been no activity to speak of—an air vent rustling the leaves of a potted ficus, a gnat illuminated like a ghostly orb—and now on Camera Four Jock and Anna appearing in the green wash of the full-spectrum IR, fussing around each other, all heels and elbows and rear ends, crouch-walking under the low ceiling before taking their places in the loft, lying side by side at a respectable distance, a narrow canal of pale mattress between them. Anna's disembodied voice from above is hushed and bedroomy and out of sync with the choppy video feed before me.

"Why do ghosts only come out at night?" she asks. "Why not during the day?"

It's a good question. All the research says it's we who are open to ghosts after dark; darkness scorches the nerves of the perceiver, puts him in a heightened state of awareness. Any fierce emotion—anxiety, terror, even love—opens us up, widening our parabolic antennae until we can hear the voiceless, see the unseeable. I am eager to hear Jock's take on this phenomenon.

"It's cozier in the nighttime," he says, as if he's forgotten everything we've learned together. "Ghosts like cozy, I guess."

"Mm," Anna says.

I open up my own receiver and watch their bodies line up next to each other on my monitor. In the green flush of the IR cam, her skin is lighter than his, blanched like sea foam, her dark hair spilling behind her in a sinuous crown. He is as stiff as a figure on a trophy, always vigilant, always stately, even in repose. They turn their heads toward each other and something—something intimate—seems to pass between them. Then, with sudden realization, Jock sits upright and faces the camera with milky night-vision pupils, as if he only now remembers he's being recorded.

"Hey, Pace," he says, with a sloppy wave.

"Hey," I say. "Don't worry. Just surveilling. Not spying."

They don't laugh, or react at all, except to look away from the camera and by extension away from me. She says something indiscernible, and on the video monitor I see Jock crawling toward the edge of the loft to talk to me. Instinctively I jerk away and pretend to occupy myself with the closest object I can find, which happens to be Jock's recorder, lying in a corner of the desk where he'd set it down before climbing up. Its red LED pulses on standby. I tap on it, press *Playback*, busy myself with the controls.

"Go do a sesh in the head, will you," Jock calls down, "and close the door behind you? It's supposed to be active in there."

"Copy that," I say, but I'm immobilized with a kind of numb incredulity. They—he—would never think to break protocol, would he? Not on a job, not with me in the room, and not with her. My irritation has no target or, rather, too many marks to take aim at, and I'm left only with a childish, throbbing, bodily sensation of maltreatment. I stare down her image on the monitor as if to make her feel my rage. Anna, our client—victim, thief.

I get up from my chair and do as I'm told, but not before clamping a mic onto the low beams of the loft overhead. I strap on a headset and summon up a phony coughing fit to cover up the noise, then stumble around Anna's couch and welcome mat and palm my way to the bathroom, the short passageway lit up by the standby signal of the recorder in my hands. I can feel them behind me, their bodies suspended in the shallow tomb of the loft.

I pull the handle of the bathroom door and let myself in, and for all my wait-and-see optimism it's hard not to feel pushed out, or, more precisely, pushed in, into this four-by-three box lined with porcelain and smelling of Tilex and seasonal hand soap, cinnamon and allspice.

Hunkering down on the pot, feeling one part angry chaperone and one part dirty voyeur, I peer across the length of the house for a sign. But from the bathroom, with little light and from my low vantage point, the loft is hidden from view and there's nothing to see, just the sense that they're up there, the two of them, adjusting their bodies in the tight gap between the ceiling and the mattress, the plywood platform making light groans, their barely audible voices amplified to whispered cotton in my ears.

I hear Jock's voice first, low but clear: "Why'd you have to leave Saganitso without saying goodbye?" Then, with a sugary drawl of uncertain origin, born perhaps of an ancestral lothario buried in the uppermost branches of his family tree, he adds, "I missed you."

"Bullshit," she says.

I max out the volume on my headset.

"I was there for you, wasn't I?" Jock says.

" 'Paying' and 'being there for me' are two different things," Anna says.

"I told you I'd go with you or whatever."

"I did it in New York anyway," she says. "Like you cared. At all. Whatever? Whatever."

"Arrow through the heart, girl. Hey. Look at me. There's always now."

"Now? As in 'you and me' now? Bull. Shit."

"Anna," Jock says. "Don't be mad, all right? But is this ghost even real?"

Waiting for her response, I feel us breathe, Jock and me in unison, though out of each other's line of sight and at separate ends of Anna's house, with me relegated to the shitter and locked up behind a door.

"Fuck," she finally says. "You. Fuck you. Fuckyoufuckyoufuckyou."

They erupt, both of them, in vicious whispers with chilling, accusatory inflections, and there are murmured defenses and scattered curses until Jock makes a weak, final appeal and Anna, exhausted by her ire, breathes her hard breaths and pushes up against his corny promise—*It's been a long time but I'll make it up to you*—and in all of this, the ghost baby begins to take shape. In the blackness of the bathroom I conjure her, Anna, not the hardened pseudo-Goth variant lying next to my friend tonight, but the straw-haired, gullible model of yesteryear with her inflated sense of urbane authority over a hick like Jock in a place like Flagstaff. I see him throwing her a toothy smile at the JV tailgate and a well-rehearsed line at the after-party, earning her secret admiration by brandishing his beer-bonging prowess and mad karaoke skills. I see them mashing behind a pile of fly-ash bricks on the gym field, his hand under her skirt, Anna foolishly convinced he's the conquest. I see one proper date, a chick-flick at the Harplex Eleven, a shared tub of popcorn, and a clumsy after-hours break-in to Anna's bedroom while her mother romps and rolls in her Ambien-fueled fantasies upstairs. I see Anna spot Jock in the hallway as the eight o'clock bell rings and bodies disappear into classrooms and he too is gone, and after school I see her alone and panicked at their erstwhile rendezvous, spring showers misting over the mud of the athletic field, a single grackle with slick onyx wings tilting its head to question her business, and I see the fog lift around Anna's delusions. I see her a month later confessing her sins to her parents, flying out to stay with her father in New York, or driving down to Scottsdale in her mother's SUV; either way, Anna cries in her basement bedroom to a John Mellencamp song.

My interpretation of their story might not be strictly literal, but after two years of ghost hunting with my best friend and studying the masters of parapsychology, I know I am close. I can feel the colors of Anna's haunting, the textures of her pain. I am hooked up to our audio system but plugged into something bigger; I'm hearing the stripped-down words and protests and apologies but listening harder to their undertow. I am hearing something ending, and I am hearing it begin. Jock and Anna's labored, postbrawl breaths slow with each counted second, capsizing into each other and plunging into a sad, molluscan, sucking wetness.

Back in the formative months of our professional relationship and in an ill-conceived bid for credibility, Jock and I once brought a third partner into the fold. Brock Chen was a self-proclaimed psychic who also happened to be a second-degree black belt in Brazilian jujitsu. It didn't take me long to realize that "Brock and Jock" were a more obvious pair and for all my intellectualizing and research and dedication I was clearly the third wheel. It was what Jock seemed to want, so I kept my mouth shut through the entire affair, even when our investigations started feeling like world-wrestling events, with the Ock Brothers introducing cuss words to EVP sessions and spraying every room with the stench of their testosterone. Things came to a head one night at the Hotel St. Michael, where the two of them were placing microphones in the haunted guest rooms while I set up base camp in the lobby. Through my audio feed I overheard Brock calling me a "dipshit poser" whose only concern was the "teenage crush" I had on Jock and saying that we needed to rethink our brand going forward and how we wanted to project ourselves to the ghost-loving public. When Jock's voice came on, it was loose and jovial, saying I was cool and I knew my way around an investigation, and that he'd got me all wrong—I wasn't into blonds. When I woke to find Brock Chen gone before daybreak, Jock attributed his departure to creative differences and insisted with his signature boorish indifference that "duos are way more epic anyway."

A guy like Jock makes a unilateral impression. It can't be helped. There are people who take up space in a room, and people who don't. Sometimes an act of providence will bring them together, the finely rendered and the invisible, united in a single mission, moving in the same orbit around a common source of light. Jock draws me line by line until I'm seen and, sometimes, even he sees me. When he doesn't, I'm still here, speaking questions into dead air, hoping for a response.

As I step out of Anna's tiny home and down into the night I realize I've been holding my breath in anticipation of this gulp of earthy, outdoor air. As I'd imagined, it's brighter outside than in, a rust-colored vapor of particulates and city lights hazing over the rooftops and desert willows, a cool, late-summer night, sixty degrees and shifting languidly into fall. A baby wails in the house next door, a real baby, and a TV comes on. Tinfoil laughter tumbles out of an open window and unravels into the night as I walk across the stone pavers of Anna's garden. I find a woven hammock hanging from a low branch of the elm tree and drop into the soft yarn, the frameless structure yielding too readily, too extravagantly, dragging my body down into an awkward, fetal pose until I'm gazing forcibly into the orange smog.

I wonder what Jock will tell Anna about her haunting.

My guess is that instead of accusing her of manipulation or vengefulness, he'll tell her that a ghost is like an image that appears in that groggy, half-dream state just before waking—filmy and ephemeral but stubbornly there, cinched firmly between darkness and morning, emphatic in its insistence on being seen. It isn't one thing and not another, a haunting is not something one can unbraid and explain away—he might say.

He might explain again the four major classifications of hauntings—Demonic, Poltergeist, Residual, and Intelligent—and clarify that while some cases fit easily into a single category, the overwhelming majority have elements of all. In demonic possessions, the chaste and noble are overcome by their gruesome passions. In poltergeist hauntings, an adolescent girl is said to channel the fury of the dead, a phenomenon driven more by the emotional tempests of the victim than souls from beyond. In residual hauntings, tragic events play and replay themselves throughout eternity like a video on a loop. And in an intelligent haunting, a once-living person, as real as you or me, dies and refuses to move on, attaching itself to a familiar site, hoping to make contact. To the ghost, the house is still a home. It remembers: an aging dog, a lap, the winter hearth, a wood spoon knocking butter into a freshly seasoned pan. There's a sense of ethereal belonging, a blurring of time and distance, everything blanketed in a velvet shroud of unconditional affection. We fear the spirit, but for the spirit the haunting is nothing short of a miracle. Let me linger, it thinks, let me stay for one more moment. So it lives inside the walls, it tugs at apron strings, it burrows into the living in the palace of their dreams. One wonders, almost, if it isn't an act of violence to ask it to leave.

Perfume Dioramas
Elaine Equi

WE MARK OUR PLACE AND IT MARKS US

I enter the building—the room—
by a door, then another door.

But it enters me through the air
I breathe in

its commingling of human and animal,
mineral and chemical, cooking and debris.

A building is made in no small part
of air.

Yoko Ono tells us to bottle the air
at different hours,

and also to send smell signals
by wind.

Today is apples, smoke,
tentacles of vomit

leftover on the sidewalk
as I fumble for my keys.

No shape
takes place
in time
without smell.

MY GRANDMOTHER'S GLASS SKYLINE

Shalimar
Emeraude
Tigress

gave her bungalow
in Chicago
an exotic air.

As a child,
looking up
at the geometry
of bottles
on her dresser,

I thought each
a liquid city—

and fragrance
the real "magic carpet"
to carry me there.

How wise the wizard
must have been
to shrink and imprison

a forest, an ocean,
a mountain—

a whole kingdom
in these glass towers.

Elaine Equi

PSYCHO-SCENTUAL

I once had a therapist
who practiced
olfactory analysis—

often declaring,
about any difficult situation,
person, or emotion I brought up:

"It stinks. It really stinks.
That just stinks all over the place."

He had a small windowless office
where oddly (I thought)
he continually burned
a vanilla-scented candle,

perhaps to infuse a more pleasing
mental attitude in his clients,
or as a form of self-protection
from the noxious cloud
of their negative energy.

It was a big deal for me
(never good at setting boundaries)
to ask him to please refrain
from keeping it lit during our sessions
as it aggravated my allergies.

He gladly complied,
but the smell of burnt sugar,
like an alter ego,

always lingered, and often
I found myself clearing my throat
as I struggled to find
the right words—and air—
to describe my experience.

THE BASEMENT LAUNDRY ROOM SMELLS

Like a combination of damp and dry things:

dirty socks, disinfectant, drains,
dust blown about by fans,

air freshener, fabric softener,

the cardboard smell of boxes
stacked up, each harboring the ghost smell
of what it used to contain,

the newspaper smell,

the broken smell of old furniture
abandoned and soon to be carted off.

LIKE FORM, FRAGRANCE FOLLOWS FUNCTION

Not always literally—

banks don't really smell
of money.

Of credit, perhaps,
a deferral of smell
borrowed against the future.

And doesn't one find
in government buildings,
the muffled odor of bureaucracy?

Scent is invisible architecture,

a binding together of place
with diffuse beams.

211

Elaine Equi

I cannot think of
gothic cathedrals
as other than ornate
incense burners.

The Wall
Robert Coover

ONCE, THERE WERE TWO LOVERS, separated by a wall that divided
their city, a wall they had helped to build, recruited by the warring
city fathers, who declared that only a wall would ensure their freedom. It was across the wall, trowels in their hands, that they first
saw each other, lovestruck as soon as seeing. Such amorous gazes
between separated wall builders were not rare, but soon were out-
lawed, stolen glances being treated like common theft and punished
with solitary confinement or, when those found guilty were deemed
incorrigible, blinding. Looking away became a way of looking, a
trowel's clicks a code, the placing of a brick a form of erotic suggestion. Every day there were reports of frustrated lovers being shot
while attempting to cross over, whether by burrowing under the wall
or by clambering over it. Most of the wall was impenetrably thick,
and there were stretches of two separate walls with a no-man's space
between, but in a few places it thinned to the depth of a single brick.
The lovers sought out these places by knocking on the wall with
their wooden bricklaying mallets, their ears pressed to it, and when
they found a thin place, they whispered into it, expressing their
desires and their frustrations. These whispers stirred a hot wind that
authorities said eroded the wall, so that too was soon forbidden and
severely punished. Posters appeared that reminded them that freedom was not a given, but was a privilege that required discipline and
sacrifice, but such admonitions only further distanced them from
the city fathers and confirmed their desires. Once, in a dark crannied
crack in the wall, created perhaps by someone attempting to break
through, the two lovers were able to touch, which only intensified
the fever of their desire. It was dangerous, they could die at any
moment, they didn't care; what they could not have, they could
imagine, and for a precious moment, in urgent whispers, they spoke
to each other of their imaginings. Curfew interrupted them, the
terrible sirens. When they returned, the crack had been filled with
cement, the wall thickened, and afterward the two lovers had only
their memories of what had been until then the most beautiful

moment in their lives, memories that brought tears to their eyes.

Slowly, as frustrations mounted, resistance emerged. Trowels were dropped. Graffiti appeared. People were seen carrying emblematic slivers of bricks chipped from the wall and wearing inflammatory "Knock It Down!" pins. Many of these early protesters were martyred, but the numbers steadily grew, each new protester emboldened by the sacrifices of others. Demonstrations sprang up on both sides, demanding the wall's demolition, and the two lovers joined them. There was no time now for stolen glances, passionate whispers into the wall; the fall of the wall became their life's project, their existence all but defined by it. Their hearts told them the wall must come down, and so did their reason, but it was not easy. Many were imprisoned, lives were lost, but yet the resistance spread, up and down the length of the wall, until at last it was broken through. Shots were fired, many of the bravest fell, but the power of the authorities was waning. They could no longer repair the wall as fast as it was being dismantled, and suddenly one night those in power simply vanished, the wall crumbling as if made of sand.

An explosion of happiness! The end of tyranny! Parties broke out across the city. Fireworks, free beer, dancing in the streets! The two lovers ran, stumbling over the rubble, through the crowds of ecstatic strangers into each other's arms, and over the hours and days that followed, celebrated their love in as many ways as possible, and over and over, almost unable to believe what was happening. How could they have surrendered so abjectly to such a bitter fate engineered by others? they asked themselves. The past now seemed as unimaginable as this present had seemed so recently.

What was left of the wall, an insult to humanity itself, was destroyed. Some kept small fragments as souvenirs, but most wanted nothing more to do with such a cruel obscenity. Streets were laid, linking the divided city, and lined by beautiful new buildings, none made of brick. The no-man's-land became a public park with children's playgrounds, and trees were planted, memorializing the fallen. The day the wall fell was declared an official holiday, celebrated with parades and circuses. The "Knock It Down!" pins became collectors' items. The nightmare passed into history, read about in school by the new generation, for whom it was something that happened a long time ago. An excuse for an annual party and a day out of school or off work.

Then, as time passed, the two lovers, along with many others who had lived through the construction and fall of the wall, found that they missed it. They studied old maps, took walks along its buried contours. Sections of the wall were said to exist still; they searched for them, getting lost from one another as they did. They accepted that, discovering that the wall had been a barrier to their desires, and a stimulus to them, but freedom had deprived them of their intensity, provided other options. It was a time of separations, divorces, reconciliations, new loves to be found and lost again. He took a position in a distant neighborhood, she raised the children with a new husband, then later by herself.

And meanwhile, slowly, though none knew how, the myth of the "city fathers" having crumbled with the wall, the wall itself, as if seeded by the chips of bricks that had been left behind, did indeed return, or seemed to, seen by some, if not by all. A kind of personal choice as with all perceptions of reality, though it did not feel like choice. Perhaps its reappearance, to those who witnessed and acknowledged it, was provoked by that longing for a significant life the estranged lovers felt, for there they were, gazing at each other across the wall, real or imaginary. They nodded curtly to each other, looked away. They could have stepped over this young wall, but did not, for their separation had seemed permanent and desirable.

But the rising wall drew them back again and again and, over time, feeling that they had something to share, even if only their disappointment, they allowed a cautious friendship to grow between them. They did not try to breach the wall or recover what they had lost, but conversed quietly over it, recalling dispassionately the tyranny of the old wall, their impassioned resistance to it. Though monstrous, the old wall gave so much meaning to our lives, one said, and the other: Well, meaning, that old delusion. Which, when sought, is just another form of nostalgia. Sort of like love, you mean. No, love, whatever it is, is real in its stupefying way. But it's not enough. No, and there's not much else. That's very sad. It is. Sometimes I cry. We had some good parties, though, which wouldn't have happened without a wall in the way. There's probably a moral, but I don't want to know it. Do you still believe in the city fathers? Sure, they shot people. Well, somebody did. Do you remember those people who were blinded for gazing at one another? Yes, it was horrible. I saw one of them the other day. He's a prophet now, or claims to be. Wouldn't you know, another blind seer. What is he prophesying, the end of the world like everyone else? No, its damnable continuance. He's a pessimist.

That made them smile, but they didn't know why. Or did know, but wished not to acknowledge it, even to themselves. Because: if bitterness overtakes you, what choice remains? They talked about their children and their children's children, the passing of the elders, what, if anything, they still believed in (well, the good, the true, the beautiful, they joked), and whether the return of the wall signaled the return of tyranny. The tyranny of time maybe, one of them said. Sounds like a popular song title, said the other: "The Tyranny of Time." Everything's a song title when meaning's just another tune to play. Like "Knock It Down," that violent sex song the children are dancing to. I have to confess I still have my old "Knock It Down" pin, but I never wear it, not even on the national holiday. The children, in their terrible innocence, just point at me and laugh. I know, my old mallet and trowel are still hidden away somewhere like secret sex toys. It's a strange feeling when the story moves on without you. Yes, at the time, I thought it was about us, but it was only about itself.

Later, they would wonder why they had remained on opposite sides of the wall, as if their conversation depended on it, as perhaps it did, the wall shielding them from anything more disquieting than banter, while serving at the same time as a kind of playing surface for it. That surface rose until their wistful sallies were more like lobs. They could no longer see each other, nor were they hearing each other as clearly as before, their voices lost in other voices behind the thickening wall. It might be our ears' fault, one shouted. Our years? the other called back. No . . . well, maybe. . . . The distance was too great. They turned away, aware that the loneliness they felt was in effect that freedom they'd been promised when citizen bricklayers still, and sadly they wished it so.

Cleeve Abbey Suite
G. C. *Waldrep*

REFECTORY

kniving the same
extravagant body
the tongue threshed—
the blunt theft
concealed, a calendar
creased
& lactant, only
a man on a ladder
could feast
on this dry island.
Wheat-ghost,
rise into the tremor.
Wheat-reef
even the bees spared,
what byred here
a tractable
ablution, wisp
of the charred depth
the almoner
turns his back upon,
nude geometry
against which now
a single bench
evitates, correcting
for the body's
warmth, its delicate
perlustration.
In pelt after pelt
we find the lock
tended,
lapse upon lapse—

G. C. Waldrep

GHOST-APSE

maze & bezel

a scaffold
crossed
with a globe

flag sewn into
raw deed's
oblate garment

it neither
wants nor needs
your muscle

only, not to be
glade
&, dirempt,

the pearl's
external depth

(roofed
with thirst)

a conic section

ROOF-LINE

scrolled in thirst
& gelded
by our new verticals

the orchard's
single lash
fleering its dense
Bethlehem

218

a green syllable

helixed
with the long rind's
choral blurt—

observed meridian

of the ear's
doubled rupture

(more datable
in its carbons)

I dreamt
the world-whale
suffered,

that is, to drink

or, straitened,
depth remits its
tined whirr,

its wildest octave

NIGHT STAIR

nothing the star allows

a panicked embroidery

let rise
these spruce pavilions

into which the ships
bear
their creased reserves

219

the whey combed
into its lambent crèche

nippling w/ bee-gauze

SLYPE

vein of door, a late
ripeness
golds forth
twins itself, a mirror
preconceived, & yet
you risk
the tongue's crutch
lapsed effigy
of the bleating
master-pain,
its city glows
with almond-hued
flight
can't you hear
the sun ticking
against the tiles
or, dusk's
paternal lemniscate
against the heel
of the soft
flocks—
tungsten wives
the shallow bay
& you, moist
tenant, briefly hive

Fractal
Joyce Carol Oates

1.

AT ELEVEN, THE CHILD was *into fractals.* Naturally then, the mother agreed to drive him to the Fractal Museum in Portland, Maine— "The Singular Museum of Its Kind."

One blustery November morning when the mother might have been doing other things, more homey/domestic things (for it was a Saturday), virtually anything she'd have preferred to driving two hours, twenty minutes from New Haven, Connecticut, to the Fractal Museum north of Portland, Maine, the (fatally unwitting) mother found herself, in fact, driving the (doomed) child for two hours, twenty minutes north on I-95 from New Haven, Connecticut, to the Fractal Museum outside Portland, Maine, which the child had discovered online and had begged the mother to let him visit.

Well, *begged* was an extreme word. This delicate child who wanted so little that adults could provide him, usually so absorbed in his architectural drawings, or a science book, or an electronic gadget, and so often (you would not want to acknowledge aloud) *withdrawn,* wasn't it a good sign, a healthy sign, an encouraging sign, Oliver had actually made a rare request of the mother: would she drive him to the Fractal Museum in Portland, Maine? Sometime? *Please.*

She'd been flattered, he hadn't asked the father. (Of course, the father would have been *too busy.*)

She'd been flattered but she hadn't wanted to say *yes.* Oh, why *her!*

Yet, being a (good) mother, of course she'd said *yes.*

For weeks then, after the date had been marked on the calendar, plans began to be made even including where to stop for restrooms along I-95 (for the child was prone to anxieties about toilets, sanitary conditions, access to bottled water, etc.), and these plans the mother and the child shared, and the father looked on, listened, at a little distance, bemused and just slightly envious, or seeming so.

And so, this fierce cobalt-blue November sky. Cumulus clouds with puckered cheeks blowing in such gusts, the Toyota SUV at sixty-eight miles per hour quaked and came near to drifting out of its lane.

"I wish you would talk to me, honey. To keep me company. Always absorbed in that damned iPad of yours."

Of course the mother wasn't jealous of a damned *iPad*. Not really. Not much.

Yet to the child, *damned* was a swear word. Not an extreme swear word like some (which he'd heard in the mean mouths of older and coarser classmates but had not dared enunciate to himself), but, yes, *damned* struck the child's sensitive ear like fingernails drawn against a blackboard; for if a parent or indeed any elder complained of a *damned iPad* it was anger that was the motive, and an elder's anger was/is wounding to a sensitive child.

Neither the mother nor the father of the child would ever have struck him. Not a slap, not a nudge or a shove—never! Not a pinch! If in a blind fury at the child's taciturnity/stubbornness the father had ever struck Oliver, he, the father, would've gnawed off the offending hand. He swore!

They were not that sort of parents. Not that sort of people. Not ever.

But words too can lash. Words too can sting.

Often too, to draw the preoccupied child's attention to her and away from the iPad in his lap, the mother would do something playful: thrust out her lower lip and blow air briskly upward, stirring the fluffy-faded-red bangs on her forehead, a clownish gesture copied from a grade-school classmate decades ago. The gesture was to make the child who did not readily giggle, giggle.

For the child was insufficiently *childish* and this creates a vacuum in a parent-child relationship that a guilty adult may feel the obligation to fill.

However, the child took no notice of this goofy-silly antic that another child (the mother doesn't want to think) would've found hilarious; instead feeling the rebuke, worse than if the child had sneered at her.

"Are you even listening, Olly? I'm beginning to wonder—why am I here? *Why me?*"

Olly and not *Oliver* meant that the mother was not scolding, not really. Chiding, teasing. Though there was an edge to the mother's voice—*Why me?*

Which could mean *why* the mother and not the father, or *why* either parent, driving north on I-95 in such a ferocity of wind. And perhaps too there was another *why*, beyond the reach of the mother's mental grasp.

That *why* you must not ask. Nor *why* you must not ask *why*.

In the passenger's seat beside the mother, safely belted in, the child had been immersed in an interactive topology game on his iPad for the last thirty miles, yet, uncannily, for the eleven-year-old who was *into fractals* and had at the age of nine declared his intention of being *an architect* was at the same time enough aware of his mother's ranting to call her bluff, and to answer her seriously.

" '*Why me!*'—because there is no one else."

Very solemnly the child spoke as if issuing a decree. In his voice, which the mother worried was *too thin, too soprano* for one soon to enter the maelstrom of middle school.

"What do you mean, 'no one else'? I don't understand."

"From the beginning of the universe. Determined to be *you*. It could not be anyone else in the driver's seat, because it is *you*."

In his solemn, methodical way Oliver spoke to the mother as one might speak to a classmate who is having difficulty with a home-work assignment. Sweetly patient, not condescending.

"That doesn't make sense, Olly. Of course it could be someone else, and I could be somewhere else. Why on earth not?"

"It isn't like that, Mom. Because if the person driving this vehicle is *you*, that is all the proof you need that there is no one else it could have been, and there is nowhere else *you* could be except here. And the same is true for me."

"You mean—here with me. Beside me."

"Yes."

Well. The mother had to concede that was probably correct. She would certainly not be driving on I-95 on this blustery Saturday morning if not for the child beside her.

"And I suppose it would have to be 9:27 a.m.? It couldn't be some other time, earlier or later?"

"Not if it's *here*. Has to be"—with a glance at the countryside through which they were moving, of the hue of bleached chloro-phyll, stubs of undergrowth and featureless trees like a papier-mâché stage set—"here."

The mother didn't know whether to laugh at the child's certainty or to be impressed. Or annoyed. She wondered if Oliver dared con-found his math teacher with such paradoxes, or whether it was his math teacher who provided the eleven-year-old with such paradoxes. (For the child, officially in sixth grade at New Haven Day, was allowed

223

to take an advanced math course taught in the high school.)

"It was of my own free will that I agreed to drive us to Portland, Olly. You forget. I might have said, 'No—too busy.' And it was an accident more or less that we left when we did, at that precise moment, so that it's 9:27 a.m. now, when we're passing the exit for—what is it—'Biddeford.'"

Oliver was not persuaded. "Mom, no. There are no 'accidents.'"

"You're being ridiculous—an eleven-year-old who doesn't believe in free will! Do you really feel as if you're enclosed in a sort of cobweb, or you're a puppet on strings, being manipulated? *Determined?*"

"What we 'feel' doesn't matter, Mom. A 'feeling' is just—nothing."

Of course, this was so. The mother knew that this was so. Yet, in her role as *mother*, she could not let things lie there bleak and forlorn as a pile of twigs.

"Well, then—'think.' Not 'feel' but 'think'—'reason.' We can *reason* that we have free will. It just seems so—obvious. . . ." Her voice trailed off, as if that were an argument.

But the canny eleven-year-old persisted: nothing could be accidental, for all things are determined. If you could wind time backward, tracing things to their causes, you would see—"There's no chance of something just swerving off on its own."

The grim prospect seemed to please Oliver unless—possibly—he was joking? For sometimes Oliver seemed bemused by his mother's obtuseness.

Oh, she hoped so! She'd have welcomed the child's joking, *joshing*. What is a family without good-natured joking, teasing, *joshing?*

"D'you know what?—you're too smart for your own good. There are plenty of 'accidents' in life—you'll see."

You yourself are an accident. Were.

What d'you think of that, smarty?

(But no. They'd decided, no, they would have the baby. That is, they *would not* not have the baby.)

(Unexpected/unwanted pregnancy a nightmare before they were married at the very worst time in the father's life preparing for law exams and not a great time in the mother's life while her own mother was undergoing chemotherapy but decided not to delete/abort. Deciding *yes all right. Yes. We will. We can.* Scarcely guessing how the (unexpected/unwanted) pregnancy would turn out: the extraordinary child whom both the mother and the father loved deeply and without whom they could not imagine their lives.)

Of course, the child would never know. No one except the mother and the father could know this secret and when they ceased to exist, the secret would die with them.

He was a beautiful if fragile child with a chronic asthmatic condition susceptible to pollen, dust, danger, heat, aridity and wind, excitement and agitation. His skin was slightly feverish to the touch; the mother wondered if this was the result of his medication, steroids, which quickened his pulse. She wondered if other children, and most adults, seemed dull to him, slow paced in their thoughts, predictable and lacking in complexity.

In her handbag she carried the child's "rescue inhaler"—as it was called. The child had not required this inhaler in years and could not bear to see it in the mother's handbag.

His vision was myopic, often his eyes squinted behind round, wire-rimmed eyeglasses that gave him a scholarly look. His chin seemed to melt away as if lacking sufficient bone. His hair was a fine, fair, gingery color, lighter than the mother's, and his skin was splotched with freckles as with droplets of water tinged with cinnamon, or turmeric—a beautiful smooth skin the mother felt a need to touch, perhaps too frequently, as she felt the need to lightly kiss his temple. Where the child had tolerated such motherly affection when he was younger, by the age of eleven he was beginning to stiffen and flinch away.

Trying to reason with him, for she loved talking seriously with her son, and being taken seriously by him.

"But we are always somewhere, aren't we? I mean—if we exist at all. . . . Why is any *where* we find ourselves a *where* that had to be? Why—*had to be*? That's what I don't understand."

Felt as if her tongue was twisted. Not sure what she was trying to say.

And where are they? Just beyond an exit for Biddeford, Maine?

Otherwise, nowhere. New England countryside, dense-wooded, mixture of deciduous and evergreen trees, thunderous trailer trucks rushing past, a *here* interchangeable with any *there*.

Oliver murmured, *OK, Mom.*

"Am I correct? Or are you just humoring me?"

Oliver murmured, *OK, Mom.*

Returning his attention to the damned iPad in his lap that had been there all along, waiting.

2.

Offhandedly the child had remarked at the age of nine that he guessed he wanted to be *an architect.*

The astonished parents weren't sure they'd heard correctly. Had their very young son remarked that he wanted to be *an architect?*

Exchanging a glance. Really! How—*funny!*

Or, rather, how impressive. And rare, a child of nine would express such a wish. . . .

There was an air about their singular child of intense curiosity, wonderment, as if he were a fairy caught in a net, his fairy wings fluttering but not (yet) broken (so the mother thought, with much tenderness and concern). He'd been a premature baby and had not thrived as an infant; eventually he'd grown, but remained small for his age, and his bones seemed thin, everything about him gossamer light, provisional. There had been some frightening asthmatic episodes when he was a small child but the condition seemed now controlled by medication, or nearly.

So far as the parents knew, Oliver had never met an architect, nor had he heard them talking of architecture. The mother had a degree in art history and had hoped at one time in her life to be an artist but there were no other artistically inclined persons in her family, and no architects. The father was a (Yale) university attorney. For each, the marriage was the first and the child was the only child.

Vaguely Amanda and Peter wished to have a second child. Possibly, a more ordinary child. For it did not feel quite right, Oliver was such a *precious child.*

Since he'd been capable of gripping a Crayola in his (left) hand the child had loved to draw. He'd had little interest in toys, children's books, but rather adult books, particularly oversized books with photographic plates. Any subject seemed to interest the inquisitive child—ancient Egyptian pyramids, constellations of the night sky, Himalayan mountains, medieval fortifications, twentieth-century "skyscrapers," Arctic marine life, meteors, bird life, "earliest forms of organic life." Before Oliver could read he was drawn to such books, and to copying from them onto sheets of tissue-thin paper with a fanatic concern for accuracy.

The mother looked on, fascinated. The child seemed to be in a trance, exuding an air of feverish intensity.

The mother wondered—*What is he doing? Is he—"taking possession" of what he draws?*

Concentrating on visual images, the child was late in speaking. But when Oliver did begin to speak it was in phrases and not in single, monosyllabic words like the speech of most toddlers; soon too his vocabulary flourished with such words as *design, wish, depending upon, accelerating.*

For a brief while, when he'd been very young, Oliver had been captivated by the word *other.*

For what did *other* mean, really? When you pondered upon it. *Other* was not this, and (possibly) that. Or (possibly) not that. *Other other other other.*

Once, he'd screamed and laughed—*Oth-er!* The mother had been alone with him at the time and had felt a moment's faintness; the child was mad.

But, of course, the moment passed. Such moments pass.

One thing was clear, the child was indeed *other.*

And then one day the child (who was an inquisitive child but not as other children are inquisitive, rather as adults are inquisitive, "nosing" about a household) discovered in a storage closet the architect's plans for the house in which the family lived, that had been built forty years before. It was a stucco, stone, and glass house constructed in a style made popular by Frank Lloyd Wright in an earlier era, though not so starkly beautiful as any house by the great architect, rather more resembling an upscale American "ranch" house. The child was excited by the architect's plans, which he'd examined with a magnifying glass and copied in colored pencils. This became his play, his preoccupation. Soon he believed he'd discovered a secret passageway in the basement—a kind of large cupboard or crawl space opening from an obscure corner of the room. This, to the mother's distress, he insisted upon exploring with a flashlight, and emerged covered in cobwebs and blinking his eyes like a nocturnal creature thrust too rapidly into the light.

Other parts of the house too the child determined to be "secret." A ghostly doorway in a corridor, a passageway of only six inches width inside a wall. You could not see these features of the house with just your eyes; you could only discover their existence through examining the architect's plans, which were unfortunately now badly faded and creased. "But what are you seeing, Oliver?"—the mother would ask, and Oliver would direct her to look through the magnifying glass at the sketch of a door, or a passageway, or a "false ceiling" in the house plans that he'd discovered.

But why is it so important?—the mother wondered. *Is this some other—world?*

227

Neither she nor the father could comprehend the child's preoccupation with this sort of "architecture." Neither had troubled to glance at the architect's plans and had long forgotten their existence. The house they'd purchased was the physical house and not the architect's plan of a house that did not exist except on paper. At the closing they'd been given the architect's plans in a folder that tied with a ribbon, as if it were a precious document, but neither had untied the ribbon.

Twelve years later the child discovered the folder in the closet, which intensified his wish to become, one day, *an architect.*

For each house designed by an architect, Oliver explained, was actually two houses: the one people lived in, and were meant to see, and the other, which they were not meant to see but which was preserved in the architect's plans.

This remark left the parents baffled. What on earth did their son *mean?*

Whatever, it was not the sum of his words. For they repeated his words to each other, and were not illuminated.

"What interests you about being an architect, Oliver?"—relatives asked the little boy, not sure whether they should be amused by him or somewhat alarmed by his precocity, which marked him as very different from their own children, and Oliver said in a shy murmur that he wanted to draw "special houses," which only an architect could draw.

"The architect is the one looking *down*, and *in.*"

In the child's room there came to be an accumulation of books, glossy magazines. No design of any house or building that included detailed floor plans failed to captivate him. His favorite architects were Gaudí, Kahn, Wright, Graves, Gehry. There came to be a new word in his vocabulary—*deconstruction.* (The (controversial, disorienting) architecture of Gehry.) His many pencil drawings were of houses that did not (yet) exist. And he continued to draw plans of the family house with "special"—"invisible"—features added.

It was bittersweet for the mother to see in the child some of her own inchoate yearnings. She'd tried to paint in her early twenties but had lacked confidence. Luminous visions in her head were crudely parodied by brushstrokes on canvas. She'd come too late for "figurative" art—too late for "abstract" art—too late for "pop" art and "conceptual" art. The child had no awareness of art as history, it was all one to him, present tense. He had no concern for being belated. The mother was thrilled by the child's skill at drawing though he rarely drew figures (animals, people) as other children tried to do; his obsession was with the interiors of buildings, the skeletal outlines of material things, which never seemed to bore him. If human figures appeared in Oliver's drawings, they were positioned for practical reasons of scale, and had no identities.

Oliver acquired notebooks, and made sketches of the interiors of places he visited, the homes of relatives and friends, transcribing what he saw (which was not likely to be what others "saw") as others chattered around him. And then he might point out to the homeowners some oddity, some imbalance or error in the architecture of their house with the suggestion that a door, a window, a staircase was in the wrong place, a ceiling too low or too high, a room too small or too large, and should be "rebuilt."

A wall should be removed—"It is blocking the spirit of the house."

A roof should be raised—"The house wants to be taller."

Such suggestions were met with blank faces, incomprehension or annoyance. "Well! Thank you, Oliver."

Or the child would say nothing to the homeowners but remark to the parents on their way home that something had happened in the house that had left its ("invisible") mark, which was evident ("visible") only in his sketching.

Did they see what he meant?—Oliver would try to show them in his sketches of the house, but the parents could never see.

Easier to dismiss the child's notions as *play, imagination.*

It was also Oliver's belief, explained to the bemused parents, that there were places (homes, school) in which the texture of the very air might become "denser" depending upon what was happening or not happening: a "boring" space (school classroom, for instance) became a "dense" space requiring literally more effort to endure, thus literally more time to endure than if it were not boring. The equation for this phenomenon was

$$T \text{ (time)} = D \text{ (density)} \times E \text{ (effort)}$$

Oliver's father laughed, saying, of course, it was common knowledge, emotions affect our experience of time; boredom makes time seem to pass slowly, as in an excruciatingly dull lecture on torts, while a pleasurable time may seem to end too soon. But the child frowned, saying with an air of rebuke that he did not mean *that.*

Nothing so obvious, so commonplace as *that.*

With infinite patience, over a period of months, Oliver copied the

229

architect's plans for the family house, until he could draw them without consulting the original. Then he began to experiment with additions of his own introduced into the drawings, which seemed to have the effect of altering features of the house.

The mother began to notice that the house "felt" different, in some rooms; its ceilings were at unexpected angles or its floors slanted; its windows appeared to be smaller, or larger, or unexpectedly shaped; through glass panes the exterior world looked different even as it was (evidently) unchanged. The very air in certain parts of the house seemed "denser"—exuding a faint sepia cast—than it had been, even as, in other parts of the house, the air seemed lighter, purer.

Were these changes the consequence of the child's alterations to the house plans, or had the child perceived discrepancies in the house in which the family had been living obliviously, which his attentions had made evident? Had the strangeness in the house been but *implicit* previously, and was now *explicit*?

The mother wondered if, gazing at her, the child might see something in her, in her (invisible) soul, unknown to her, unfathomable.

Feeling a wave of something like panic, fear. That the child who was *her child* yet might acquire a perspective from which he could view her as dispassionately as he viewed the interiors of houses.

One day Oliver asked the mother to participate in an experiment he called the "Zone of Invisibility." This involved the mother waiting in the hall outside his room and knocking on his door several times; each time she knocked, if he answered, *No!* she was not to come inside, but just to wait a few minutes and then knock again; only when the mother knocked and received no answer was she to open the door, and come inside.

These instructions the mother followed, at least initially. It was not often the boy requested anything from her, let alone her involvement in his life, or rather in the life of his architectural imaginings, which were usually kept private and secret, and certainly not shared with the father. But after she'd knocked on his door several times she couldn't determine whether she heard the boy's voice, or just imagined it, and so she opened the door impulsively—discovering that Oliver wasn't in the room after all, so far as she could see.

"Oliver? Where are you?"—the mother tried not to sound alarmed.

It was some sort of game, she supposed. Though the child had never cared for children's games like hide-and-seek.

The child had never cared for *pranks*. His play was serious play, and not ever a waste of his time.

230

"Oliver? Oli-ver?" The mother looked in the child's closet, and stooped to peer beneath the child's bed, and even lifted the comforter on the bed though (certainly) she could see that no child was lying flattened beneath it and hiding from her.

"Oliver?—where on earth . . ."

She had to laugh, if nervously. The child was (certainly) in the room somewhere.

There were two windows in the child's room but these were shut tight, locked. If Oliver had crawled through a window to jump down to the ground outside he could not have shut the window behind him, still less locked it.

Not that Oliver would have played so crude a trick on the mother. He was far too fastidious for such behavior.

"Oliver! This isn't funny. . . ."

Was it possible the child had the power to create, somehow, an actual *Zone of Invisibility* in his room? But what did this even mean? A kind of hypnosis, a mirage that obscured the mother's vision so that Oliver might be actually present but she could not see him?

"Oliver? I—I don't like this. It isn't . . ."

How could it be, Oliver seemed to have vanished in his own room? That was not possible.

Desperately the mother yanked open drawers in the child's maple bureau, as if Oliver could have squeezed inside one of these and shut the drawer upon himself!

The mother took note of light fixtures in the ceiling. These were of ordinary dimensions yet the mother found herself wondering fantastically if the child had somehow *shrunken himself* to a miniature size, to hide inside one of these?

It was not likely, and yet—the proof of *Invisibility* seemed to be that the child had become *not visible*.

Nor did the mother sense the child. Surely a mother would sense her child, if he were present. . . .

As, years ago, the mother had felt her hard-swollen breasts ache with milk, hearing the infant begin to whimper, in another room.

How brainless she'd been, in those (happy, unquestioning) days! Like a creature with its head cut off, sheer instinct, breasts and womb, female body.

However, it had not lasted. The fever-trance of motherhood had lifted, faded. Now and then she yearned for its return as one might yearn for ether, a fat thumb to suck in one's mouth.

But no, the prospect filled her now with revulsion. Really, the mother was eleven years beyond that stage in her life and did not want its return.

Of course, the parents spoke vaguely, smilingly, of another child. In conversation with others, especially relatives, they were prone to say how nice it would be, how ideal, if Oliver had a baby sister. *He is too much the center of our lives, that is not good for him or for us.*

Once upon a time, a man and a woman had as many children as God sent them. That is, the woman had as many children as God directed the husband to inflict upon her.

There was no refusal. Not of the man, and not of a woman's task.

"Oliver? Please don't scare me, honey. . . ."

A spell of vertigo overcame her brain. She sat down hard on the child-sized bed, which yielded to her weight. The wild thought came to her that cunning Oliver had attached himself monkey-like to the box springs below the mattress and was hiding beneath the bed but not on the floor, so she'd failed to see him. . . . But when she knelt panting to peer beneath the bed another time, of course there was no one.

A world without the child. A world depleted of the child.

The child who held the marriage together like cartilage in the (shared) spine of conjoined identical twins.

"Oliver! P-Please . . ."

Realizing that she lived for those moments when Oliver was (again) hers. When the child would smile spontaneously at her.

It could not be, that this vivid presence might vanish from the world. As you'd switch off a lamp and be plunged into darkness.

But then, suddenly: "Mom? Hi."

Out of nowhere the child appeared. Behind her, on the farther side of the bed.

Smiling at the astonished mother, pleased and excited. The experiment had been a greater success than he'd expected.

"Oh, Oliver! You frightened me. . . ."

She would chide the beaming child, she would strike her hands together in a display of motherly exasperation, but also motherly pride, vanity. He'd been naughty, hiding from her; but he'd been very clever too, for he had fooled her utterly, because he was such a clever child.

Quite the most clever child she had ever encountered.

She embraced him, kissed his fevered forehead. Later she would think—*He must have been hiding in the closet. Of course.*

232

3.

"Oh, Oliver. Oh *no*."

The Fractal Museum was closed! Closed Saturdays and Sundays, November through April.

What a disappointment! All the way to a desolate interstate exit on the northern outskirts of Portland, Maine—to discover the damned museum closed. . . .

The website that had posted Saturdays and Sundays as *open* had not been updated since September—that was the explanation. The child could not be blamed but the mother blamed herself: why hadn't she telephoned ahead, just to make sure the Fractal Museum really was open?

It is the *off-season* now in Maine.

But there is a good side to the disappointment: more time to explore the beautiful Atlantic coast a short drive away. Walking with the son, just the two of them. Rare for the mother and Oliver to be alone together in a place like this.

Arm in arm, when the walking is treacherous. Rocks, boulders. Crashing surf. She will take pictures of the rocky coast, white-capped, frothing waves pounding against the shore at Prouts Neck, which Winslow Homer depicted in his extraordinary drawings, watercolors, and oil paintings.

They will visit the Winslow Homer Studio at Scarborough, which is on the way home.

Out of a kind of shyness the mother has never told the child about her love of art and her hope to be an artist, before his birth. Her awe at the work of Winslow Homer in particular. She is excited now at the prospect of sharing Winslow Homer with him. . . .

4.

In fact, the Fractal Museum is open. It is a Saturday morning, and the museum is closed on Mondays and Tuesdays: the website was correct after all.

Thank God! Oliver would have been disappointed, sullen and sulky. The mother would have had to find some other quasi-intellectual diversion for him, museum or otherwise, in Portland, before daring to suggest walking along the coast at Prouts Neck or stopping at the Winslow Homer Studio in Scarborough.

"Well—here we are!"—for her own sake as well as the boy's the mother is trying to sound upbeat, cheerful.

It is rare for Oliver to scramble out of a vehicle so eagerly. Usually he is scarcely aware of having arrived at a destination, reluctantly looking up from his iPad.

"Oliver—don't *run*."

Parking the vehicle, the mother feels something like a (ghost) hand pressing against her chest in warning—*Go back. This is wrong. It is not too late.*

5.

You may enter at any door. All doors lead to the same place.
(The reverse is not true.)

*

How strange, the Fractal Museum looks as if it is composed of several buildings simultaneously!

Oliver tells the mother *no*. That is an illusion—"simultaneity."

But—what does he mean? The mother is perplexed.

Politely Oliver explains: "We don't see all sides of the Fractal Museum simultaneously. We see just one side at a time—the museum is deliberately constructed so that we 'see' what is being presented to us to be seen. It's 'fractal architecture'—there are sides of the museum that appear to us in sequence but our perception is that they are 'simultaneous.'"

Adding, as the mother ponders what he has said: "Nothing is 'simultaneous' with something else—that's an optical illusion."

Oliver is eager to take pictures of the Fractal Museum. He has been planning this, the mother assumes, for weeks.

Seen from the front, the Fractal Museum appears to be made of some attractive but commonplace material like sandstone, with narrow vertical plate-glass panels in a pattern that repeats itself (one would assume) on all sides of the building; it is foursquare, three stories high, set back from a state highway. Seen in a partially filled asphalt parking lot, and resembling a moderately well-kept medical office building.

But that is only the facade.

From the (west) parking lot the Fractal Museum is revealed to be, behind the sandstone facade, a private house, or what had once been a private house: a renovated old Victorian shingle board painted dark

Joyce Carol Oates

purple with lavender trim, bay windows, steep slate roofs, lightning rod, and weather vane—exactly the sort of distinctive old property given away by heirs to townships for charitable purposes, to escape property taxes. Overlapping shingles suggest a fractal pattern that repeats itself top to bottom, bottom to top, impossible to measure with the eye as a result of its repetition; as the visitor's eye moves about this (visible) portion of the house, it comes to seem, uncannily, that there are more tall, narrow windows here than could possibly fit into the limited space; it is an effort to move the eye horizontally, left to right, right to left, and not rather vertically, as if something in the structure of the building is an active (if subliminal) impediment to the visitor's curiosity.

Seen from the (east) parking lot the Fractal Museum is revealed to be, behind the sandstone facade, another private house, very different from the Victorian: a large Colonial with weatherworn white shingles, dull-green shutters, a greeny glimmer of moss on its roof, exactly the sort of distinctive old property given away by heirs to townships for charitable purposes, to escape property taxes. Here too there is something uncanny about the windows—there are not enough windows for the space and they appear to be of differing sizes; the observer is led to glance quickly from window to window, to see how they differ, yet there is some sort of impediment (instant amnesia?) preventing "seeing" the windows in relationship to one another, so that each sighting of each window is distinct from its predecessor, and forming a comparison is not possible.

Also, there appear to be in the windows remnants of holiday decorations, candles or Christmas lights, unless these are but (fractal-like, repetitive) reflections in wavy glass.

The rear of the museum is a blank, freshly painted (beige) stucco wall that might be the rear of a fast-food taco restaurant—blunt, pragmatic, windowless, and so textured that if you look closely you can see the suggestions of fractal designs in the material, leaflike, overlapping in seemingly infinite repetition. There is a single large metal door marked EXIT and below this a smaller sign: NO REENTRY. From a stoop, a short flight of concrete steps and a ramp to the parking lot.

As he has been taking pictures of the museum with his iPad Oliver has been trying to explain to the mother that the Fractal Museum is considered a "living paradox"—a "living conundrum." Measured from the outside its square footage is (reputedly) considerably less than the square footage measured from the inside—"interior fractal space."

235

Oliver plans to take pictures inside the museum to determine for himself the authenticity of *interior fractal space,* at which online commentators have marveled.

The mother has listened, or half listened, to the child chattering about the Fractal Museum for weeks. But this is new to her. How can the museum be smaller on the outside than on the inside? And how can a museum, which is nothing but a building constructed of wood, brick, stone, stucco, *unliving* materials, be *living?*

The mother hesitates to ask the child another time to explain what he is talking about. (Especially, the mother hesitates to ask the child to explain what the hell he is talking about. *What the hell* will be registered by the child as exasperation, dismay.) The mother is self-aware enough to dread that hour when she hears in the (prepubescent) boy's voice the equivalent of *Oh Jesus, Mom! Please.*

At the entrance of the Fractal Museum a woman of about Amanda's age, looking both harried and flushed with a mother's eagerness to please, is ushering inside several children of whom the eldest, lanky limbed, with round eyeglasses, resembles Oliver to an uncanny degree.

The mother holds her breath, waiting to see if the two boys notice each other: they do not.

6.

It is just 10:28 a.m. The Fractal Museum has opened at 10 a.m. Inside, there is a surprisingly long line for tickets. Families with young children, a predominance of mothers. The Fractal Museum advertises itself as a *family-friendly museum.*

While the son studies an interactive floor map of the museum that bristles with lights and animation like a casino game, the mother purchases their tickets. She is surprised that this obscure museum in a quasi-rural suburb of Portland, Maine, is expensive: thirty-five dollars for adults, thirty for seniors, twenty for children under twelve. *Twenty for children under twelve.* Is this even legal?

"Another year, and I'd be paying the 'adult' price for my son here."

Just a mild observation. Not a complaint. The mother understands that the Fractal Museum is privately owned and probably isn't subsidized by the state.

"Eleven? Your son is *eleven?*"—a query from the woman selling tickets isn't intended to be rude but, yes, it is tactless.

"Yes. He is eleven."

With a pang of dismay the mother sees that the child who so often seems to her immense in his intelligence and imagination and will-fulness is indeed small for his age. Not short, as tall as an average eleven-year-old perhaps, but painfully thin, with underdeveloped shoulders and arms, the slender neck of an aquatic bird, and that pale, cinnamon-freckled skin—*vulnerable* is the word that comes most readily to mind.

In his dark-red flannel shirt he'd buttoned crookedly, and she'd had to rebutton. In wire-rimmed eyeglasses that enlarge his eyes, which glow like bees.

Fiercely the mother thinks—*I will protect him with my life.*

But Oliver isn't so frail, to himself: Oliver is strong-willed, even defiant. He has been an only child for eleven years—a lifetime!

Edging away from the mother, frowning as he struggles to clip the bright blue Fractal Museum badge (which is, in fact, several fractal-leaf badges conflated as one) onto his shirt without her assistance. Though he hasn't heard the exact exchange between the ticket seller and his mother, the mother's friendly chatter with strangers is embarrassing to him.

Especially since the child knows that the friendly, chattering mom is not really *the mother*—just some silly mask and costume the mother puts on in public.

Adjacent to the foyer is the gift shop. Adjacent to that, a planetarium with hourly showings—OUR FRACTAL UNIVERSE. Also a café that is brightly lit and buzzing with customers.

Oliver suggests that the mother have coffee in the café and meet him afterward in the third-floor exhibit—for he knows how badly she would like coffee (very black, strong!) after the stress of the drive—but the mother quickly demurs. "No! I'm not letting you out of my sight in this weird place." Adding, as if it were an afterthought, with a smile, "Sweetie."

It is the mother's nightmare that she might lose the child in some unfamiliar place like a museum, airport, subway. Perhaps an out-dated nightmare since the child is not of an age to be easily lost any longer.

Sweetie is a signal the mother is pleading with him. The child is stiff backed, not in a mood to be pleaded with.

If she didn't know that the child would ease away from her like a cat not wishing to be stroked she'd have taken his hand. Just to feel the small, hot-skinned hand in her own and to claim—*See?—I've got you. Safe.*

*

"Oh, Oliver! *Look.*"

Their first exhibit is on the third floor: NATURALLY OCCURRING FRACTALS. This is a massive and dazzling display that winds its way in brightly lighted glass cases and interactive presentations through the entire third floor. Crowded with visitors (including the harried-looking young mother with a son who resembles Oliver), this exhibit appears to be at least twice as large as the mother would have anticipated, given the (apparent) size of the museum from the outside. Just to gaze into it, to the farther walls of the museum that seem to dissolve into the ether, is disconcerting.

Giant illuminated photographs of seeds, leaves, flowers. Feathers, hairs, fur, scales (snake, fish, lizard). Many-times-magnified snowflakes, crystals. Magnified cells, neurons, ganglia so tangled and so beautiful, they evoke a sense of vertigo in the brain. And there are, scarcely less startling and strange, skeletal trees with fractal branches, fractal twigs, fractal-veined leaves. Fractally dense evergreen cones looking sharp and lethal as spikes. With his iPad Oliver takes multiple pictures. He is particularly interested in a sequence of highly magnified photographs of the New England coastline, in ascending order of magnification.

No matter how many times magnified, the fractal pattern of the coastline recurs. The mother can see this but can't quite see the point of magnification. Is there to be no end of things?—no *end*?

"What you think is a straight line," Oliver says, "actually isn't. There are all these little breaks and creases, that go on forever." The child speaks with a sort of grim glee as if *forever* were not a terrifying prospect.

"Oh. But—why?"

"Just *is*, Mom."

"I mean—why pursue it? Why would you want to know so much that has no use?"

Oliver retorts that most of science is "useless"—plus math, fractal geometry. That something is *useless* is not a description of its essential properties but is irrelevant. *Useful* is also irrelevant.

The mother feels rebuked. For a mother is of all things meant to be *useful*.

Before each dazzling display the mother lingers. She is (half) aware of time fracturing, fractal-ing. Unlike Oliver, who seems to be familiar

238

with much of this information, the mother needs to carefully read, reread the descriptive passages on the walls. Her brain feels gluey. Her eyes feel the strain of so much to see.

Her arms ache from the effort of having held the damned steering wheel steady for so long, to keep the SUV in its proper lane and prevent a sudden catastrophe, a crash into an abutment (just beyond exit nine at a place called Elk River) and two lives *snuffed out just like that.*

But, no, that did not happen. Without incident they'd passed the exit where they'd been most at risk, at about 9:05 a.m. Arms trembling with effort, the mother held the steering wheel firm as an enormous tractor-trailer truck thundered by in the adjacent left lane.

The child had not even noticed. Absorbed in the intricate puzzles of the iPad.

The mother wonders: is there such a thing as fractal time? She feels a thrill of dread that this must be so. Each hour, each minute, each second broken down into its components, to infinity, and in each, an alternative fate of which she knows nothing.

Up close, life is but life. At a little distance, life is fate.

Crushed, broken amid the wreckage. Steam lifting, stink of gasoline.

Snuffed out just like that: two lives.

To the husband she'd have said, *Serves you right! You have abandoned your child and your wife and now you have lost them.*

Something is staring—glaring—into her face. Another of the giant illuminated magnifications. Reduced to its fractal components, the photograph (rock, lichen) is unrecognizable as a swirl of molecules.

Yet, the fractals abide. No matter the degree of magnification.

The mother has certainly underestimated the Fractal Museum, she is thinking. She'd meant simply to humor the child, driving him here. She'd hoped that, if there was an extra hour, on the way home she could stop at the Winslow Homer Studio at Scarborough, about which she has read in the *AAA Maine Guide*, and that would have made the long trip worthwhile for her.

But now, she is quite absorbed in the exhibits. It is a new world to her, close beneath the surface of the world she believes she knows without needing to examine how she knows.

Naturally occurring fractals seem to encompass virtually everything in the physical world—all that the mother has been seeing with her eyes (and not with her brain) through her life.

The fractal is the basic unit of design.

The fractal repeats itself endlessly and yet each fractal is unique and unlike any other.

Trying to grasp this. Like stepping out onto ice. Possibly it is rock solid and will support your weight. Possibly it is not.

*

"Shall I take your picture, Olly?"

Shakes his head *no*.

Ducks his head. Smooth-freckled pale skin reddening as if slapped, for certainly the mother must know that the child hates being called *Olly* in a public place.

Well, in fact—the child isn't comfortable being called *Olly* at any time this past year.

Stubbornly resisting. No picture!

The mother feels a surge of something like fury and wants to take hold of the child's skinny shoulders, give him a shake.

But consider: she is *the mother*, she is not *the child*.

In a contest of wills *the mother* does not need to vanquish *the child* to establish her power over him.

"Come on, sweetie. Please. Just stand here. We can mail the picture to Daddy, to make him envious he isn't here with us."

This is very mild sarcasm. This is not actually a condemnation of the father, who is oblivious of much in the household.

"Actually, Daddy asked me to take your picture. And send it to him. So he knows we got here safely. OK?"

None of this is true. But the mother exudes such sincerity, the most icy-hearted child could not resist.

And the mother has exerted her authority by taking the iPad from the child—virtually unhooking it from his fingers—and positioning him against a wall, as if he were a much younger child.

(The wall display is one of the gorgeously colored magnifications of—is it a nebula? a multifoliate rose? a neuron in the human brain?)

"There! That wasn't so bad, was it?"

The child has allowed the picture to be taken, to humor the mother.

The fear that our likenesses will outlive us. The image of a being in a (future) time in which the being has ceased to exist.

This is a morbid thought that has leapt into the mother's brain like a sly louse or tick, out of the gorgeous fractal display on the wall. But the mother casts off the morbid thought as she always does such thoughts, by ignoring it.

The time is 10:31 a.m. But—how is that possible? The mother stares at her (digital) watch, baffled and uneasy. She has given the iPad back to the child, or she would check the time on the electronic gadget as well.

Hadn't they arrived at the museum shortly before 10:30 a.m.? The mother is sure she remembers the time correctly. And if so, if at least forty minutes have passed in the exhibit, it would now be 11:10 a.m., approximately; how then can it be only 10:31 a.m.?

Something is very wrong. The mother's brain reels.

If time moves with such glacial slowness in the Fractal Museum they will never be released from it. They will never return to their home in New Haven, where someone, the third party of the triangle of which they constitute two-thirds, awaits them.

The mother gives her watch a shake. Damned battery must be slowing down.

"Oliver, wait!"—the child is eager to move on.

CULTURALLY APPROPRIATED FRACTALS is an equally massive and dazzling display sprawling through the museum's second floor. Here are walls of illuminated mandalas, rose windows. The mother will spend many minutes here entranced as one who has been deprived of beauty and is now blinded by it.

Astonishingly elaborate, intricately designed Hindu mandalas. In these you can lose yourself. That is, *self*.

The mother is mesmerized by the great illuminated mandalas. These are as different from one another, and alike one another, as fireworks in a night sky. Seeing one, you have seen them all; seeing many, you have seen one.

Like the infinite faces of God.

The child is less intrigued by (mere) visual beauty. The child is drawn to the cerebral component—the fractal structures that underlie beauty.

In the beige tile floor of the museum are several stripes: green, red, blue, yellow. Each leads to an exhibit. It is the green stripe that Oliver wants to follow to bring him to more cerebral exhibits, video puzzle games, and interactive robots that mimic/mirror the individuals who stand before them typing on keyboards. There is the promise of the Sierpinski Triangle Labyrinth, which is a "challenging" maze game in the form of a triangle containing countless triangles in which time as well as space has to be navigated.

Oliver plucks at the mother's wrist to move her along but the mother finds it difficult to break the spell of the mandalas. The

241

exhibit area is enormous, the size of a football field. Always there is more to see: another gorgeous, dazzling, intricately wrought mandala that seems to hold a secret—a secret meaning. Beauty exudes a powerful spell upon the mother, like a heady perfume.

The mother becomes aware of an agitated hubbub of the air about her as of a crowd pressing near but when she looks around, there is virtually no one else (visible) in the enormous room.

At the farther end of the room a museum guard motionless as a mannequin. His face is generic and friendly, of the hue of skim milk.

Oh, where is Oliver?—the mother hurries to locate him. And there Oliver is, around a corner, in a corner, absorbed in an interactive video that makes him laugh.

Something about fractals, of course. Fractal topology? Vivid colors, like explosions in the brain.

The mother tells the child please don't move away from her. It is crucial for them to stay in each other's sight. The museum is much bigger than she'd thought, and—how to express this—"Time moves differently here."

The mother dislikes video games, which she interprets (correctly) as an alternative reality not congruent with her best interests. *She* would like to imagine herself the emotional center of the child's life, and not a brain-exhausting game.

(Can a machine love her son, as she loves her son? Of course not.)

Being of an older generation to whom such antic video figures will never exude familiarity or comfort, the mother instinctively distrusts humanoid figures. She knows that they are "programmed"—she thinks that "programmed" means "safe"—but this makes no difference to her. She *cannot trust* any machine.

As Oliver interacts with the video game the mother loses herself in an exhibit of eerily incandescent, shimmering flowers of diverse varieties and colors. These too are fractal mandalas. Peering into them is like peering into the soul.

From all sides, Ravel's *Boléro*. Ever faster, ever louder, musical notes turning frantically upon themselves like snakes in a cluster.

7.

"It's OK, Mom. I can go alone."

"Oliver, no. I don't think so."

The Sierpinski Triangle Labyrinth, located on the mezzanine floor of the museum, takes up the entire floor.

The child cannot think of anything more disappointing than to have journeyed to the Fractal Museum only to be forced to undertake the labyrinth, the museum's major interactive exhibit, about which he has been reading online for weeks, in the company of his timorous and uninformed mother. No!

And yet there is a warning posted above the entrance: CHILDREN UNDER TWELVE MUST BE ACCOMPANIED BY ADULTS INTO THE LABYRINTH.

Though Oliver is hardly a small child the mother intends to enter the labyrinth firmly gripping the boy's hand. It isn't likely that he would run ahead of her, or become lost, for after all the labyrinth is finite—no larger than the mezzanine floor, you can see. Still the mother is reluctant to let the child push ahead and leave her behind. She is somewhat dazed by the effect of the mandalas and rose windows in the preceding exhibit and feels reluctant to leave them so soon.

Amanda has not been a religious person and has not (consciously) felt the need for spiritual solace. A great hunger is opening in her, in the region of her heart, that will never be filled.

And yet—she is obliged to use the women's restroom. This is not so spiritual.

Instructing the child to please wait for her in the corridor. Or use the (men's) restroom himself, which is just across the hall, and wait for her. And then they will proceed—together—to the Sierpinski Triangle Labyrinth just a few feet away.

The child agrees. Seems to agree. *OK, Mom.*

Standing very still, deceptively. With an expression of utter innocence.

On surveillance cameras it will be recorded: the mother addressing the child, the child seemingly docile, a lanky-limbed boy of ten?—with ginger-colored hair, in a dark-red, or maroon, shirt buttoned to his throat, jeans, sneakers.

Mother disappears into women's restroom. Child waits obediently for two seconds before edging away into the entrance to the labyrinth.

(Not that Oliver was a rebellious child. Rather, Oliver was oblivious of the fact that while he *was* he was a *child*.)

In the Sierpinski Triangle Labyrinth each individual who enters is designated a *pilgrim*, overtly; covertly, from the perspective of the program that governs the labyrinth, each individual is a *subject*.

There is (allegedly) a direct path that leads from the entrance of the labyrinth to the exit, at which there is posted EXIT: NO REENTRY. If you make the right choices each time you are confronted with a choice (that is, a fork in the path) you will exit the labyrinth after a breathless forty-fifty minutes.

Has anyone ever exited the labyrinth in this relatively short period of time? Legend is, no one has (yet). Thus, each *pilgrim* imagines himself potentially ranked number one in the labyrinth competition; the child Oliver is, or was, no exception.

Like human intestines that might measure, if stretched out, more than twenty-five feet, yet are condensed into a much smaller abdominal space, the devious path of the Sierpinski Triangle Labyrinth is far longer than one would guess; calculating the numerous (fractal) turns, each of which involves an equilateral triangle replicating the larger equilateral triangle that constitutes the outermost limits of the labyrinth, and factoring in the time fractal as well, the labyrinth is many miles long, perhaps as many as one thousand. Examined minutely, however, the labyrinth might be said to be infinite, for each smaller triangle in the path might be deconstructed into its parts, to infinity.

The *pilgrim/subject* makes his way into the labyrinth, confronted with forks in the path at intervals of only a few seconds; he must choose to go right, or left, for he cannot go backward; having made his choice, he will be confronted with another fork within a few seconds, and must choose to go right, or left, and so on. As soon as he has entered the labyrinth the *pilgrim/subject* is moving through time as well as space, and this movement into both time and space is irrevocable—though it is not likely that the *pilgrim/subject* realizes it, as none of us do.

Having calculated a route beforehand, Oliver has a plan to take the left fork of the path, then the right, and again the left, and the right, in a pattern of strict alternation; in this way (he deduces, plausibly) he will always be hewing to the center, and will not be drawn off into peripheral, fractal branches that may culminate in dead ends. Oliver is very bright and quick and has a near-photographic memory and so tells himself—*I can't become lost.*

It has been Oliver's aim—his dream—to complete the labyrinth in record time, or at least to tie with the previous number one *pilgrim* whose likeness he has seen posted on the museum's website: a seventeen-year-old boy from the Fieldston School who intends to major in cosmology at MIT.

And so, the bold child enters the labyrinth without a backward glance. At once the atmosphere is altered—he finds himself almost weightless, disoriented. Surprised too to see that the maze walls are not solid as he'd anticipated, but rather translucent, or giving an impression of translucence, opening onto sunlit areas, fields of poppies, Shasta daisies, wild roses that seem to stretch for miles. There are high-scudding clouds. Fleecy, filmy cirrocumulus clouds in a cobalt-blue sky. Cries of birds, or perhaps they are human cries—a young family at the beach, laughing together. All is vivid and then fleeting, fading. Forks in the path come rapidly—more rapidly than Oliver has expected—but each fork seems to lead into an identical space so that it is possible to forget one's strategy and make a blunder, "choosing" randomly, with the assumption that *left* and *right* are interchangeable; and since the *pilgrim* can't reverse his course he has no idea if *left* and *right* are in fact interchangeable, or in fact very different—as radically opposed as *life* and *death.*

Once a choice has been made it is irrevocable, for a powerful momentum draws the *pilgrim* forward, as a mist of amnesia trails in his wake.

Soon then, the child has entered an industrial landscape. Factories in ruins, dripping water. The sky is leaden, sinking. All color has vanished. Suddenly he is in dark, rank water to his ankles. (Is the water *real*, or is the water *virtual*? In the Sierpinski Triangle there is no clear distinction between the two states.) A strong chemical odor pinches his nostrils for the water is poisoned. It is the reeking landscape of the Russian film *Stalker*—Oliver's favorite film since he'd first seen it at the age of ten.

How many times Oliver has seen *Stalker*! He has been mesmerized by the long dreamlike excursion into the interior of the Zone in which all wishes are fulfilled including those wishes we do not know we have. Recalling how a black dog suddenly emerges from the contaminated water, to befriend one of the pilgrims . . .

There is no doubt that Oliver must continue forward, ever deeper into the Zone. Dank, dripping water, a tightening in his chest. No friendly German shepherd appears (yet). Oliver has not time to wonder how so abruptly he has stepped out of the comfort of the Fractal Museum with its clean restrooms and brightly lit café buzzing with customers and the planetarium show—OUR FRACTAL UNIVERSE—which he might now be seeing safely with his mother, except the line of mothers and children was too long, and the lure of the notorious Sierpinski Triangle Labyrinth irresistible. For weeks Oliver has planned how, if he follows his plan unfailingly, he will exit the maze in "record time"—his name and likeness posted on the Fractal Museum's website for all to see.

For the father to see. For kids at school to see.

Yet Oliver has a strong feeling that he should turn back. Even if it is against the rules—perhaps the program that drives the labyrinth will make an exception for him. (He is a special child, isn't he? The fuss his parents have made over *him*.) He has made a mistake to push ahead into the exhibit without his mother—they will make an exception, for he is just a child. He has deceived his naively trusting mother.

She will be upset. She will be angry. Her eyes will smart with tears. Her lower lip will tremble. *Oliver, how could you! You must have known that I would be looking for you, I would be sick with worry over you.* . . .

Hesitating on the path, uncertain which fork to take. Now there is not only a right-hand fork and a left-hand fork but a middle fork. Three!

Oliver had not known that some of the choices would involve three forks in the path. He is confused, uncertain. How deeply has he penetrated the Zone? Will there be a way out?

Always there is the promise, if you are an American child and your parents love you, there will be a *way out*.

Even if you have rejected your parents there is a *way out*.

The polluted air is difficult to breathe, the child's chest begins to tighten. Airways in his lungs begin to tighten. He begins to choke, wheeze. He is panicked suddenly. It is a violent asthmatic attack of a kind he has not had in years. In another few seconds his eyesight will blotch and blacken and he will sink to the floor gasping for breath, unconscious. . . .

Oliver, darling! Here.

He feels the mother's hand on his shoulder. He feels the mother's panting breath on his cheek. The mother has brought Oliver's rescue inhaler in her handbag. Of course, the precious rescue inhaler, the almost-forgotten inhaler, the despised inhaler that will save the child's life.

I've got you, darling, you are all right. Your mother has you now, just breathe. . . .

8.

At the entrance to the Sierpinski Triangle Labyrinth the warning cannot be clearer: CHILDREN UNDER TWELVE MUST BE ACCOMPANIED BY ADULTS INTO THE LABYRINTH.

Yet when the mother emerges from the women's room to glance about inquisitively the child is nowhere in sight.

Oliver has entered the labyrinth by himself—has he? The mother is exasperated with the son but not (yet) upset.

Noting the time: 12:29 p.m.

Reluctant to enter the labyrinth, for the mother knows that it is the most challenging of the Fractal Museum exhibits, indeed an "ingeniously" difficult maze, the mother looks prudently about to see if, in fact, Oliver might be somewhere else. Perhaps he has wandered into another exhibit, around a corner. Into the men's restroom? With mounting anxiety she waits outside the restroom. In case Oliver is inside. Oh, she hopes so! If he appears, she will not scold him. *Oliver! Thank God.*

Though she is not by nature an *anxious mother*. Minutes pass; Oliver does not appear. Other boys emerge from the restroom, one of them closely, uncannily resembling Oliver, the boy who'd worn the dark-green Newtown Day hoodie, coming to join the mother waiting for him outside the labyrinth, but Oliver is not among them. Finally the mother asks a museum guard if he will please go inside the restroom to see if her son, Oliver, is in there—eleven years old, "small for his age," gingery-red hair, wire-rimmed glasses, dark-red shirt, jeans, sneakers. The museum guard is willing to oblige but returns from the restroom without Oliver.

Is she sure he hasn't entered the labyrinth?—the guard asks.

The mother confesses that she doesn't know. She'd asked the son to wait for her, but . . .

At 12:36 p.m. the mother again approaches the guard: should she enter the labyrinth to search for the child?—or should she assume that he will emerge at the exit, when he completes the maze?

The museum guard is a skim-milk-skinned individual of no discernible age with an affable smile, museum uniform, and badge. He does not appear to be armed except with a device that might (the mother thinks) be a Taser. He assures the mother that the maze is a "challenge" but it is "finite"—"It is guaranteed to come to an end." He recommends that she wait for her son at the exit, which she can access by taking the stairs or elevator to the first floor, walking to the rear of the museum, then taking the stairs or elevator back up to the mezzanine. She will encounter *pilgrims* leaving the maze there, and possibly someone among them will have seen her son.

This, the mother does with some misgivings for it seems not a good idea to leave the labyrinth entrance in case Oliver shows up there after all. Bitterly she regrets not having insisted that the child carry a cell phone so that she can contact him easily but Oliver (who does not want to be contacted easily by his mother) is interested only in the damned iPad.

At the labyrinth exit the mother waits. Surely Oliver will emerge from the maze soon!

Each person who appears at the labyrinth exit—many of them boys Oliver's age, or older—looks familiar to her, for a brief moment. Her heart is suffused with hope even when she has seen a face clearly and knows that the person cannot be Oliver: the child out of all the universe who is precious to her as her very life, perhaps more precious, for he is *her child*, and the promise is—*Our children must outlive us, and remember us, else we cease to exist utterly.*

An older, white-haired gentleman exits the labyrinth appearing distracted, distraught. It is unusual to see an individual of such an age in the labyrinth. The mother tries to speak to him, to ask if he might have seen Oliver inside the maze, but the white-haired man seems reluctant to meet her eye, and hurries unsteadily away.

The mother tries to reason with herself: it is (probably) foolish to worry about Oliver—the labyrinth is only a museum exhibit, a maze for children to navigate, nothing like a Ferris wheel or roller coaster; a child is obviously not in danger of his life in the maze, nor is it likely that a child could become *lost*. She knows this, certainly.

Strangely, it is only 12:29 p.m.—how is this possible? Amanda could swear it would have to be an hour later at least. She is becoming increasingly anxious.

At the labyrinth exit is a sign in emergency-red letters: EXIT ONLY— DO NOT ENTER. Amanda hesitates, wondering if she should try to enter, or should she return to the entrance and try to make her way through the maze, to find Oliver? Reaches out her hand to the door-way—her hand is confronted by a very slight resistance in the air. (Is this real? Imagined? She feels a sensation like a mild, warning shock.) A museum guard approaches her to inform her politely but firmly that visitors are not allowed into the maze at the exit; if they wish to enter, they must return to the entrance.

She stammers that her son is somewhere inside the maze, she's afraid that he is lost, that something may have happened to him— "Please? Please help us."

On his walkie-talkie the guard summons an aggressively friendly woman in a museum uniform (jacket, pleated skirt), badge identify-ing her as *M. W. Pritt*, who assures the mother that of course it is natural to be worried, for some children get "mired" in the labyrinth and take longer to complete it than others, and it is natural—understandable!—for a mother to *worry*. But there is (after all) only one way out of the labyrinth, even if the labyrinth turns upon itself, in mimicry of a fractal universe, in ever-tighter "pathways" within ever-smaller triangles, and even if, as all visitors to the museum are clearly informed—in fact, it is printed out distinctly (if in a very small font!) on the reverse side of all museum tickets—the Sierpinski Triangle Labyrinth is also a maze *in time.*

What does that mean, the mother asks—"A maze *in time?*"

"It means that the maze is ingeniously imagined as a maze *in space* and *in time.*"

"*In time . . .*"

"The pilgrim who undertakes the labyrinth is moving through space but also, inevitably, through time."

"But—why is that different from what we are doing, just standing here? Aren't we moving *through time?*"

"Of course. It is not possible not to move *through time.* But *time* is a kind of spectrum, and there are different rates at which one moves. The labyrinth experiments with 'time'—at least, that is what the inventor claims. Very few of us, on the staff, have actually *gone inside* our interactive exhibits."

"You've never gone into the labyrinth? Why—why not?"

"But why would we?"—the woman regards the mother with a quizzical smile. "We are here to manage—not to be entertained."

Seeing that the mother is looking distressed and confused, *M. W. Pritt* repeats again that the labyrinth is *finite*, and if the child is still in the labyrinth he will be found.

The mother asks what does she mean by *if?*

If. If the child is still in the labyrinth, or *if* the child ever entered the labyrinth.

The mother asks if there are security cameras inside the labyrinth and is told that there are not, for reasons of privacy, as there are not cameras in restrooms; though there are security cameras in the museum generally, in the exhibit rooms and corridors.

"But—I don't understand. 'Reasons of privacy'—what does that mean? In the maze?"

"Ma'am, I am just relating museum policy to you. I did not set the policy!"

M. W. Pritt escorts the mother downstairs and into the security office, where she is allowed to observe a wall of TV screens. On each screen humanoid figures are moving at a distance, blurred and indistinct, with only intermittent colors, as if seen undersea. It is very difficult to distinguish faces. In fact—are there faces? A preponderance of children, young adolescents, some adults, a white-haired older man drifting about like sea anemones in an invisible current. When the videotape from the labyrinth entrance is rewound and replayed the mother stares so intensely she almost cannot see— "Wait! Is that Oliver?—Is that me? Or, maybe not . . ."

A mother and a boy, obviously her son, yearning to slip away from the mother, listening to her anxious prattling with an air of barely restrained impatience; a young boy, not yet an adolescent, in what appears to be a jacket or a hoodie, standing very still.

The mother enters a women's restroom, and vanishes from the TV screen; the son remains for a beat, two beats, before turning away decisively and entering the labyrinth.

Last glimpse of the son, a defiant little figure, entering the labyrinth without so much as a backward glance.

The mother stares at the screen, perplexed. Again, she is so agitated she has difficulty seeing.

"I—I think that might be us. Though that doesn't actually look like us. Especially me . . . that isn't *me*. But the boy resembles Oliver. Oh—I just don't know."

The recorded time, noted on the screen, is 12:25 p.m.

The head of museum security is very sympathetic with the mother. He rewinds the videotape, replays it. The mother stares avidly, as a starving person might stare at (a representation of) food, imagining it in three dimensions, smelling it. She is thinking how human beings recorded by such cameras are diminished, soulless. Flattened and distended like sea creatures of so little consequence they would not require names. Their limbs grow stubby, flaccid. Their faces are melting like wet tissue. It is particularly curious that on some of the screens you can distinguish adults from children only by height, and even that is not a reliable measure.

The mother demands that she be allowed to enter the labyrinth, that a security officer escort her, that they find Oliver, immediately. She is excited, her voice rises. Calmly it is pointed out to her that the boy has not been in the maze very long, by their calculation less than ten minutes, and that, if he is making his way through the maze as the brighter children do, he will need at least forty or fifty minutes to complete it.

"You don't want to disappoint your son, ma'am. He may make

250

excellent time and be a top-ranked *pilgrim* posted on our website. Why don't you wait here in our security office for a few minutes at least, before we enter the labyrinth and create a commotion? Maybe your 'Oliver' will show up on camera, at the exit."

The mother is about to burst into tears—*No! You are lying to me. Something terrible has happened to my son, I want to see him at once.*

But hears herself saying weakly, yes, all right. Suppose that is sensible. Probably the child in the video was Oliver, though the woman did not much resemble her, the mother, in which case if Oliver entered the labyrinth at 12:25 p.m., it is only 12:38 p.m., and not much time has passed.

Many hours have passed. The mother is exhausted, her bones dissolving.

"Why don't you have a seat, ma'am. Try to relax. We will watch the camera trained on the labyrinth exit, and see when your son emerges. And we will station a guard there, to bring him immediately to you. Shall I get you a coffee from our café?"

9.

In the labyrinth there is no *time*. There are many *times*.

The child is beginning to suspect that each *time* he chooses a fork in the path he is choosing a *time* that does not "differ from" but has no relationship at all to other *times*. His experience in the labyrinth is not (he supposes) synchronous with the *time* preceding his entry, which has continued in his absence, nor with the *time* in which (he supposes, guiltily) his mother is now looking for him.

Beginning to appreciate the ingenuity of the labyrinth, which is more properly described as a *Labyrinth of Infinitely Receding Triangles*.

For when the child makes a choice—left, middle, right—right, right middle, left middle, left—there is the alternative child self who takes alternative paths. And each of these selves has engendered, or will engender, alternative selves.

Already the (defiant) child is lost to the (overly trusting) mother. As soon as he'd stepped into the labyrinth loss suffused them each like a smell of brackish water.

In the Zone, the child has been alone. The friendly black German shepherd dog has yet to appear.

And then, at a subsequent fork of the path, the child is greeted by the friendly black German shepherd dog!

251

Delighted, with childish relief. The child takes a seat in front of the German shepherd, who is (obviously, the child can see this) a robot, though a very realistic-looking dog. The child pets the dog, wanting to think that the stiff synthetic fur is actual fur, coarse from the brackish pools. The tawny-golden eyes shine.

The child is invited by the Friendly Dog to participate in an interactive game. *Your Fractal Twin.*

Though the Friendly Dog is a "dog," he/it is also more essentially a mirror of the child.

Oliver laughs; the Friendly Dog has made him very happy. Though he is eleven years old and not a young child, he is not thinking so clearly now, to be made very happy by the Friendly Dog, and to trust the Friendly Dog when (he can see) the Friendly Dog is but the carapace of a machine that has (probably) not been programmed in the child's best interest.

Sierpinski triangles within triangles. Oliver tries to calculate how far inside the labyrinth he actually is, how many triangles *in*. Five? Six? More? He'd intended to navigate the maze by reverting always toward the center but has been distracted in the Zone.

Begin with any key.

Oliver strikes the return key. On the screen instructions appear. These he follows. Questions appear, he answers. Oliver almost laughs; the game is not so difficult as he'd expected.

Strike any key. For all keys are a single key and no single key matters.

Oliver hesitates. Which key to strike? But, of course, it does not matter—all keys, like all doors, lead to the same place.

Oliver strikes the letter O, as a capital. For *O.* means *Oliver.*

In that instant the Friendly Dog reaches out in a swift, unerring gesture of a foreleg, seizes the child by his upper body, and with a powerful wrenching snaps the child's upper spine and neck, as one might snap the vertebrae of any small mammal. There is no resistance, the child had no idea what was coming, and in the next instance the child *ceases to exist.*

The small limp body lies broken on the floor. Still warm, though no longer breathing, within seconds it is liquefied. Through vents in the wall a vacuum sucks the remains away and within thirty seconds nothing remains of the child except shreds of clothing, pieces of a sneaker, a glaring-white fragment of bone. A smashed iPad.

By the time the next *pilgrim/subject* takes a turn in the path, and discovers the Friendly Dog, these pieces of debris too have vanished.

10.

It is 12:47 p.m. The anxious mother has returned to the entrance of the labyrinth and is making a spectacle of herself, as visitors to the museum look on gravely.

Demanding again to be taken into the labyrinth by museum officials. Threatening to call the police.

But is she *absolutely certain* that her child entered the labyrinth? Yes, she is certain. Yes!

Doubt is being raised. Witnesses have been discovered who do not agree with the mother's charges. A museum guard says that he'd seen the mother with a small boy, a "sweet-faced, shy" boy with eyeglasses and a school hoodie, but not in the vicinity of the labyrinth: in the museum café.

A middle-aged man whom the woman is certain she has never seen before steps forward to volunteer that he'd definitely seen a "red-haired boy, a little mischievous scamp, ten or eleven years old" playing the Fractal Topology video game—but that had been on the first floor of the museum, at least two hours before.

Weakly the mother protests, that could not have been Oliver. There is only one Oliver, and he must be in the labyrinth, except the museum officials won't allow her to look for him, she will have no choice but to go to the police. . . .

Rehearsing how she will plead with the father—*Our son has disappeared. I have lost him. Forgive me, our son is lost in the Fractal Museum.*

11.

"Ma'am."

A kind person is pressing damp towels against her forehead. She has no idea what she looks like. In the security video her features seem to have melted, her face is a blur. She is of an unknown age: somewhere between twenty and forty. But no, she has not been twenty in a long time. Her hair is faded red, possibly it is laced prematurely with silver. Her skin is drained of blood, the redhead's pallor, an Irish complexion perhaps, freckles like splotches of rust-tinged water.

"I don't know why I am here. I'm not sure where I am. Though I have been drawn to—fractals."

This is hardly true. She isn't sure what fractals are. Something to do with—math? physics? computers?

253

"... mixed up with black holes. Gravity—events."

She has been a wife, and a mother. She has wrestled with the conundrum: inside the laundry dryer, which is a (finite) space, how can articles of clothing disappear?

If a pair of socks disappears, you do not notice. Only when one sock disappears do you notice. So possibly there are more disappearances than are perceived.

In the black hole, gravity sucks light inside. You must imagine, for you can't actually experience or measure nonbeing. Indeed, the universe may be mostly nonbeing.

She is feeling better. She has forgotten what it is she has forgotten.

Amnesia! It is a rare malaise of the spirit that amnesia cannot heal.

Strangers are whispering about her. She is both anxious to leave and yet reluctant to leave. She is desperate to flee this place of confinement yet she is wary of being excluded, expelled. She knows: if you exit the museum, there is NO REENTRY.

She has come to loathe and fear the atmosphere of the Fractal Museum, which is a constant murmur of fans, air vents, machines. A constant murmur of voices. Children's complaints, small ticking sounds like the manic heartbeats of crickets.

She hears too acutely. All of her senses are too acute.

Needs a tissue. Her nose is running, eyes leaking.

In the tote bag are receipts for many (old, recent) purchases. Two tickets to the Fractal Museum. Adult, child.

Obviously a receipt for two tickets must belong to someone else for she'd come to the museum alone. Must've fluttered into her tote bag or been given to her by mistake. She crumples the receipt and sets it aside as if it were an annoyance.

"Are you feeling better, ma'am? You are looking a little better—not so pale. Still, we should call an ambulance. . . ."

"Please don't call an ambulance!" Suddenly she is begging.

She will not sue the museum, she promises. Oh please!

Can't imagine why she is here. Whatever this place is.

It is explained to her that she is approximately two hundred and fifty miles from her home. If indeed she has come from New Haven, Connecticut, which her driver's license indicates is her home, as it has indicated that her name is Amanda.

Directions to her address by car have been printed out for her by the kindly museum staff. (As if, having gotten to the Fractal Museum, she could not simply reverse her route, to return home!)

But she is polite. She is a polite person. Trained to be polite, and by nature polite. Thanking the museum people. The woman with the *Pritt* badge. Courteous museum guards. Individuals practiced in dealing with hysterical visitors. Mothers who have lost their children. Adults who have lost their elderly parents in the Fractal Museum. Husbands who have lost their wives. Miscarriages?

A stillborn baby is not a fetus. A fetus is not a baby. A fetus has no history.

They have been very kind: they have brought her to this warm, interior room where it is quiet. She can lie undisturbed on a sofa, she can rest. For if she tries to stand too quickly the blood will drain from her head, and she will faint. It is an effort to keep her eyes open.

Gradually she becomes aware of something strange about the room. The walls. On all sides, walls that are not covered in wallpaper, or with a coat of paint, but rather with something like—could it be *skin*? Soft leather skin like the skin of a (not-yet-born) creature.

Exuding an air of warmth. Blood warmth. Thinnest of membranes, lightly freckled.

"Ma'am?"—smiling *M. W. Pritt* stands before her with tawny, shining eyes, offering a very black cup of coffee from the museum café.

12.

Days dark as Norwegian nights. Rain pelting against windows, rushing down drainpipes. The husband away and the wife, the mother, at home with the baby cuddled in her arms. Both naked.

Flesh of my flesh. Blood of my blood.

Before the birth, cells from the embryo made their way through the placenta into the very marrow of the mother's bone. After the birth, cells remain in the mother that might one day be required for the restoration of the mother's health.

How happy she is! Suffused with joy.

He'd told her *no*. That is, he'd told her *yes*.

*

Pregnannt.

No: *pregnent.*

No: *pregnant.*

Her tongue was numb. Her tongue had become a desiccated old sponge. Her tongue could not manage speech.

"Amanda, what did you say?—*preee-*"

Fear. Wariness. Caution. The (instinctive) male response.

They'd made their (his) decision. Well, it was hers (his) too.

Will you love me, she'd asked.

Will you love *me*.

He took her to the clinic. Of course—he'd driven.

Waited with her. Held her hand. He'd brought work to do. He always brought work. His eyes danced with work. His soul festered with work.

He was/was not the father. Yet.

At that age, has the fetus a soul? No.

The correct term is not "age"—I think. The terminology is weeks: how many.

The crucial thing is, you don't name them before birth. That is not a good idea.

Primitive people often do not name babies/children until they are several years old. So that if they die, the loss is not so great.

An unnamed child is not mourned as a "named" child would be mourned?

Her name was called. A name was called, beginning with *A*. *A* was unsteady on her feet, for they'd provided her with a round white pill and she had not slept the previous night nor many previous nights lapping leaden against a hard-packed shore. Her companion who was/ was not the father walked with her to the door gripping her icy hand and his eyes were damp with tears hot and hurtful as acid. Asking her yet another time if she was *all right* and what could she say but *yes of course.*

Stumbling back to his chair in the waiting room. He would wait, how long. The actual surgical procedure was not more than a few minutes. They knew: they'd researched the procedure. They were the type to (carefully, exhaustively) research all things that touched upon their lives that challenged their control.

Prep took a while. Anesthetic is recommended. Absolutely. Cervix is forced open wide with a speculum, very tender, interior of the body, best to be numb, asleep. Suction.

Oh Peter—I took a tranqizziler. Feels so funny . . .

Tran-lil-lizzer?

On the gurney, legs spread. Shoes off, in stocking feet. Naked from the waist down. Very cold, shaking. OK to keep the bra on. Otherwise, naked. Paper smock, pale green like crepe paper.

This will pinch a little. Hey—that vein just wriggled away . . .

. . . small veins. Maybe use a children's needle . . .
. . . will take twice as long. Let me try.

Suction. Suck-tion. It did not hurt, she was miles away. If there was hurt in the room it was not hers. Head was a balloon bobbing against the ceiling. Heels pressed hard against stirrups.

The vacuum sucked thirstily. The gluey remains vanished.

In the other room the distracted father was logging into his laptop.

Password, invalid. What the hell?—he types it again, alarmed. This time the screen comes alive.

* * *

In another story, the son hopes to be an architect.

"An architect is the one looking *down*, and *in*."

13.

"Ma'am? You are looking as if you have lost something."

Yes, she has. She has lost something. She laughs awkwardly for she isn't sure what.

Is it so obvious—the terrible loss in her face?

The uniformed woman is smiling at her. A smile stitched into the face. *M. W. Pritt* is the name on the plastic badge.

"He was just here with me, a few minutes ago. He—I think—went into the labyrinth . . . I suppose he must still be in the labyrinth."

It had been a child. Or an elderly white-haired gentleman with kindly eyes that would not engage with hers.

Uncertainly Amanda speaks, almost apologetically. Her heart is beating rapidly as if hoping to outrun her anxious thoughts.

He is gone gone gone. You have lost lost lost him. You are damned damned damned and this is hell hell hell.

"Ma'am—'Amanda'—I'm sure that I saw you come into the museum about an hour ago, and I'm very certain you were alone. In fact you'd come into the museum at the same time another woman came in, a woman of about your age, who had several children with her, and I'd thought at first that you were together, friends who'd brought their children to the museum together. But that wasn't the case evidently. You were alone. You are alone. You bought your ticket and you made an awkward joke about the tickets being expensive— 'for such an obscure museum.' And our ticket seller Mary Margaret said: 'Distances are deceiving in the museum, ma'am. Visitors are

257

Joyce Carol Oates

often surprised.' For some reason, you laughed at Mary Margaret's remark."

It might be her passport Amanda was afraid of losing. Many of her dreams are of losing her passport in a foreign country where she doesn't know the language. Often she'd lose her plane ticket as well.

"But—this isn't a foreign country, thank God!"

Laughing nervously. *M. W. Pritt* in boxy jacket and pleated skirt, bosom hard as armor, regards her with something beyond pity but does not join in her laughter.

"There are many variants of 'foreign,' Amanda. Some people are surprised to learn."

And: "I don't think you quite realized why you were laughing, Amanda. Sometimes it's better to think before you laugh."

That is certainly correct. Amanda has no idea why she'd laughed that morning purchasing a single, overpriced ticket for the Fractal Museum in Portland, Maine.

14.

After the Fractal Museum she will drive to Prouts Neck at the shore, to hike along the beach in a swirl of icy froth. The Atlantic has been whipped to savagery by rushing winds on this November afternoon. Scarcely is it possible to imagine another season, a warmer light—waves peacefully lapping to shore, expelling foam like harmless tongues lolling on the beach.

Perhaps this afternoon she will hike out beyond the crashing waves, beyond the seaweed-shrouded boulders. Icy waves pummeling her slight body against the hard-packed sand. The end will be swift, merciful—her (unprotected) skull cracked against a great rock puckered as if for a kiss.

But no: she has brought her small, inexpensive camera, she will take pictures of the sea, the seashore, the November sky ragged with clouds. Ocean debris, seaweed and rotted things, desiccated fish, corpses of unnamed creatures, skeletal remains like lace. When the husband sees the digital images he will squeeze her hand and say half in reproach—*You see, darling? I've always tried to encourage you. Everyone has tried to encourage you. You have an eye for beauty in the least beautiful things.*

Also: she is thrilled at the prospect of examining close up Winslow Homer drawings and paintings she has never seen before.

There is beauty, and it is outside us. Yet, it is us.

258

That is why she'd driven so far that morning, she realizes. Rising early in the dark, driving against the wind until her arms and shoulders and head ached. A purpose to her most impulsive acts, she must learn to have faith and to combat depression settling like a shroud of mist around her, through which only the sharpest and most corrosive sun rays can break.

Yet she is reluctant to leave this place. For still, after so many hours, she is in the Fractal Museum.

A warm room, if slightly airless. No windows. No security cameras. (That she can detect.) No one to observe how strangely she is drawn to the wall beside her, to what covers the wall, taut and tight as skin.

A thrill of horror comes over her. For it does seem to be—the wall's surface is neither paint nor wallpaper but a sort of membrane, a skin, soft, heartrendingly soft, exuding a barely discernible warm pulse like a living thing. It is lightly freckled, like droplets of water tinged with cinnamon, or—turmeric. . . . In wonderment she touches it— just the lightest touch, with the fingers of her right hand.

"Ma'am? We're sorry, the Fractal Museum is closing now."

Yes! Of course. It is time for her to leave.

By the rear exit with the blunt admonition EXIT: NO REENTRY.

Only one vehicle remains in the parking lot. If the key tightly gripped in her hand fits the ignition, obviously that vehicle is hers.

Built in 1890, the Westinghouse Air Brake Company General Office Building
("the Castle") recently sold for $100,000 at a sheriff's sale. Once intended for
employee recreation, the Castle is now being converted into a boutique hotel to
serve the Greater Pittsburgh area.

My Wilmerding: Wheelhouse or Runaway

Lawrence Lenhart

> *Winnipeg, Winnipeg: snowy, sleepwalking Winnipeg. My home for my entire life. I need to get out of here. I must leave it now. What if I film my way out of here? It's time for extreme measures.*
>
> —Guy Maddin, *My Winnipeg*

IN THE LOWER TURTLE CREEK VALLEY—where there are no longer turtles in the crick (for decades, I've checked), no turtle soup on its cafés' menus either—a borough surrenders its castle. On a Saturday morning, the last contents of the turreted sandstone castle are dragged onto the lawn: three chairs from the old high-school auditorium, a big drum that belonged to the Polish Falcons, and an antique Westinghouse roaster stand ("calibrated to match the temperatures in your cookbook with super-super exactness"). I drive around the Castle once, twice, a few times more. The tally ticks upward. I'm in indefinite orbit.

For years, there has been a protracted campaign to resuscitate the glory of the old castle on the hillock, which for ninety-five years served as the Westinghouse Air Brake Company General Office Building. Now, just weeks after a rash of vandalism and weeks *before* the public option, the vacancy seems to dignify the Castle. That's what I'm circling, witnessing, authenticating—its reset dignity. The Castle's clock tower, which once signaled work shifts at the nearby Air Brake factory, has become a vestigial architecture. I discontinue my circuit of bygone industry, trying not to read the "Commerce Street" signage as ironic, and drive toward the decrepit downtown, where I park outside the Dollar General.

In *Species of Spaces* (1974), Georges Perec calls the neighborhood "a familiar space [which] gives rise to an itinerary . . . a pretext for a few limp handshakes." Wilmerding's grip has often been firmer than my own. Occasionally crushing, white-knuckled. How many times I've been introduced to a "machine hand" who once worked with my grandfather at the Air Brake.

Two young girls enter the Dollar General, singles fanned out. I notice they're barefooted. Their toes flex against the tile as they do candy-bar arithmetic. "I think we can get five of this size," one says. I buy a package of pens and leave.

I begin at a four-way intersection on the other side of the creek, the westernmost point of Airbrake Avenue (just outside of Wilmerding in Turtle Creek)—a pen clipped to my notepad and tape measure clipped to the waistband of my Levi's. I've decided to measure the avenue's sidewalk cracks, the ones my father once leapt to spare his mother's back. Even though she's gone, her back now parallel and subterranean with her husband's at St. Michael's Cemetery, I keep my ear to the ground and listen for her sound as I crouch, measure, and record every breakage in the cement. This is borough forensics. I am closest to the surface across which Wilmerding's feet glide, and I am picking through all the let-go litter. By the time I arrive at Valley Laundromat (and Donut Shop), a few scant paces from my point of embarkation, I've already genuflected six times to measure the side-walk cracks (SC).

SC #1: 8¼"
SC #2: ¾"
SC #3: 1"
SC #4: 3½"
SC #5: 1"
SC #6: 1"

My methodology is wack. I ignore cracks smaller than ⅜", am prone to approximation, am not yet sure what to do about the croc-odile cracking. Am I to measure each fracture of its concrete web-bing? The first step in calculating pavement condition, according to Mahmood et al., is to "determine severity, and the extent of each dis-tress type for a pavement section." I see the houses to my left shoul-der, their paint cracking too, and remember blight can be vertical. Blight is the pall that mistakes our cities for tombs, begging us to look away.

A man balances a laundry basket on his bare shoulder as he opens the trunk of his LeBaron, parked at Pinky's Billiard Parlor. "It look like you on the chain gang," he says to me as I kneel to measure a crack just a stride away from his back left tire. "First down?" he asks, extending his arm perpendicular to his body—down "field," that is:

down Airbrake Avenue. Inside Pinky's, people are watching the second quarter of the Steelers-Niners game.

"First down," I confirm, recording *SC #7: 3¼"* and its lengthy tributary, *SC #8: 10"*. The pavement-distress density can be calculated by dividing distress length (or number of potholes) by section area. "That's it," he said. "That's the way." He fist pumps before freestyling his limbs through the armholes of a just-laundered Lawrence Timmons jersey.

I amble toward Better Feed, whose windows advertise wild birdseed, pet feed, nursery stock, hanging baskets, and bedding plants. In George Westinghouse's biography, Henry G. Prout documents the aesthetics of old Wilmerding, the forgotten project of beautification. Many years ago, the Westinghouse Air Brake Company held contests for the best gardens and lawns, making "the little town . . . a focus of taste in a commonplace and even dreary region." Among the original planned cities in America, Wilmerding was the first true company town. For the earliest decades of his life, my father lived in a "Westing" house contracted for workers of the Air Brake Company, workers like his father and his father's father.

What happens, though, when the plans are aborted, the planners deceased or dispersed? Weeks ago, Mary Comunale petitioned the Wilmerding Borough Council: "I was here last month about the house next door to me, where grass and weeds are over six inches. Nothing has been done . . . We need some help." Over the minutes, members discuss the catch basin in Lilac Alley (not working), the curbs in the business district (crumbling), and the water weeds outside of Wilmerding Beverage (need spraying). I imagine Mary Comunale, sitting on her porch, swinging beneath awning's shade as the grass grows up to her eyes. I imagine her miniaturized by the wilderness, turning pest-like. If only she went inside for the scissors, slipped her thumb knuckle past the brim of the eye ring, snuck into the neighbor's yard, and sheared.

When I was very young, my uncle explained that the men of my family—my father, his father, my father's mother's father, five "great" uncles, six once-removed cousins, and even the women during WWII—had collectively contributed over three million hours of labor to the Westinghouse Air Brake Company. "That's a minimum," he told me. Once released at shift's end, their heels clobbered the cement sidewalks, homebound.

Lawrence Lenhart

For weeks, I have been phoning Human Resources at Westinghouse Air Brake Technologies Corporation (the modern incarnation of the Air Brake), but nobody returns my calls. I leave messages, plead: "I just want to see the inside of the place. It's very important to me."

There's an apocryphal story from the 1920s in which my great-grandfather, Nick, applied for a job at the Air Brake. The manager allegedly became uninterested, even dismissive when Nick shared his Italian surname (Lenbratto). Nick was crestfallen; before leaving the factory, though, he glimpsed the roster, looking for a name near to his own. His curiosity evolved into deceit. Within a week, Nick was an employee of the Westinghouse Air Brake Company; he had returned to the factory and fibbed about his surname to a different shift manager. This is how we became Lenharts.

"Hello, it's Lawrence again. Lenhart. Will somebody please look into my previous requests?" Don't you understand? The Air Brake named me. I am a rightful pilgrim. I imagine my voice mails being played ad nauseam in the modern break room, the undersized workforce (7.5 percent of what it once was) laughing at my vibrations; in a postnostalgic town, my pleas become mawkish prattle.

Long before George Westinghouse invented the air-compressed brake (before 1868), train cars freighted through the Lower Turtle Creek Valley along the Pennsylvania Railroad to or from Pittsburgh, stopping unsteadily, jolting as the engineer quit the engine and the brakemen turned handwheels, tautening chains that forced the brake shoes against the locomotive's headlong wheels. Generally, the cars streamed through the valley toward the city. If the flag was raised at the request station, though, the train's whistle squealed as it approached a small timber dock where coal carts from the Oak Hill Mine waited to be backed onto a railroad car. The stop was known as the Joanna Wilmerding Station (after the mine owner's daughter). In time, it was shortened to Wilmerding, her name broadcast over the valley.

When the state denied Wilmerding new signs for its centennial gala in 1990, boosters financed a small-scale Hollywood-style sign constructed on the borough's hillside. This act of reactionary boosterism glamorized blue-collar W-I-L-M-E-R-D-I-N-G. After dinner each night—my tongue eroding the bits of Grandma's pork chop sticking between my teeth—we'd drive home to North Versailles, and I'd practice the borough out loud. It became the first three-syllable word I knew how to spell.

*

It starts to feel asinine, collecting these measurements (*SC #49* through *SC #56* totaling 11′, 4½″). One doesn't have to look this hard to detect the blight—the discolored awnings with cracked numbers, leaning fences, for lease/for sale signs, shuttered storefronts, and shed letters off the Sub Alpine Society marquee. Still, though, I'm striving for something more quantitative. I need a number to calm my father's speculative woe. Because it's Sunday—the few in-business businesses closed (all the welders, mechanics, and contractors saddled on barstools or nestled on couches somewhere else in Allegheny County, watching the Steelers besting the Niners (the coal rush versus the gold rush))—the streets are mostly deserted.

Eventually, I *do* see one child pushing a doll carriage on the sidewalk. Closer, I realize she's a teenager. She grips an actual stroller, its canopy closed. She swerves into the street as a courtesy. The shabby stroller swoops off the curb, scraping over a square of hot patch. The baby moans, and I apologize, though I'm not sure why.

Scores of us were born in this borough, and some of us (not me) raised by it. Hear the polyrhythmic sobbing of every generation buzzing from the carriage as if through a boom box. I feel guilty for hijacking this swath of sidewalk. I am no Wilmerdinger. Is that even the right demonym? I've likely been misusing it for years.

If I add up these cracks, I'll have summed up the parameters of neglect. I'll know exactly how our family's flight contributed to the blight surrounding me. Sometimes by taking one dramatic step "toward," I give myself permission to run states away. If first we packed our boxes and left for the suburbs, I'm now returning for the morsels in the cabinets, the cigarette burns on the rug, the moss in the grouting. With the last crumb and char and clump dropped in my pocket, there will be no reason to come back. I am finding new ways, more final ways, to vacate this borough. If I could just, as Georges Perec has claimed to do, manage to "inhabit my sheet of paper . . . invest it . . . travel across it," then I will never have to go back to Wilmerding again. It will all be here in the lignin, a static portrait that gets no worse (, no better). Hurry, before it's full-on terra nullius. Before it redeems its lottery ticket.

First, the Elvis impersonator came to the Castle on select weekends.

And for every child . . . stands a castle tall and proud . . .
the warm wind crawls through the castle walls.

Next, a registered paranormal investigator was hired to certify that
the Castle was haunted (thus began the dubious business of Wilmerding ghost tours). Finally, to pay the bills, the offices were leased to
a funeral directors' association. These harbingers of borrowed time—
the impersonator, the investigator, and the director, all coconspira-
tors in the art of the uncanny—were predictive of the Castle's mortal
future.

In its next incarnation, the Castle may be bought and converted
into a boutique hotel by the Priory Hospitality Group (PHG). In an
article in *The Pittsburgh Tribune-Review*, former Wilmerding mayor
Geraldine Homitz praised PHG President and CEO John Graf: "With
everything that people have . . . tried here, nobody else has the imagination to do what he's doing." In an article in *The Wall Street Journal*,
Graf "acknowledged that Wilmerding's charms are faded but said the
Castle, if renovated, 'creates its own destination.'" Offering billiards,
croquet, and lawn bowling, the Castle could be a venue for a "romantic weekend" in Wilmerding.

I've known *romantic* to be the verbiage of gentrification. *Romantic*: not just a word, but a lifestyle too. Think settlement movement.

Now, the bellhop's tears keep flowin'
and the desk clerk's dressed in black.

I am wary of the nostalgia industry; its guise of restoration is a
blueprint for social stratification.

Well, they've been so long on Lonely Street . . .
they'll never, ever look back . . .

What utility is there in a boutique Wilmerding? What futility?

Just take a walk down Lonely Street to the Heartbreak
Hotel.

It's halftime on the avenue, the Steelers leading 21–3. Three boys
play tackle football between hedgerows. Their field is less than ten
yards long. They notice me, and the boy with the hard plastic ball

yells, "Catch!" I catch the wobbling red football and hesitate before choosing my receiver. Two of the boys clamber in mutual defense. The third, runty looking, a shaved head and small left eye, presumes I won't be passing it to him. When I do, this jilted playmate juggles the catch before dropping it.

"What are you measuring?" the runt asks, noticing the conspicuous tape measure on my hip.

"His dick," his friend says before I can answer.

I fix my face into a compulsory frown.

The runt throws the ball to me, an underhand shovel pass. He beelines on a route, arriving at a statue of the Virgin Mary. I fling the ball, and it's another failed reception.

"Who lives here?" I ask.

They exchange looks. No one seems to know. The ball is thrown back to me. They are from Middle Avenue, also known as the Flats, but they come down to Airbrake Avenue to play football. They explain this to me as they juke indeterminately. For a moment, I forget I have the ball. It's as if they have induced hysteria, the way they dash and jitter their fingers.

"They've got all the yards down *here*," one boy says, unable to conceal his envy.

"What are you measuring?" the runt asks again. "Really."

"I'm measuring the cracks in the sidewalk," I say.

"What for?"

"Because he's a crack dealer," the jokester jokes again.

Ignoring him, I explain to the runt, "I'm on official borough business." It's unclear if he knows I'm bluffing. "I'm conducting a manual survey of the pavement. Have a good day, guys." I roll the ball from the sidewalk to their feet, and continue walking.

"On a Sunday?" the jokester yells at my back, sounding doubtful that anything "official" can happen on a Sunday. "Bull. He's measuring his dick with that tape."

With thirty-two patents to his name, perhaps Westinghouse's most significant invention was the weekend. He was the first American industrialist to inaugurate the weekend: imagine blue-collar workers crossing the Air Brake's viaduct midday on Saturday afternoons in 1869, freed from their labor to picnic with their families. Among them, my great-grandfather: released!

Two generations later, my father and his brother used to teeter on the rail of the viaduct, on the precipice of a new weekend. There, they waited for *their* father. "First, you'd see these young guys sprint out of there like they were just freed from jail," my father says. "Then, the next group, a little older, would walk out naturally. That's the group Dad was in. But if you stuck around, about five minutes later, you'd see the guys with a limp. And finally, the last ones: they moved like they had just barely made it out of there alive. That explained the whole life cycle to me."

The valley managed to maintain its attitudes toward workers' rights long after Westinghouse passed; nearly a century after the Air Brake's first weekend, The Vogues (of Turtle Creek) insisted through the blue-eyed soul of "Five O'Clock World": ". . . when the whistle blows, no one owns a piece of my time."

If the Castle has a resident ghost, let it be my paternal great-grandfather, Nick, the Italian who swapped his name for a wage.

If there's a second ghost, let it be my father's *maternal* great-grandfather, Patrick, little Irish pistol who pushed the scrap cart around the factory, scavenging the metal chippings from the floor into a bucket, wearing a skullcap with no beak, collecting union dues, but running numbers too, indebting men whose wives would soon come to collect checks to buy groceries at the A&P, checks that always weighed less than they should.

And if there's a third, making up a spectral triumvirate, let it be George himself, preparing now to topple wickets on the lawn because the people of this town play football, not croquet.

Turtle Creek empties into the Monongahela River, eddying toward Braddock, four miles west of Wilmerding. In a recent commercial depiction of Braddock, a silver train passes a campfire as a blue-eyed dog and his scruffy owner invoke urban pioneerism.

Levi's Braddock is thinly veiled poverty porn: see the decommissioned bridge and plywood windows, the abandoned car engorged by knotty vine, busted auditorium seats, and scaffolding. In *Monthly Review*, Jim Straub and Bret Liebendorfer write, "As far as scenic ruins go, the Pittsburgh metropolitan area sets a high standard. The natural beauty of the Monongahela Valley and the built legacy of deindustrialization make gorgeous scenery of blue-collar defeat."

In the commercial, a young narrator suggests, "Maybe the world breaks on purpose so we can have work to do." By framing deindustrialization as an entirely natural process, like a controlled burn in wildfire ecology, the implicit message is that blight is an acceptable form of ruination. The active voice ("world breaks") forces the consumer to retract her pointed finger ("was broken"). Maybe it's Levi Strauss & Co.'s way of making sense of the devastating economic upheaval it caused its stalwart workers following the successive closure of all its American factories.

"People think there aren't frontiers anymore," the girl narrator says. "They can't see how frontiers are all around us." The commercial ends with the camera accelerating down a quotidian street similar to Airbrake Avenue. Then, the camera takes flight—the skyward lens is Icarian—and an imperative is stamped on the screen: "GO FORTH."

If I was to make a commercial for the bygone borough, my Wilmerding, I might focus on the variant cracks—alligator cracking, block cracking, edge cracking, longitudinal cracking, transverse cracking, slippage cracking, bleeding, bumps and sags, corrugations, depressions, joint reflections, patching, potholes, rutting, swelling, weathering, and raveling—and I'd soundtrack it to pithy poetry, maybe Leonard Cohen singing "Anthem":

> Forget your perfect offering.
> There is a crack in everything.
> That's how the light gets in.

In a 1904 article in *The Wilmerding News*, a visitor to the borough pointed out that "every foot of street will have been paved [with fire brick] in the near future. All streets are sewered . . . and lighted by arc lamps." The visitor also mentioned Wilmerding had been improved by its "fine paved sidewalks." Nearly a century later, a door-to-door contractor walked the avenue, offering exclusive prices for concrete slabs. Wilmerding needed new sidewalks again, and the residents were expected to pay out-of-pocket. While some residents refused to pay for the maintenance of a public path, my grandparents—wanting to protect their home's curb appeal—added their names to the list. After the concrete was poured, my grandmother offered the $400 to the contractor. He refused her payment. In a karmic twist, the borough footed the bill only for those who were initially agreeable, those who bought in to the project of beautification.

Just a few years after these new sidewalks had dried, I pedaled my tricycle from its parking spot next to the Chevy Caprice in my grandfather's garage. I'd sail the rectangular sidewalk while my grandparents sat on the porch swing. Each time I reappeared—it took a minute or so per circuit—they'd call out a number, tallying my laps. Sometimes, when the neighbors were outside, they'd shout the number too. In *Sidewalks: Conflict and Negotiation over Public Space*, Jane Jacobs calls sidewalks "'the main public places of the city' and 'its most vital organs' . . . sites of socialization and pleasure . . . [which keep] neighborhoods safe and controlled."

I measure thirty-one sidewalk cracks, *SCs #90* through *#121* (21', 4"), on this main section, the old block where my grandparents lived and died. I used to mow my grandparents' lawn. As the yards were small, I would sometimes push the mower over the neighbors' grass as well—it was just easier that way—but my grandmother insisted I discontinue this practice. "Everybody has to keep up their own," she explained. The sidewalk, though, public *and* parochial: to whom does it belong?

To the east of my late grandparents' house, two octogenarian sisters live next door to one another. When a sidewalk crack appeared between their houses this past year, straddling their property line, the two argued over who was responsible for its repair. I stand on the property line now, the wary impasse. Sociologist Lyn H. Lofland has called sidewalks "simultaneously public and parochial—open to all and yet a space over which a group feels ownership." I peek for longer than I should, squinting at the crack in question, offering silent unsolicited arbitration.

After my grandparents' block, the measuring feels more perfunctory. At the beer distributor, Wilmerding Beverage (once a soda manufacturer that made the signature pop, Mission Orange), I see the water weeds that were mentioned in the council minutes. I yank a few so that I can properly measure the cracks from which they are sprouting—six alligator cracks, *SC #158* through *#163* (7¼").

When I check my phone, I see three missed calls from my parents. Originally from Wilmerding (1947), my father has moved farther and farther eastward—to the suburbs (1970s) and then to the newer suburbs (1990s). Before I left for his hometown this morning, he warned me that it's "gotten pretty bad. All the windows are boarded. People have just given up."

In 1904, it took ninety minutes to get from the Turtle Creek Valley to Pittsburgh on the trolley line. Now, one can reach the city limits in less than twenty minutes. Industrial boroughs like Wilmerding are necessarily dependent on the industrial centers nearest to them. From *The Wilmerding News* (1904): "Reduced orders for air brakes" or any specialty product will affect the company, and "naturally when business is slack, there is slack in the town, also."

In President Barack Obama's 2009 statement ahead of the G-20 Summit in Pittsburgh, he lauded the city for "[transforming] itself from the city of steel to a center for high-tech innovation—including green technology, education and training, and research and development . . . a beautiful backdrop and a powerful example." However, the city's transformation further abandons the outer boroughs whose works exclusively served the once hyperindustrial city. In this case, transformation looks a lot like desertion.

One of America's first company towns, Wilmerding was deindustrialized in the 1980s. The row houses pictured in this old postcard were built as Westinghouse employee housing but are now managed by absentee landlords.

After the day's long walk, 680 sidewalk cracks (collectively about a quarter of a mile in length), I park outside the house in the Flats where my father was raised, before his parents could afford the two-bedroom home on Airbrake Avenue. When I was young, I referred to it as the Westing house. It's late evening as I lower the windows and recline the car seat. My dad used to petition his parents to be allowed to sleep on the porch in the summers. In his pajamas, he'd settle into those balmy nights, rubbing his toes together in sync with the stridulating crickets.

I listen for them now, but only hear subwoofer. On that porch, a red light bulb glows. I drift to sleep, ignoring calls from my parents. They're worried that I haven't come home yet. How to explain I *am* home? They're the ones who have left.

At 1:04 a.m., I wake to laughter. I peek over the passenger window's ledge to see a young black couple climbing the stairs to the porch. Their laughter is so genuine, it becomes a self-fulfilling prophecy: I start chuckling myself. At what? I recall the ugly line in *The Wilmerding News*: "Wilmerding is fortunate in having few foreigners and negroes of a low type among its population." I hear this century-old index still ready on the tips of tongues as the eminently affordable Wilmerding is repopulated. It's hard to point the finger at the borough's real problems because they're in hiding: behold the absentee landlords of Greater Pittsburgh. No town breaks on purpose, just as no town gets fixed by accident.

As an adult, it seems unfair that I have to ask permission to sleep outside the old row house. It's almost 2 a.m. when I finally call home. "If that castle hotel was open," Dad says, "you could check yourself in."

John Graf will buy the Castle eight months later for $100,000 at a sheriff's sale. This is less than it cost to heat the Castle annually in its previous incarnation as a banquet hall. At fifty-five thousand square feet, Graf's investment will be $1.80 per square foot, or as far as commercial spaces go: only 8 percent of the national average. My father will call it the deal of the century. My godfather, "a steal." It's hard for me to really discern what is being stolen. I'll remember the last contents on the lawn, those three auditorium chairs displayed in what was once a backward-looking museum, and I'll wonder if my father once sat in the middle one, flanked by his two buddies from high school, Artie and Charlie. If these seats are permanently extracted from the borough, then where will the three young football players from Middle Avenue sit in a few years' time? Geraldine Homitz will say, in the *Pittsburgh Post-Gazette*, that the "the whole town is happy" about Graf's purchase. The businessman plans to spend up to $9 million (jackpot!) in renovations, and it is a certainty that the spirit of

Westinghouse will be invoked when the ribbon is finally cut with oversized ceremonial scissors next year.

In Pittsburgh's Schenley Park, Daniel Chester French (sculptor of the Lincoln Memorial) created a monument to George Westinghouse. A schoolboy, "The Spirit of American Youth," lingers before panels depicting Westinghouse's accomplishments. Nostalgia has the facade of a wheelhouse, but the momentum of a runaway. Months later, as we're driving through the park, I'll ask my mom to stop at the memorial. Barricaded by chain-link and orange safety fence, the memorial is green tarped, the ground around it dug up like an excavation site. I climb an oak tree to see past the oversized signage laying out plans for the "Westinghouse Memorial Restoration Project."

When I wake at 6 a.m., the red light bulb is still on. I hear a baby sobbing from inside. As I study the house, where my uncle (Baby Johnny) slept in a drawer next to my father's bed, always wailing, dying from hydrocephalus, I realize that I've only entered this house through narratives. It's a dangerous habit, constructing monuments only of the past.

This is my moratorium on the story of this house. What's the point in imagining it as it used to be? Now I think I'd like to see it as it is. I read a book about Nikola Tesla while waiting for the red bulb to go off. In 1893, Westinghouse (with the help of Tesla) underbid Edison's General Electric Company for the honor of illuminating the World's Columbian Exposition. Nearly one hundred thousand incandescent lamps were installed alongside neoclassical architecture and Frederick Law Olmsted's palatial landscaping. This world's fair was the starting line of the City Beautiful movement. From a distance, though, those in Chicago's boarding houses thought the city was on fire.

It's too reckless to worry from afar. Instead, dispatch the espirit de corps to the avenues of these boroughs whose cracks need tallying. Assume the mantle of the postnostalgic flaneur. Become an honorary Wilmerdinger. Wade through the streets. Beg for a signal. A summons. Wait for someone to finger the switch.

At some point, the light goes off. My vigil is over. I leave my car parked, tires kissing the sidewalk, and I climb the stairs to the porch as if just heading home. I hear the righteous sound of my knuckles knocking on The Door. Several hundred feet above Airbrake Avenue,

273

above Turtle Creek and the great factory, I've never before enjoyed this view of the valley. I'm waiting in Wilmerding to be let in. The man opens the door and nods before saying hello to me. We are strangers, verging on a homecoming. In that moment, with his feet inside and mine out, he is home and I am nearly so. I make my case, and he opens the door further. The Westing house swallows me home.

NOTE. Quotes in this essay about sidewalks come from Jane Jacobs and Lyn H. Lofland's writing on the subject in Anastasia Loukaitou-Sideris and Renia Ehrenfeucht's *Sidewalks: Conflict and Negotiation over Public Space* (MIT Press, 2009). Some quotations about Wilmerding come from an article, "The Ideal Home Town," found in the September 2, 1904, edition of *The Wilmerding News*, as accessed from the digital collections of the Library of Congress. This essay was developed as part of the Writing Pittsburgh project through the Creative Nonfiction Foundation.

Six Poems
Mark Irwin

MEMORY

The magnesium flare of lightning
freezing the church steeple and town. We run

and run then walk more slowly toward the statue we'll become.

The room's always cold just before dawn when the ghost appears.
His pills are little ladders where he climbed.

—Candles and sparklers on a birthday cake. Laughter. Smell of burnt
sugar and wax. The fabulous

present for each of us: sunlight penetrating wood, or so deep
into sleep's wool it resembles

cloud. Under a microscope one can detect traces of gold
in the blood.—Marveling, to push

being out of forgetfulness. The swooping head of the black swallowtail
resembles its once

caterpillar face, and where grass borders granite, a name
pooling water shines.

SHIMMER

A high-rise lobby mirror's lobbing
suited bodies back and forth while ten thousand
blue screens flicker toward a new ocean
we navigate from land, but to throw a window open
with the entire force of your body's not the same as pushing
a power button on a laptop, or a remote
electronic detonator. Watch this in your room
along with the Ilulissat Glacier melting, the portable
become monstrous illusion. Like the man watching late TV
who shoots his sleeping wife. Just a bad dream,
he tells her, then soothes her back to sleep before
shooting himself. The smoggy stars above
the city's flickering lights, fire thrown down and back, just look
from any jet and marvel at the astral makeup, a grave
of aging, prickling light.

IF

If we knew as much as the trees, the hours and miles

of sap, sun.—But how? *Listen.*—Doorway to what? Memories

gone to chalk: You and *you* into the dark but the present's

still bustling, the fringe of each second sliding through grass, or

wind hustling a plastic bag down the street as April's chlorophyll

scent builds through the rain, and there in a distant sun-stabbed

tower, someone gazes down at cloth-gusseted folk streaming

in, out—just fine, just fine—while here ants gather granules,

doming the soil. If I were an Aztec, I might understand more

this *summarium* of light building above the silhouette

of peaks and clouds like cities. Sometimes the money floats

down and no one looks up, each body a little sack of flesh.

Sometimes I need to grip the earth, or sometimes I become tall

just to see what I'll never have but will give to others.

Mark Irwin

HORIZON NOT MUCH FARTHER THAN A HOLLER

What remains unclear grows

clearer. That all this

solitude was good for

something like building a pine

from an abandoned

house's shattered boards. Look

how fast it grows in

shadow, how the pieces summon

faraway birds

carrying green needles.

—For Forrest Gander

PROGRESSION & ZIGZAG

To build a tower on the causeway, then a bridge to approach it,
and when the population triples, a tunnel beneath the river, and a high-speed
rail from the airport where the jets weigh in and out, uploading minutes,
    hours, emblazing

the nights, debriding them, our sleep with thousand-beacons
                    till it's no longer late or early.

If we could only hear the night sooner, then the breathing darkness might seem
possible, and all the *tos* and *froms* would seem like swallows'
                    veering paths,

something fast and slow at once as the dusk light pours continually through
    glass.

LANDLINE

Please, I wanted you to hear me. Please, the character
of each word like touching the chains of a swing after
a son has gone. Please, sit down. It's about someone
close to you, the river's engravure, the dug-in trees. Please, are
you sitting down? The gravitas of houses at dusk, or imagine
a panther asleep. You sound so close. Yes, I'm sorry. They
found him in his apartment. No, there's no static. We once made
a fence of sticks and I remember mooring the boat, tying
a wet shoe, and yes, his horse hitched, that skittish mare. Funny how
as you get older there's less to hold on to. Did you know
there's a seed vault tunneled in a mountain on the Svalbard archipelago?—No
microwave frequency interference. The seeds are sealed in special four-ply
heat-sealed plastic, and the entrance is lit up with highly reflective
stainless-steel art so we can find it. Yes, finally each is left
with his or her own energy. I've been reading about orphaned
stars, which makes me still thankful for the grid of utility
lines. *Yes*, facedown in the tub. Today, I almost wept for the minutes
to pass. Birds darken the wires during these times when the trees are less.

How It's Gone and Done
Justin Noga

I BUILD MY FIRST HOUSE. It would've been home to flowers and birds and a lone antelope, a home alive with the promise of a harmony that exists across nature—but then Anton comes by. Anton, he blinds all the birds, pricking out their eyes with knitting needles. The antelope he rides into a crevasse, bailing before the burst of flesh and bone. And then all I have left is the house I was asked to build for us, bloodied birds writhing in the sunshine, cracking against the siding.

"Will you at least help me clean up?" I ask Anton.

But he's singing scales by the pin oaks now, and has already forgotten. I prod him, frown in a way that shows teeth. One look at me, he sniffs and says, "B-but our mother said—," and lets the silence speak for itself.

The second house I get halfway through before Anton tells me his worldview. When he's done, it is as if Anton has swallowed the sun.

"You see," he says, "that's why it's always pink."

The terror I feel seeps into the drywall, the carpet tacks. I can barely keep my hammer straight.

Anton sees an opportunity and lights a fire and follows the fire to the house. In the ashes he makes a kind of wrestling pit for him to wrestle mud crabs. Soon Anton tires of the mud crabs. In the evening, he puts a loose tarp over the pit, fashioning it into something he calls a rub-off tent. "Mom would've wanted a house with more panache," he says, stroking off onto a mud crab. "Think on it."

I skip the third house to try a fence, just a goddamn fence. Four fingers lost in the first hour.

Anton finds my pile of fingers behind a bush cooling in a bucket. Three go in his pocket, and the pinkie he hollows out to tootle on like a limp kazoo. He glances at the fence, goes back to the kazoo.

281

"I can never get these things right," he says, blowing, blowing. "But Mom said it was always about focus, you follow?"

Scratching at my nubs, I don't follow.

"Jeez, she never told you that, Henry? I'll be damned." After he gnaws the nail down to the cuticle, the kazoo finally sounds off. Anton gives me a big smile.

All night I watch the mangled fence from my bedroll by the creek, and think. A mud crab spackled with Anton's seed clacks by, claws at my toes.

Anton says he's taken some time off to think about Mom being dead and just wants to watch me at work. "Just don't think about how she's dead, OK? Skip it entirely. I'll do the thinking for us, about her being dead, about her saying you're in charge."

To be a good sport, he massages my shoulders as I make the starter cuts.

This fourth house I try to improvise so Anton won't presume its function and make off with its parts before I'm done. In his deep-tissue technique I can feel him trying to unlock my head, parsing the thought before the action.

Anton, by noon that day, has rubbed my shoulders for six hours. Every time I shake him he clamps back on.

"You're doing good, buddy," he says. "Real good."

As the days drag on, the shoulder muscles stay loose but the skin's worn and blistered. "Just keep going," he says. "Don't prove our dead mother wrong. God, think of the look on her face if you did. I mean the look then, when she was alive, not now, rotting in the dirt."

In the end, it's a house wormed with wires and holes and it forms a shape that, when Anton tips his head to it, I can only say, "Well, it's not supposed to . . ."

"You beefed it, buddy." And he stops the massage. Leaving for his rub-off tent, he smells his fingertips, intrigued.

Pocking the land are these houses I'm supposed to build for my older brother and me now that we're on our own, and Anton points to a tree.

"OK," he says. "Watch me be all casual."

He hacks at it with a bow saw, and it becomes a live weeping tree, arms and eyelids, wispy curves. Birds congregate in its hair.

"My mother," the tree says, and cracks at the base from its own terror.

Handing me back the bow saw, he says, "OK, now you try, Henry. Do it from the pink."

Anton watches me at the fifth house, where I keep it tight and true.

Little box: One door. One window. One lamp.

As I admire my work, my knee slips at the doorjamb. I feel the stringy snap of something complex and inoperable. Lump it in with shredded feet, the herniated discs, the egg-white effluvia leaking from my nubs. Yet through it all the house stands proud in the light.

Anton gives the house an up-and-down. "You think Mom would've built something like that if she were alive?" He points to a catalog, page two. "Look, you can just order it here." Then he's off to his weeping tree with the mother issues. It has a wound, and he pokes at the wound.

Yells back over: "Mom said always give it a little life. A little life and a little zing."

House six, I weep in a ball at Anton's feet and beg him to teach me what Mom never taught me. "I can see it all in my mind—all the wires, all the screws—but it's like my fingers have their own shit logic they're following. I want Mom to be proud. I want you to be proud."

Anton looks down at me. "Sheesh, way to get me to feel the exact opposite." He's smiling, though, lifting me, dabbing my eyes with his sleeve. "OK, fine," he says. We bear hug, thinning ribs on thinning ribs. "Just pay attention this time, you fucking baby."

House six goes up like a dream. Side by side, we're climbing scaffolding like in the days when Mom was alive. I think of her in the other room calling me for nails and wood, for ideas and takes, and Anton no longer in the basement with the piping but here, now, boosting me onto the planking. How to sand an edge. How to see the micro for the macro.

We finish and do shots on the carpet in the foyer. We joke. I give him my spare bathrobe. "This is nice," I say. "This is really so nice. I never thought I could do it."

"I?" He scratches his head.

"Aye-aye," and I click my heels and salute the work.

Anton, as I haul myself half drunk up the stairs to the master bedroom, he hangs out on the staircase looking at all the old family pictures I mounted.

The moon has crawled away when smoke trickles into my room. The only light's from the fire chewing at my floor, rolling up the sheets I've tangled myself in.

Outside, Anton's pacing around the yard. I want to ask what happened but I know what happened. This is what he did to our old house after Mom died. Back then he said he'd love to see what I'd do with my own vision.

And now he balls up his bathrobe for the fire, tossing it in with the lawn whimsies.

"You think you tricked me, don't you?" There are tears in his eyes.

"When did I ever trick you?"

"I'm just here for the grunt work, aren't I? I know what you two talked about. You the brains? Me the helper mule? You tricked her, and now you think you've tricked me."

I just slump against a tree. Anton spends the night feeding our house to the flames. Two-by-fours and a mailbox, clumps of grass and a plum tree—they all bounce into the flames like sheep to dream to, sheep that snap awake in the pyre.

The next day Anton's wandering around in the raw, combing his chest hair with my lost fingers. Smirking at House Four. Grimacing at House Two. Sometimes he sticks leaves to his naked body, and if I catch his stare he peels them off to give me a looky-loo.

We keep our distance.

Across the way from the smoldering house I start anew. I go slow and rejigger until it's time to show Anton. I feel like a newborn turtle, fresh from the egg and racing to the sea before the gulls catch me. I call Anton over, and he goes, "Again with this cookie-cutter shit, Henry?" I can see him seeing me from above, circling.

"Why not give it a looky-loo? I added something Mom showed me."

"Mom never showed you anything."

"No, really, go ahead," I tell him, retracting chin to chest.

And Anton goes into the house. The flooring gives. He drops fifty feet into a long cone I dug out, his legs twining together at the base like ribbon stuffed into a stiletto toe. Mom loved stilettos.

"Poor planning," he yells up. "It's not baked into the design."

I bring in the rocks. Dangling my legs over the edge, I look in and let the rocks tumble down. Rocks can only be dodged so much. He says he gets it, he gets it. He says, "Way to beat that dead horse. Mom would be so proud."

I hold a rock up, and he says he's kidding, he's kidding.

"But really," he says, and whinnies up through the cone.

I use sandstones. I like how they clap together.

You can picnic atop the filled-in cone to the rhythm of settling rocks, and I do. Waffles, bacon—the full English. After a nap, I stretch oak flooring across the pit, and decide to build a new house over the cone-floored house.

When I'm done, I walk inside the redesign and hear Anton wheezing under the floorboards. He asks, "Got a good paint job at least?"

"You'll see, my friend."

"Friend?" He coughs something out I swear I can taste. "Not good to start a house on a lie."

He sounds parched so I smash a hole in the floor and piss into the cone. I hum him a little ditty while I connect the cone to the chimney. This is the way Anton can hear the new world I create.

"Did you know Mom loved my humming too?" I ask.

The creek goes by and the windows rattle, and I know this silence means, "Of course, buddy, of course. Keep it coming."

This new house has a door and a roof and a little tilt to the chimney I can say is my own stylistic fingerprint instead of the mortar I over-mixed. The house is painted the color of a shining liver. Less and less do I hear Anton echoing up the chimney—no shifting stones, no whispering.

I feel a tug of the heart.

I go to the weeping tree, dry its tears, tell it a joke.

"Oh, you're such a rag," it sniffs.

"You saucy flirt, you know what you do to me."

We bed together. In the woods, in the tent, on my roof beneath the bright moon. The birds in its hair fly off for dwellings less voracious. But I have trouble sleeping. Into the chimney I whisper, "Anton, Anton," but nothing comes out. I piss into the chimney and put an ear to the trickle.

The tree wakes up, and soon our hands are all over each other's wounds.

"Bray for me," I say. "It gets my blood up."

"Like this, Henry?" The tree tries to bray, but I have to shush it.

"Goddamn it," I say. I am staying calm. I am staying professional. "For once in your life use at least half your ass, OK? Pay the fuck attention." I bray loud and long and I can feel my blood shoot up into the unknown. It's sunrise, and I'm still presenting tone and tenor and the sweet subtleties of my own musicality.

Pushing in a loose shingle, the tree says, "OK. Got it. Let me try."

I look at the tree, and I know I haven't gotten through. "You're still gonna beef it. Listen again, OK? You never listen right."

Anton, Anton, I wish you could see how my house is now, how it is I do this alone.

Reconciliation Story
Karen Hays

ONE DAY WHEN YOU WERE in preschool your mom took you to a craft fair at a pavilion with a roof shaped like a pyramid. The pyramid was similar to the Louvre's except its ceiling was clad with acoustic panels instead of glass, and rather than shelter the lobby of a world-class art institution, its use was contracted out by the local old folks' village, an enclave that grew like arterial plaque at the atrophied heart of your hometown, a suburb whose metastatic sprawl was well on its way toward gobbling up all of the Civil War landmarks and green, karstic topography your father remembered so fondly and so well.

When he saw the new developments with their monochromatic box houses, treeless sod, and cul-de-sacs shaped like empty thought bubbles or defective light bulbs, your father pined for the spacious austerity and neighborly self-reliance of his own childhood, for netting paddlefish and shooting quail and smothering biscuits with preserves made from stone fruits his or some nearby family grew and picked and blanched and put up themselves. A home ought to shelter you from the wide wilderness of the nighttime, not spare you from the sight and eyes of strangers who scurry between hidey-holes like crawdads. No. When he saw what your hometown was turning into, and in how hell-bent a fashion, its artless growth and deluded independence from the land, your father itched in a big, forevermore way for elbow grease and elbow room.

Back when you were a kid, your parents were what you were made of and yours held polarized views of the world. For your dad, better was a condition that predeceased you; for your mom, better was the future you were finally and doggedly on your way to. The space in between their counterpoints was the time line whereon you and your sister dwelled, like a shot at the center of a sling, momentum vectoring out in both directions. Maybe that's why it was a relief to you when the tension between them firmed into something real and geographic, when it turned out that between your mom and dad there existed a no-kid's-land that couldn't be entered so much as squarely circumnavigated, but only in your dad's car and only on every other weekend. That's when he shuttled you back and forth between the little house he mortgaged with your mom and the five places he lived before finding an ear of land he could piss on whenever the urge struck him, a damp curl of floodplain where, an hour or two after the sun wheeled down the cicadas and spun up the mosquitoes, it was sometimes quiet enough to hear the peristaltic squelch of night crawlers extruding themselves for their mysterious moonlit adventures, by which point you were old and spoiled enough to traverse between points M and D all by yourself.

Until such time as you had wheels of your own, however, your dad picked you and your sister up two Fridays out of every four, returning you two days later to the town whose most memorable building from the road was a multipurpose pyramid, your dirty laundry slung over your shoulders and a too-precious child-support check cupped into one of your palms. Your dad folded the check down the middle to protect you from knowing the financial cost of your growth, the paper sweet with his unsmoked tobacco and astringent with the ink of his felt-tip, the dyslexic 2s and 5s drafted carefully and without a single curve and often in red, like the numerals on the bombs whose explosions were always imminent on television. Your body was a temple. You were what you ate. Your parents loved you, each in their own separate ways. In the middle of crises, a tiny winged cow poured so much milk into each Kraft Single that if you consumed enough of them you were sure to fossilize yourself alive and therefore not slouch or break when, at some unfathomable point in the future, you had the tragic misfortune of looking into the mirror and finding there the reflection of an old person, some cloudy-eyed lady whom you would've never known back then but who, looking back, would always, always know you. Even when she remembered very few others. Even when she remembered very little else. *Here is the church*, you used to think, attempting to stand the child-support check upright on your mother's dining-room table. *Here is the steeple. Open the doors and . . .*

One day when you were in preschool your mom bought you a necklace in the pavilion whose roof was shaped like a pyramid. The pyramid was similar to the one in the picture of your grandmother wearing that red hibiscus behind her ear, except its exterior was made of ordinary roofing materials instead of stone, and rather than travel to it by Mexican tour bus, you rode past it countless times in your mom's car on the way to and from the dance studio where, for entirely compul-sory reasons, you took tap, jazz, and ballet lessons, never once with cause to stop and enter whichever of the pyramid's giant leaning tri-angles harbored a door. Until the day of the craft fair, the old folks' pavilion was a shape you could occlude with your palm or frame between thumbs and forefingers against the car window.

Your mom would've had a cow had she known that weekends he had to work, your dad trusted you to your own devices in his car or alone in the closed lawn-mower shop. In the parking lot you sat in your winter coat reading library books about a girl who rode dolphins in water of a shade that would not submit to your crayons. You twid-dled your favorite necklace as you read and meted out the car's bat-tery life by only checking for good songs between chapters and during slow sections. First your toes succumbed to prickles and then to a stony numbness. When it drizzled or rained, you lifted your head from the glass to stare at the rivulets through the clear spot your hair had mopped in the condensation. Alone in the car, your bodily and social hungers sublimated into appetites that could be satisfied with the nullity of the written word, while somewhere outside—in a whole other realm—your sister helped your dad and uncle by fetching ciga-rettes, passing wrenches, and pressing some ailing engine's gas pedal on cue.

In the lawn-mower shop, its lights off and heat lowered, the two of you sat on the riding mowers, either pretending by bouncing up and down on their seats that you were driving or pretending by talking in manly, grinning voices that you were salesmen—imaginative dead ends both. Sometimes one of you dared the other to Frogger her little body across the busy road and into the taco shop with the empty parking lot and the ten-gallon hat on its roof, its cowboy lights blink-ing in parallel like a Venus flytrap and a drunken landing strip, but neither of you had the taco money to make the treachery or risk to life and limb worth it. Sometimes you upended the empty paint bucket in the bathroom and stood on it to reach the vertiginous stack of porn perched on the plywood plank nailed over the toilet. Some-times you stood in front of the black, sweet-smelling sink and ex-truded the longest strand of vermicelli that the greasy soap could hold before breaking from the dispenser and coming to rest in a white turd-like coil below the faucet.

The most disturbing thing about the porn was not the orange women who beckoned like the taco joint that you smelled and surveilled from the lawn-mower shop's darkened storefront, but the metaphors

289

and lies of specificity in its captions. The fake names, fake want, and all the animal-vegetable-mineral euphemisms. The failure of its presumptuous second-person pronouns to jibe with its readers in that particular bathroom in those particular moments. Your body was a temple. You were what you ate. Someday when you were a big girl a man might mistake you for a cat named Candy or even a piece of food on a plate. Was that the secret the big, smug adult world was trying to keep? If a woman lying on her back makes a peace sign with her bare legs, what does a woman standing on her own two feet make? In more years than you could comprehend, you would graduate from high school in the RLDS conch just a few blocks down the street, the church's molluscan spire jutting heavenward as if some temperamental god had reached down and given a warning tug to its navel, its internal spiral so nacre slick and steep in its state of unravel that you'd barely be able to navigate it in the pumps your mom would loan you for the occasion. In the auditorium you and your classmates would sweat and answer to the names that your parents felt would give you the best shot in life, even if they weren't the names you went by. You would graduate in a town called Independence because no venue in your suburb would be big enough to hold you all. Though your father would decline to attend, your mother's father, who refused to attend her graduation thirty years before, would be there, and he would cry and tell you that you looked pretty as you sweated and teetered and clung to the rail to maintain your balance in the heels. His tears would reveal a bit of what your growth cost him, the egg of you tucked away inside his own daughter while she was still a mystery curled in the salt of his wife's wild womb. Everything, cocooned. Everything, sheltered. *Here is the church. Here, the steeple.*

On the day your mom bought you your favorite necklace, your sister had a dance recital inside the pavilion whose roof was shaped like a pyramid. The pyramid was nothing like the one on the green butterflies your mother teased from her wallet to buy you that little necklace. Those were crowned with all-seeing eyes while the one in your hometown appeared blind or else simply more introverted, its dull opacity swallowing light rather than emitting it. Your hometown pyramid was an inanimate fixture in your life and yet your feelings toward it were ineffable and complicated. The pyramid felt like your best impersonation of a grown-up—a pairing of grandiose and boring affectations, at once jokey and too self-serious. It tempted but without much promise, like a dome your grandmother might lift from the table when it was OK to tuck into the ziggurat of divinity and fudge she'd assembled for a holiday gathering, which desserts you were never particularly fond of and which party you were as likely as not to vomit after. On the day of the dance recital, your sister was recovering from strep throat, and your mother was hoping against the odds that you would not succumb as well.

When one of you was sick, suffering was the cause as well as the result of your separation. The rest of the time, suffering was merely the result. Yours, mostly. That's because as different as your parents were from each other, your sister occasionally was from you. You hated how readily she dissolved into her group of friends, how instantly your pairing lost its significance when a new opportunity arose. You even sometimes hated the girls. They tittered and flitted about like the sparrows that swooped around gathering up crumbs at the con-cessions area of the municipal pool. Conspiratorial and ornery and impossible to catch up with, they left you to trail lamely after your mother instead. The older girls were reckless with their estranging perfection—cruel, you felt—and your heart would've had room for nothing more than a green, stalwart desire to fall into their fold at any given moment, at *that* given moment even, if it weren't for the deep, toothed gullet they were doomed to perform in.

Did you have any idea before that day? That a pyramid to the ground is a square? Or that a pyramid, like a tree with hidden roots, might actually only constitute the upper half of a submerged diamond? Stepping inside, it became immediately clear to you that things were not at all as they had seemed from the road. The perimeter of the pyramid was lined with card tables where locals were peddling their homemade jewelry, candles, pot holders, and paintings, and the center was carved into a theater as deep and cavernous and spotlit as you felt your very own groaning belly was. At the bottom of the pit was the bright platform whereon your sister and the rest of her tap class, composed of a dozen or so six- and seven-year-olds who were just then patting their sprayed hairstyles and plucking nylon leotards from their rear ends, would perfunctorily execute their shuffle-ball-change routines. Meanwhile a troupe of girls who waited in posed silence on the stage looked like a bunch of sparkly stalagmites whom the music would magically animate, the pyramid's providential eye beaming upward—*beaming upward*—at them. When your mother turned from one of the card tables and held up a necklace for you to reject or ap-prove, you stood at the exact interface between the upside down and

291

the right side up, your stomach articulating in lurches what your mind could not in words. The portion of the pavilion accessible to your body was the geometric reflection of what your eyes had sized up from the road, the bright, belowground spotlight echoing its dark, aboveground apex—the latter open to the sky, the former enclosed as a basement.

Nothing you'd seen before had prepared you for the space that was at once light and tomb-like, expansive yet crushing. Where you grew up there were no mountains and what you knew of real caves you gathered from the billboards and drippy limestone roadcuts you blew past on the highway. How unto yourself you felt in the back seat, and how invulnerable. How easy it was to confuse insularity with safety when what physically encapsulated you sealed your mind off as well, a trusted parent behind the wheel. You moved through the geography of your life as if the scenery were composed of giant vertical canvases that time whisked away as you approached with gaze outstretched, like an inexhaustible stack of tablecloths yanked out from beneath a handful of fixed landmarks and celestial objects, or a flip-book whose pages the wind sheared off before you had a chance to fathom their individual illustrations. A magic trick. A dozen or so years would pass before you'd clap eyes on your first etching by M. C. Escher. You'd be sitting in the top tier of the recessed amphitheater of your high school's art room when your teacher would project the maze of gray scale stairs onto the screen below you. The image would be new to you, but the queasy feeling of walking on the ceiling would be one you would instantly recognize from navigating the plunging aisles of the inverted pyramid. Your fingers would search in your jugular notch for the plastic bead on the blue woven cord, the necklace by then a choker. On both sides of the bead, a wan blue rose would still have the same old second thoughts about blooming. Your hair would still catch in the clasp that unscrewed like a miniature metal version of the barrel you once kept your plastic monkeys in. The bead would still keep its cool in your jewelry box but assume your body temperature just as soon as you put it on, matching you, like a proxy or a good friend. You would still receive compliments on how the bead's design echoed your own color scheme, as if it were your third eye and not a plastic bauble on a string. The only difference in the necklace that day would be its numbing accrual of associations, a cloud that the memory of the pyramid would swiftly burn away. Perhaps the old folks' pavilion became surrealistically ingrained in your mind because you were on the febrile edge of your sister's strep throat on the day that you entered it. Or perhaps a sickly, giddy sensation in-sinuated itself through your eyes that day, like a kind of mnemonic virus, and stayed there until the conditions were just right for it to resurface, reuniting the necklace with its source, and you with yours, to each her own duality, no one as simple as her outward appearance or reducible to the sum of her parts. If memory obeys the laws of nat-ural selection, then the stories that survive in you are also the most adaptable and therefore the ones you ought to trust the least and for-give the most. It stands to reason that each retelling is a distortion as well as a distillation. A reminder as well as an act of defiance. Equally true and false. *Art doesn't grow wider*, said Degas, whose pirouetting girls you wouldn't meet until college, *it recapitulates*. How many times in one day do you find yourself standing in a room confused about your path and purpose for being there? How does your mind look to you when you need to talk with your teenaged son about the plastic disc-shaped thing he keeps getting stuck on the roof of his high school and the only word you can think of to recall that way-ward flying object to his mind is wrong, is *zebra*? Your exterior voice repeating *zebra* and your interior voice, the you who speaks beneath the I, screeching like locked tires on asphalt, split thoughts careen-ing within the frame of your mental collage, your son laughing as he corrects you, *Close, Mom, close,* and making you laugh too, blessed-ly dowsing that subterranean caterwaul?

Suffering has a way of inserting itself between you and the ones you love and throwing out its elbows, whether as the initial cause or the growing effect of your separation. Whether as the germ or the fruit of human sickness. Once or sometimes twice a year your father, sister, and you converge in three cars in the parking lot shared by your grandmother's apartment and the old folks' pyramid, your dad from his house on the floodplain, your sister from her home in the moun-tains three states away, and you from the seaside town in California where you landed after a journey of a couple decades.

    Sometimes your grandma still makes fudge, but divinity you haven't seen since you were a kid. Often you picture her with that red hibiscus in her hair, or smoking cigars with your dad at your wedding. She introduced you to Georgia O'Keeffe and Joyce Carol Oates when you were a kid—the latter introduction scandalizing your mother—and still jokingly refers to the local library as the *Incon-tinent* rather than the *Midcontinent*. She's the only other reader in your family. You, the first to graduate from college. She complains about how the most recent expansion of the old folks' village has led to the neglect of her older, lower-rent unit, same as its development once led to the neglect of another less lucrative set of residences. Life's conveyor is unrelenting even at the margins. The enclave has apartments, an assisted-living facility, a nursing home, and hospice care, but the apartments are the only dwellings that seem to keep expanding in count and grandeur and scale. Your grandma's apartment is luxurious with the scents of cumin and lentil soup and potting soil and roses. The theme of the art on her walls is maritime. After almost a century, she's seen enough to weigh in on whether it's better for your mind to go first or your body. After almost a century, she's sharp enough to weigh in on pretty much everything, her edges well stropped on her fellow residents, many of whom she finds too preachy or conservative. For the few hours you're all together each year, the conversation crackles with politics in various states of ventilation. The time reminds you how easy it is to confuse insularity with safety when what physically encapsulates a person seals his or her brain off too.

On the Sunday drives back to your mom's house, your dad used to adopt a style of reminiscence that excluded narrative, as if the grief it failed to disguise was inarticulable or possibly even metaphorical. Often he pointed out changes to the landscape as he drove you and your sister back to the tidy little house where you girls and your mother still lived, your hair, skin, clothes, and sleeping bags reeking of the smoke your mom deplored but was too dignified to complain about in your presence. *This used to be wooded,* he would say, his elbow straightening from its crook to point out the window, a cigar jutting from his peace sign like the middle finger your uncle lost to a saw when he was a kid fresh out of high school, the cigar's cauterized end underscoring the need of some injuries to smolder and to do it in plain sight if not a place of high honor. *This here, a farm.*

In the car, your dad used to indicate the whereabouts of the bloody skirmishes between the Confederate bushwhackers and Union Jayhawkers, and tell you which prominences were named after which brutish guerrillas, overlaying your view with a taxonomy you neither understood nor cared much about back then. Myopia wrapped itself like a well-meaning hug around the entire protected span of your childhood, depriving geography of history and history of relevance. You were a girl first and a child second—too young and saturated in your culture to articulate all the sides of otherness your body

294

tumbled on, your gender imparting a palpably gross lowliness, your skin color a palpably gross privilege. The effect of your dad's captioning was not to crack your insularity but to lend suspicion to the flip-book his car made of the land. Entering the pyramid on the day of your sister's dance recital, repeatedly losing her affections, nestling into the fissures of your mother's heart, reading porn in the bathroom of the lawn-mower shop, receiving your dad's terse auto tours on Sunday afternoon drives into the suburbs—each had the unsettling effect of expanding the world from the x-y plane into some other more dangerous dimension, hinting at a whole new set of swallowing and burying prepositions, an *over*, an *under*, a *through*. *Around* began to seem less and less like an option. Nothing could witness what this land had seen and remain so passive, so forgiving, so self-contained. At some point you started to think of the earth as some kind of anesthetized animal and not a drippy old hunk of dissolving craton. You imagined it mammalian, its fur thin at the knuckles and shaggy where little creeks forded its resting haunches, uncombed prairie rising in tufts between its gentle undulations, limning the ditches, bristling at the tree lines. You imagined the land genderless and deceptively dormant, but unquestionably alive. You pictured it storing history beneath the strip malls, the housing developments, and the traversable mesh of tic-tac-toe grids whereon you were precisely nowhere and therefore precisely no one, also unquestionably alive. You tasked the land with remembering everything your dad was afraid the world would forget, because you weren't up for the job yet and might never be. You grew and imagined and played optical games within the frame of the window, unable to zoom out enough to surveil your own context or voluntarily merge with a reality that was any more threatening. Now you imagine the countryside rehearsing stories like a baby songbird practicing its father's notes in its sleep. You picture the land dispersing enmity through no malice of its own, silently and indirectly, via the blood seeped into its aquifers and the ash turning to clay in its humus. You imagine fear and suspicion making their way up the food chain, decaying with some long and incalculable half-life in the steeples of bodies, towns, and states. Once, you were what you ate. Your body was a temple. Open the doors and there you all were, all of you, all of your land's people.

After your annual or sometimes biannual visits with your dad and grandma, you and your sister, each with her sons and secrets and fissured hearts in tow, return to the countryside where your mother and stepfather have happily retired, in the same county where Jesse James and his Quantrill's Raiders once planned their cross-border ambushes. After their 1863 massacre left a couple hundred abolition-ist boys and men dead in Lawrence, Kansas, Union General Ewing attempted to flush the county of Confederate bandits by ordering the area depopulated and torched—its livestock shot, its grain confis-cated, its crops incinerated. Almost a century and a half later, the county's historical society put on a fund-raising raffle in which a local jewelry store distributed guns to lucky ticket holders at the rate of one per week. 52 GUNS IN 52 WEEKS, the waving banners read. Your kids love visiting their grandparents but a part of you is hell-bent on dividing the past from the future, as if geography were a cure and not a buffer. Like your dad after he split, you moved and you moved and you moved, each time stretching the distance between your worlds a little farther, tighter, like a rubber band between the tines of a sling. On the drive back to your mom's, through the sod farms and dairy pastures, up the gravel road and past the pear tree swaddled in the cotton candy that spells tent worms, you try to impart some of the regional history to your kids, though the stories they most want to hear are your own. *The ambushers and the ambushed, don't you see, they were just your age,* you say. There's no question your kids are troubled about what they see on the news these days— your oldest wants to move to Canada and your youngest wants California to secede—but you feel it's important to pair their recent loss of innocence with the ancient loss of the country's. *A real suck cycle,* is how one of them summarized the content of this inter-minable history lesson, signaling he gets it and needs to move on to something more pleasant. When you reach your destination, your mother, in whose face you are getting better and better at recog-nizing yourself, asks, once again and therefore incomprehensibly, whether you had a nice visit with your dad. After the grown-ups go in, the kids stay outside among the frogs and mockingbirds and mud-bugs, throwing the zebra around in the field. Smarter than you, your oldest son is teaching himself Latin; he knows that *pavilion* derives from *papilio*, for *butterfly*, or *tent*, and as such there is something obscurely redundant and funny in *tent worms*, since tent worms are really caterpillars. Maybe one day you will tell him and his little brother about the time when you were in preschool and their grand-mother took you to a craft fair at that dumpy old pavilion they've ridden past countless times, the one whose roof is shaped like a pyramid, but whose form is really a diamond. Looking at their two reflections, you swear you will always know your kids, have in fact known them your whole life. Looking into their faces, what choice do you have but to believe with all your heart? Better is a future you're stubbornly marching toward.

The House That Jack Built
John Madera

THIS IS THE HOUSE that Jack built, an "existential reflection," as she'd have it, its frame and foundation made of earth-packed rubber tires, the driveway itself made of rubberized asphalt, the crumb rubber and concrete amalgam a noise reducer, the jalopy, whenever it left the garage, which was rare, making nary a sound as it rolled along the long driveway, Jack preferring to walk whenever she went somewhere, which wasn't often, not if she could help it, she'd say, or think—she wasn't sure anymore—and what did it matter, since there wasn't anyone to overhear, the days when students came over long over, Jack hating the university's classrooms, those "claustrophobia-causing boxes" with their "sullen walls," thin photovoltaic panels set within her house's load-bearing walls, which she considered dermal, bark-like, the house rarely receiving visitors of any kind nowadays, the busybody next door occasionally "popping in," notwithstanding, he, former rat racer, actually enjoying Jack's delivering lecture snippets about building and dwelling, about how the body "inscribes space," she referencing Mali's Dogon society's houses and settlements' esoteric anthropomorphisms; Carlo Mollino's *guêpière*-garbed voluptuary's torso-inspired Teatro Regio in Turin; Santiago Calatrava's *L'Hemisfèric*, that "ever-discerning eyeball"; Frank Gehry's *Dancing House*—"Fred and Ginger's swerve, elegance, and élan rendered in steel and glass"—said minilectures invariably landing on the door-step of *Womanhouse*, Judy Chicago and Miriam Schapiro's famed feminist installation and performance space, Jack sometimes tangentially referring to "Edith's House," a 108-year-old farmhouse, its eponymous owner a real estate holdout, who'd famously rejected hundreds of thousands of dollars to allow her house to be torn down to make room for a five-story commercial monstrosity—"But what about the red house over yonder?" the neighbor would ask. "Way back yonder 'cross the hill?" Jack would respond.

*

298

This is the desert surrounding the sustainable house that Jack built, no grim wasteland but a smeary palette of raw and burnt umber, whimsically shaped cacti standing in clumps, their arms prayerfully upraised, mountains in the distance jutting out from the sandy expanse, she having moved there decades ago, away from "the megalopolis and its sky-pricking phalluses," its concession-cart hot dogs marinating in tepid water, its rock pigeon shit smearing down windshields, etcetera, etcetera, the comparative silence of the sandy surroundings conducive to her work, the house a sanctum sanctorum, a space where Jack could design zones free of binaries, essentialisms, fixed taxonomies, and "all those other hang-ups," where Jack would work, work, work, her skin tinctured pink by the sun, her granitic hands sweeping across toothy vellum, drawing lines, erasing lines, Jack shifting her head, squinting, drawing again, erasing again, her graphite-blackened palm brushing away gray eraser fibers, Jack drawing again, her marks a crosshatched nest, a net capturing volume, light, and space, Jack always wanting something beyond marks on a page, beyond art—"the map isn't the landscape," she'd say—but there was something missing, always some *thing* missing, thus always this obsessive searching, where lines situated forms in space, thus these explorations, delineations of the "where" where every *thing* is related to everything else, thus these lines, through lines, searching lines—a line a dot out for a walk, as Klee said—lines and lines and lines, relentless whorls, linear "excavations," like Rodin's turbulent surfaces—where, as Rilke said, "nothing necessary was lacking"—Jack drawing and erasing until she ripped a hole in the paper, whereupon she'd laugh, a "queer divine dissatisfaction," as Martha Graham would say, settling upon her.

This is the window overlooking the desert surrounding the house—a meditation on wall and floor and roof—that Jack built, a massive circle of glass overlaying a massive square of glass, or vice versa, who could say, inspired by da Vinci's *Le proporzioni del corpo umano secondo Vitruvio*, which realized the Roman architect's claim about proportion and, by extension, the assertion of "man" as microcosm, as measure of all things, ideas Jack—who often stood there before the window, her quick brown eyes scanning the arid stretch—flatly rejected, the image nevertheless still serving as inspiration, Jack still revering the so-called triad of virtues: *firmitas, utilitas, venustas*; and wasn't this house solid, useful, and beautiful?, its rammed-earth-encased-in-steel-belted-rubber walls making it virtually indestructible, its heavy, dense mass making it a battery to store heat, these structural aspects making it durable and sustainable, yes, a house that took care of itself, yes, but also making it beautiful, its wide-open spaces, odd-shaped windows, curvaceous columns, and arabesqueing walls, not to mention the textiles hanging from walls, draped over furniture, twisting around banisters and handrails, further individuating its beauty, the house, a museum too, filled with paintings and sculptures they'd purchased over the years, like Jack's beloved "rusts," metallic entanglings made of discarded steelworks, the organized whole making it beautiful, the house not just warmly lived-in but so seemingly alive in its own right you could almost hear it breathe, hear its heart beat, Mní, her long-dead partner, still somehow present, not as some ghastly apparition or even friendly phantasm, but imbued within the house's materials, its substance, its elemental composition, memories somehow actually taking form, Jack sensing this presence, feeling it as something real but still always just out of grasp, Jack also mixed within those selfsame walls, for hadn't she been inspired by hornets, paper wasps, and yellow jackets, who mix masticated wood bits and their own saliva to make their nests, and by Formosan termites, who build their nests with wood, dirt, and their own feces, forming a "scatological force field," to mix her own spit and shit and menses within the walls of the house she'd built so many years ago?

This is the cat who gazed out the window overlooking the desert surrounding the house, a "smarter house" Jack had called it after the cyber attacks that wreaked havoc on residential artificial intelligence systems a few years ago, millions of people not only unable to use their houses' tactile displays—interconnected appliances, entertainment centers, etc., left to their "own devices," ha ha—but unable even to enter or exit their houses, the house that Jack built, where "time had stopped," as many had insultingly claimed, left unharmed, the house where the cat sat as always, his eyes seemingly vacant, every blink a judgment, who seemed asleep even when awake and vice versa, Jack, her once angular nose, slit-like mouth, and chiseled chin a bit limp these days, still taking care of him despite never really caring for him, Hopper, the cat, having belonged to Mní, who'd claimed that according to myth cats were the moon's progeny, Mní devotedly following the lunar phases, cats, for her, also representing fertility and eternity, the intuitive and the unconscious—"Look at the way Hopper wraps his tail around himself," she'd said, "incarnating the yin and yang," said symbol annoying Jack, who rejected dichotomous formulations of any kind, such formulations, which *Womanhouse* at best complicated and interrogated, Jack's own structures completely dismantled—the cat's name certainly not endearing him to Jack either, since she'd never cared for his namesake painter, whose spaces and motifs—offices, diners, movie theaters, etc.—those "domains emblematic of American dread and decay," bored her, his paintings of women in bedrooms, and *Morning Sun* (where a strangely proportioned woman gazes out a square-shaped window, the width of which oddly equaling that of the bed upon which she sat), particularly, making her angry.

This is the dog afraid of the mask-and-mantle cat, who gazed, orange eyed, out the window overlooking the desert surrounding the house that Jack built, the dog a whippet–border collie mix, all genius and velocity, in other words, the evening he arrived finding him gathering all the shoes in the house, from underneath beds, chairs, and tables, by all the entrances, subsequently lining up the flats, heels, sneakers, and boots in neat rows, Jack finally calling him Maddox, the dog always sitting at her feet at meals, the kitchen and dining room—where windows also overlooked the desert—far too spacious for two, the cabinet and table and floor's reflective surfaces electrifying the space, Jack remembering the last meal she and Mní had eaten together, a meal set off with a butter-poached lobster soup, followed by crème fraîche agnolotti (a succulent, exceedingly soft ravioli of sorts), and a turkey-fig concoction that was both ambrosia and aphrodisiac, these appetizers followed by Chilean sea bass surrounded by smoked eggplant puree, wilted arugula, and garlic confit, and marinated cherry tomatoes, one of the orbs of which squirting juice on Jack's neck when she'd forked into it, the meal punctuated by a trio of sorbets: scoops of strawberry, raspberry, and peach on pebbly beds of walnut nougatine, all of which had made her want to sing, and she had, silently, the song reverberating in her chest, the way Monk's music would, particularly the pieces from *Misterioso*, an album Jack listened to repeatedly, the maestro's disjunctive compositions, melodic angularities, and his singular approach to soloing, with its various delays and knowing dissonance, its humor too, largely deadpan, with the occasional pratfall—Monk sounding, at times, as if he were falling *up* the stairs, "accidentally on purpose," of course, but unexpected all the same—all working together to itself create space, "a sonic architecture," Jack thought, *The Seer*, one of Giorgio de Chirico's *pittura metafisica*, used for the original album cover, the image, with its contradictory orthogonals and vanishing points, a source of continual inspiration to Jack, who also loved, and was sometimes even unnerved by, the painting's eerie, and seemingly armless, manikin, an L-shaped hinge scale nevertheless held by it, its egg-shaped head turning away from a chalkboard drawing, a solitary, encircled star for an eye on its forehead, a third eye—the first and second presumably blind—a locus of insight and power bathed in light.

This is the door that let out the always fidgety dog, who was especially afraid of Hopper, an indoor-outdoor cat, who'd already established himself as hunter par excellence by placing mice and birds in conspicuous areas of the house: at either end of the various serpentine hallways, in the center of the living room, where light pouring from the massive circular ceiling window would brilliantly enframe the "gifts," the cat, who gazed out the window overlooking the desert surrounding the house that Jack built, the house with four doors, one for each cardinal direction, a door without locks, a door always an "energetic possibility," Jack would say, the stresses within itself, that is, exit and entrance, opening and closure, etc., adding up to the same thing, that is, possibility, Jack's parents, who'd once been held at gunpoint in their home in the Deep South by desperate meth heads, always worrying over whether she and Mní were actually ever safe in their unlocked house, her parents equating locks with safety, implying that an unlocked house could never be a home, a notion that Jack, who created inclusive spaces, could never support, but they too had long since passed, her mother of breast cancer, her father, always the weaker of the two, dying of a kind of willful withering away, Mní, in any case, always ready to move house if they had to, her having been born in a military-issue tent pitched near an endangered riverbank perhaps having something to do with it, her having stayed in one place for decades surprising *her* more than anyone else.

This is the neighbor who opened the door that let out the dog who was afraid of the cat who gazed out the window overlooking the desert surrounding the house that Jack built, the neighbor—whose sixty years found expression in an overall concavity of form, in his skin's constellation of flat black and brown spots—once again fulfilling his promise to Mní to periodically check in on Jack, the neighbor surprised by Maddox's mad rush to leave the house, his commands to the dog meeting with failure, his subsequent calls to Jack met with silence as he stamped his sandy boots on the entrance mat, the neighbor shouting for Jack as he walked through the foyer, the floor's fibrous appearance calling up a hot spring's calcareous deposits, Maddox still standing outside the door, barking his refusals—or were they warnings?—the neighbor, two dark buttons for eyes, fearing the worst as he entered the living room, the massive circumference of it shushing him, the walls' aggregated structure resembling the quincuncial pattern of a cluster of pomegranate seeds, the neighbor climbing up one of the house's spiraling stairs, and arriving at the landing, where he called out to Jack, who, he imagined, would be in her work space, the neighbor picturing Jack slumped over her desk, imagining tapping Jack's shoulder, touching her face, the skin feeling like a hairless cat's, or something even creepier, his forearms tingling, his knees wobbling, his stomach a cold stone, the neighbor imagining Jack's face looking like oven-fresh pizza, her slack nose and chin and cheeks chewed off by the dog and cat, the neighbor, a veteran of this country's perpetual war, recalling his first tour of duty, months into which he'd found a child dead—bloody lines radiating calligraphically beneath the body—the child naked, his or her skin dark brown like a wet paper bag, the body bloated, as if he or she had swallowed a watermelon whole, the child's face drawn into a fierce rictus, teeth flashing a maniacal smile, which mocked his silent repulsion, itself a kind of reverie, viscous liquid flowing from the child's rectum: a chasm of darkness, like death itself, a wormhole sucking him in, disintegrating his body, balling it up as pure energy, sucking it through a long tunnel, his body finally reemerging whole again on the other side, the other side of *what* he hadn't cared to find out, the neighbor finally entering Jack's work space but finding nothing, nothing save walls lined with books, piles of magazines here and there, various ergonomic chairs, rulers and tape measures and engineering scales, rolls of onionskin paper, and long white tables—lamps craned over them—and long, lateral file cabinets, the neighbor, realizing the house was empty, retracing his steps, leaving the house, wondering where the dog had gone, where Jack, who'd built this house, had gone, the neighbor finally thinking, "She's taking a walk," the thought subsumed by a succession of images, movements, sensations: lemon-yellow sun; Jack waking up from an uneasy, dreamless slumber; Jack, static; a spiraling stair; a door opening; the desert, vast, quiet, full of daybreak; Jack walking and walking; Jack disappearing; footsteps dotting the sand as far as the eye could see; wind eventually blowing the perforation away.

Here and There
Karen Heuler

NOLA POTERRI BUILT HER first bridge with alphabet blocks, and so discovered her life's calling. She built bridge after bridge and sat back on her legs and studied the bridges. "It's unusual," her mother said. Her father merely watched. They didn't know if this was a phase, or if they were reading into it, or whether it showed an actual precocity. They were interested, however; they took her to real bridges, stopping and getting out to study them. They went to abandoned, picturesque bridges, bridges they could walk on and lean over railings to stare at rushing water or murky pools. Her parents began to love bridges too; it was obviously some sort of genetic inclination. They could look at bridges all day long. They could look at keystones and suspension bridges, at stone bridges and bridge-tunnels, even at photos of woven bridges way up in the mountains, dangling over precipices. "Not solid," the mother said. "Not really a center to it, is there?" the father asked, moving his finger along the photograph. "A bridge should have weight."

And then they'd look at Nola. What did Nola think?

She seemed to think through her fingertips, always reaching for shapes that she could use to build her bridges. She liked keystone arches up until she was about nine, and by twelve she had progressed to building small suspension bridges, and their backyard was a series of rudimentary bridges rising just three or four feet aboveground. Then she moved on to box bridges, girder bridges, tubular bridges, and skyways, and instead of removing the first layer of bridges, she built over and across them, forming a crosshatch of bridge layers, with new, higher bridges spanning the bridges below them.

The stacks of bridges formed different journeys, as she called them. One led to a neighbor's house, who liked it for a while because it functioned as a balcony, until the structures Nola built above that one put his house permanently in the shade. He talked to other neighbors who had been watching the increase in bridges with alarm. There were ordinances about backyard structures.

Her mother was dying, at that point, and her father talked to

305

neighbors as best he could to placate them. But soon there was a petition and then they brought an action.

Nola moved indoors and built wispy arches around her mother's bed, listening to the rhythm of her mother's breath, intent on building a bridge that would cause her mother to stay. She never succeeded.

After her mother died, Nola got very still. She slowly took away the arches she had built around her mother's bed and moved them into the yard. Her head was bent, her hands were slow. She began removing some structures piece by piece. One neighbor reported this, and some of the complaints subsided while they waited to see if all the structures would come down.

They did not. She was just making room. Nola was testing out what she called reverse-suspension bridges.

Her father, still mourning, was inclined to let her do whatever she wanted. Let the neighbors sue him if they felt like it. What was a reverse-suspension bridge?

"On suspension bridges, the cables carry the weight from the roadway and transfer it to the towers," Nola said. "The cables hold the roadway up. But what if the roadway has to be held down instead?"

"You mean it pushes *up*?" Her father thought he was being ridiculous so he laughed. His first laugh in a while.

"Exactly," she said. "What if the weight of one end forced the other end up, like a seesaw? And the point was to hold that higher end down? Wouldn't that be interesting?"

Her father got some rebar, and together they dug under the cinder blocks of the foundation. She put one end of the rebar there as a kind of lever, and then tied cables to the other end, forcing it down and refining it until it achieved what she wanted. Then she built a larger one, still small enough to be unimpressive, but that worked as well. Then she restructured a tower on one of the lower bridges so that the end of the roadway bent under it, and then had the other end go up to the third layer of bridges, straining to leap up but held down by cables.

She fooled around some more so that cables going up and cables going down balanced themselves out, eventually building a bridge without towers, balancing between its urge to go up and its need to go down.

The mesh of bridges grew again, and suddenly there were new papers with court dates in them, and orders to cease and desist.

"Nola," the father said finally. "They're taking us to court. And we really can't afford it. The bridges were fine for a while, when they were really just garden structures, but the neighbors are complaining that we're not zoned for architecture like this. And we aren't. You're exceeding building heights and building codes. I'm sorry—"

She looked at him intently. "What heights? What are the limits?"

He gazed at her, nodded, and wrote her questions down on paper. The next day he consulted the commissioner of buildings and some architectural firms.

"I have it," he told her. "You can't build more than three stories high in this zone. You have to have a setback of ten feet from your neighbors for any approved structures. It looks like you can call some of it a gazebo and some of it a tree house—both are permitted, but we need approvals. But the interesting thing is that the higher you go, the less they can regulate. You get into air rights. It looks like we technically have air rights up to about a hundred feet, if I understand it. And it's tricky. So the problem is that you can't build things above three stories, at the same time that you own air rights up to about a hundred feet." He looked at his daughter anxiously. "Sounds crazy, huh? An interesting technicality."

"Can I fly a kite?" Nola asked.

This disappointed him. He didn't want his daughter to give up her bridges; he didn't want her to be interested in kites. "I don't see why not," he answered slowly.

"And how far down can I dig?"

He smiled. "You can't impact on the integrity of the neighbor's dirt. That means you can't dig anything that would cause their yards to collapse or be changed in any way." He was more hopeful now.

"Right," she said, and set to work.

She got a huge kite, spanning about eight feet, added a loop and a long string through the loop, and flew it up. She tied a cable to one end of the string and pulled it up and through the loop and used that to anchor the kite some ten feet from the left neighbor's yard. She dug down under her own foundation at an angle, and she placed a stanchion there, also at an angle, using the house as a fulcrum. This was twenty feet from the right neighbor's yard.

She connected the cable from the loop in the kite to the stanchion below the house. Her father came out to watch it as she finished. The weight of the cable kept the kite from flying too widely. It appeared to rest stably in the air.

"But what is it?" her father asked.

"It's the bridge," she said. There was pride in her voice. "From the earth to the air."

307

"But won't it move?" he asked.

At that she smiled. "There is a center point at each end," she said. Her father looked up at the kite and blinked; he lowered his head to look at the stanchion in the earth and pursed his lips. "I don't follow," he said.

"Watch," Nola answered, and she spread out her arms and put her foot on the stanchion and walked slowly up to the kite and then halfway back, where she paused and surveyed the scene. The view was as lovely as the views from the bridges of her childhood, when they'd all gazed over the railings and down to rushing water. There was a moment, when she looked down and her father looked up, when she felt astonished. The world was sharp and poised and she felt happiness like a perfect movement.

"Nola!" the father cried automatically. He was shocked to see her twenty feet above him, smiling down with a strange, bemused look.

"All right," she said, and walked back to him.

He grabbed her and hugged her. She leaned into him, lifting her arms to pat him gingerly. "It's all right," she said soothingly. "There was never any danger."

"Why didn't you fall?" he said. "It's so narrow."

She shook her head. "I walked in the center, that's all. Just think— if you painted a line on the ground, would you fall off the line?"

"But it isn't a line, it's a cable." He was getting his breath back, and he didn't know whether he felt foolish or annoyed.

"I ran the cable along a series of points. All the centers of the points," she said, thinking this would make him understand. "Try it," she said. "Just walk on it, you'll see."

He didn't know if he was a brave man, or a risk-taking kind of man, or the kind of man who went through life without learning anything. But he did know he trusted his daughter and he had seen it with his own eyes. He took a step on the cable.

His foot found a calm, clear purchase. He looked down and he saw nothing, just his foot and the cable. He lifted his other foot and the same thing happened. He straightened his back and walked gingerly forward. He saw Nola's face turned toward him and at once he felt a great sense of vitality. He gazed back and forth at each end, and there he was between them, happy.

He felt lighter in a new way—not just about weight; there was a mental feeling of lightness. He might say *truth*. He might say *meaning*. But he never used those words. He was between two places, here and there.

Nola touched the cable. And he walked back.

He took deep breaths and looked around. "It was solid," he said faintly.

"The center is only where the radius begins," she said. "And of course there's more than one radius. They're like cables for the points you want to use."

It made a fleeting sense to him; he had felt at the center of something. But whatever he understood began to slip away. Still, he knew what he had felt was rare.

"How do you know this?" he asked.

"I see the centers. I've always seen them. I've always been building from one point to the other, and all the points are centers."

"I don't see that," he said sadly. "And, Nola—is there any use to this? Any practical use?"

Her glance moved away from him, miles away. Even her body pulled taut. "I can build a bridge with a single line," she said. "And no one would be interested?"

"But what would they use it for?" he asked. He was trying to be delicate; he was trying to understand.

"For beauty," she said. "For the beauty of having it. I can build a longer one, a taller one; I can build as far as the eye can see, and then I can move farther, and build onto it again."

"But what will they do with it?" he persisted.

She looked at him attentively. She shrugged. "What do you do with the spot you're standing on?" she asked.

He frowned.

"It's a place, a point, a center. You touch it and you stay until you wish to leave. Just like every step you've ever taken."

But he continued to frown, and it struck at her heart, a little bit. She went back to building her bridges—adding a few suspension bridges, so her father would feel comfortable, but also building the ones he couldn't understand. Her bridges were delicate and sometimes hidden behind things, hard to visualize. She would anchor a bridge to the roots of a tree, or to a big rock in the earth. She would walk up the cable to the kite and then fly another kite from there, held by a thinner wire, small and sheer. She studied the way it moved. From across the street, she seemed to be in the air, gesturing toward another spot in the air.

Far away, she saw an unusual point. She couldn't reach it yet, but it seemed more distinct than the other points around her. It stayed there in the sky as if waiting for her.

One day the police arrived with a city marshal. The father let them in; they were serving a warrant and said they would give him more time if he cooperated. He took them to the backyard. There were only a few of the larger bridges now, old ones that weren't in the way as Nola moved on to lighter bridges. And the kites.

"Those?" the marshal asked, using his chin to point to the bridges. He had looked at the kites and dismissed them.

"Those," the father said. "I'm sure I can remove them."

The police and the marshal conferred. "Were there other structures?" the marshal asked.

"Yes. My daughter took them down. That complaint must be old."

"Your daughter?"

"She built them." At that point, Nola came home from school. She stood beside her father.

"This little girl? They're complaining about this little girl?" the policeman asked. "What do you weigh, ninety pounds?" Nola had always been slight.

"What does her weight matter?"

"It doesn't. I'm just trying to put this all together." He looked up. "You got a kite or two, I see."

"Bridges," Nola corrected him. Her father's hand on her shoulder pinched her. She nodded. "I like kites," she said.

They walked around a little, took a few measurements, said there were no longer any violations, and began to leave. The kites remained. "My kid likes kites," the policeman said. "I fly them in the park. Maybe I'll see you there."

"All right," the father said. "And thanks."

"She'll be dating in a few years anyway," the officer continued. "Then it's all shopping and boys. You'll see. I have one."

"Yes," the father said. His voice was faint.

Her father applied to special engineering schools for her, asking for scholarships. He included photos of her bridges. One school sent an interviewer, who stood in the yard, chewing like he'd bitten off a piece of suspect meat.

His eyes roamed all the levels of the structures. "A little girl did this?" he asked. "You didn't help her?"

"I wouldn't know how," her father said. "I'm a ticket agent for the railroad."

The interviewer looked at the father steadily, then walked around, tapping bridges. He stood on one and jumped a little. "They're models," he said. "She makes models. Not the same as new insights."

The father could tell the man was not interested, didn't believe what Nola had done, suspected something—whatever the reason, he was set against the bridges.

"I'm working on a point-to-point bridge," Nola said, looking up at the kites.

"That's a kite," the man answered.

She studied him for a moment, shrugged, and stepped up on the cable. When she began to walk, he yanked her down.

"I've done it," the father said. "It's safe. I've walked on it."

"And no one had to grab him," Nola pointed out. She bent down, took a ball she used to test the straightness of bridges, and rolled it up the cable. It went halfway and then rolled back to her hand.

The interviewer watched it steadily and finally shrugged. "What's the point of it? You can't transport anything on it, and, really, I can't see the trick but there must be a trick. At any rate it's useless. An illusion or magnets." He looked at her. "You're a tricky girl, aren't you? A Houdini-ette or something."

"There is no trick," she said. And then, injudiciously, she added, "You just don't understand the science."

"There is no science like this," he snapped. He drew himself up as if reacting to his own irritation, and his eyes roved back up to the bridge she'd built. He took a moment, wavering, but then he looked at Nola, her father, and back to the bridge. "This is a strange presentation. A toy? I don't know. There's something here I don't trust. It would be a shame if I passed over someone who shows me a talent in engineering that will work in the real world. I wouldn't want to regret passing him up, for this." He nodded.

"Has anyone else her age ever done anything like this?"

His head wagged a little, left to right. "I don't know what 'this' is, so I can't say."

Nola filled out applications for colleges and engineering schools. She wrote an essay on how she wanted to build new, portable bridges.

"I don't think there's much need for portable bridges," her father said gently.

"I mean, to get them in place in remote areas. Quickly. All at once. And leave them there."

"I see," he said. He still didn't know if that was a real need. He

311

went along with his daughter, out of loyalty and conviction. It was a joke between them—how no one could understand what she did or why. "What do you see?" he once asked. "When you go from point to point?"

"I see the points and how they align themselves. I see a point and I see the links to the points that constellate them. I go for the ones with the most links. They're obviously the strongest." She looked at him. "I always wondered. You don't see what I see?"

He shook his head. "No one does."

She pursed her lips and stared off thoughtfully.

And then of course something went wrong.

She was experimenting with flying bridges ("What?" her father had asked. "These kites aren't flying bridges?") that could tie two points together and then have one point release and another point catch. A kind of slinky-in-the-air.

She was reducing the size of the cables as well. She knew that some points could hold almost infinite amounts of weight, and she had been testing the points, mapping them. She occasionally crossed a bridge so she could peer at a point twenty, thirty, forty feet away. She was creating a science, and as happens with any scientist, one of her tests failed. The point she thought was stable simply wasn't, and she fell from her bridge, hard. Landing on her shoulder, wrenching her neck severely. She lay stunned, in agony, unable to move.

Her father called an ambulance, and the police came and took more notes. There were questions, since she was only sixteen, and social services was called to check on living conditions. She was a fair student, no problems noted. The neighbors said merely that her father used to build too many things in the backyard, but now things were better. She had fallen off a ladder. Or fallen off the roof. She was a strange girl.

She had headaches after that, and her shoulder was never the same, but nothing interfered with her experiments.

She began building smaller bridges. She used a pin to anchor one, and when her father asked, "What if I pull out the pin, what will happen?" she laughed and said, "What happens when half a bridge collapses? You can't cross it, that's all. The sky won't fall." This sarcasm was not like her, her father thought, but she had been surprised by the accident; she had learned she was mortal.

Mortal and alone. She had no friends, and she was of an age when her looks should matter, but she went her own way, always. She cut her hair straight across above her shoulder blades, because she didn't care. She wore indistinguishable, unfeminine clothes. Her high-school adviser, a kind woman, had called to delicately ask if she could take Nola shopping, but Nola had refused. It reminded her of the day care she'd been sent to once when her mother was sick, where they'd insisted she wear tutus and draw with pink pens.

She was determined to get into college. But her grades were only fair, nothing to tempt any school into giving her a scholarship. She was sure that if she could perfect the invisible bridge, her success would be guaranteed. Her father was caught between admiration and caution. One of the neighbors, a nice enough person, had suggested that she was really creating art. He said he couldn't think of a single female engineer. And the female scientists—well, everyone automatically said Marie Curie. But her husband did a lot, didn't he? Makes you think.

She got into a school, not the best school, and she hoped that some of the teachers would be able to guide her into a breakthrough on the invisible bridge. They didn't. One of them was kind, but the others merely pointed out books on bridges, or websites, or a few chat groups. For anything online, she used only her first initial. There was hostility to women.

Coming home late from class one night, she was raped. She went to a hospital and insisted on a rape kit. The police came and took the rape kit away, took down some notes, and then she heard nothing. She called to check and was told that the kit had been lost.

She got an IUD. If men were going to rape her, she was not going to be trapped by them. There were only a few engineering or structural classes of any kind, so she dropped out. The college was beneath her anyway. She saw no reason to continue her education.

The bridges in the backyard—the old ones, the traditional ones—began to show their age. Her father was showing his age too. He even listened slower at this point, cocking his head and thinking about what she'd just said. He knew about the poor grades, but not the rape. He knew that she was trying to get a job with any kind of civil engineering company, but their eyes looked at her steadily when she went for the job interview, and then, regretfully, she was told there was an opening with the administrative or secretarial departments. Just until she got her degree, of course.

Her father died after she changed the final traditional bridge into a freestanding deck. The neighbors explained to her where a deck belonged. One man in particular explained the difference between a bridge and a deck. These were new neighbors, unaware of the troubling

313

bridge history of her youth. She was much more guarded than she had been then. She did not tell him about the weightless bridges, or explain the concept of going point to point. She had told those things to her father, who was prejudiced and hopeful on her behalf, but who understood nothing. She was terribly afraid, after her father's death, that there would never be another being in the world who understood her.

Still, she continued.

Her father left her the house and a small amount of money. The money would allow her to keep the house; she would need more money to live and to experiment.

For all this time, she was still working on the invisible bridge. Why had her progress slowed down? She had created the point-to-point bridges, though no one had ever seen any value to them; she had made attempts to create flying bridges, but had been tempered by her fall, years before. Even she knew that there was no need for an invisible bridge, and yet she wanted to build one. It was a need, unexplainable and unavoidable. Years ago her father had asked her, what did she want with her bridges? Where did she want the bridges to lead to?

"Lead to?" she had murmured. "Why, all bridges lead to the other side of the bridge, which leads right back to this side of the bridge."

"I had thought," he began hesitantly. "I had thought maybe they went somewhere . . . different. Different from what we know."

"No," she said, shaking her head. "They lead from one point to another point, and then back again."

Her father was silent.

"It's not magic," she said, almost crying, but not crying, she didn't cry. "It's not magic," she whispered, her head lowered, trying to control herself.

"OK," he said. She heard disappointment in his voice. Did he want to go somewhere else? Is that why everyone was so harsh, so disappointed? Because in their secret hearts they hoped the bridges would lead to—another time, another place, another dimension? Were they so stupid? Didn't they understand she was dealing with science, not magic?

If you bridged two points, all you did was create a relationship between them; you did not create another world. Of course, she had to admit, you altered the world. A bit. Not much. You changed the geometry, just a touch, because no one had tied points together before.

She told herself that the point far off in the sky was merely a point she wanted to reach, like any other point. She refused to admit that she hoped that it meant something, that it was there specifically for her. That it led to something. She would start to think about it and then hold her thoughts in check. She missed her father.

She was nearing forty now. She went to museums, to lectures; she bought books, but expenses began to pile up. She sent in descriptions of her bridges to various competitions (some of them were really art competitions, not engineering) but there was only an occasional, shallow interest. A neighbor's child did a report on her once and that led to an article in the local newspaper. She got a call from someone who worked at an assisted-living residence, asking if she would like to do arts and crafts twice a week, minimum wage, unfortunately.

She thought about it. She was alone too much, she felt uninspired (she hadn't worked on bridges for a while now). She went to the library and looked in the crafts section. Folding paper looked interesting, so she checked out a few books and bought different kinds of paper on the way home.

The paper folding was magical. So many shapes! Such intricate forms! She practiced for hours each day and went to her first craft session with papers and diagrams.

There were three women and one man there. She set them around the table and they began folding. One of them had shaky hands, another squinted. By the end of the hour they were all in love with folding.

The folding was setting her mind free. She was studying form again, and shapes again, and the surprise of transformational space again. She loved the smiles she got, the murmurs of appreciation. The seniors began reading books on folding as well, and they all began work on lacy hanging lamps and bowls that could collapse. They laughed easily together. Mary and Jim and Rosalie and Fran. Wonderful people.

On the way home one afternoon, she saw how the folding and the bridges might go together. She should give up the invisible bridge; it would be problematic if she could build it—would people slam into it? Fall over it or off it? Would they even admit that it was there? Her own experiences made her doubt it. But if a bridge could be folded and unfolded, surely they would admit that they could see what it was and could see its value. It would be her portable bridge.

She studied the designs she had made for her previous bridges. She took some of them, drew them finely on thin paper, and began to fold the paper. Paper fans and creased papers and thin strips with accordion edges surrounded her.

There were now six students at the residence. Marty joined, as did Sheila. They grinned at her and looked at images in books with descriptions as they began to fold paper into vases and picture frames. "I'm giving this to my daughter," Rosalie said. "She's a snob. But I think she'll like this, it's art. It's beautiful."

After a few months, Nola's work on the paper bridges began to come together. She could build a bridge from the daily newspaper; the thinness of the paper was actually an asset, because she could crease it so perfectly, spiral it, lattice if need be.

She built a small bridge with her class, now numbering eight. It was a model, taking up a corner of the room they met in. But they could see it, they could put their hands on it; they could place books on it just to test its strength. Only she could see how to place it, but once it was placed it was perfect.

Nola was happy with her experiments with paper bridges, which at home grew increasingly large. She built one from her roof to the crook of the nearest tree, and walked back and forth slowly. That moment of suspension at the center of the bridge, removed from earth, resting in air, always gave her strength again. Squirrels ran along it until the rain brought it down. Birds landed and cocked their heads. She could stand there and be in a different life. Perhaps that's what her father really wanted. It never mattered when the rain made it shred; she liked the way it moved back to earth.

Another residence heard of her and she now had classes four days a week. She had access to the newspapers they were about to throw out. She impressed the seniors with her folds and her creases and pleats; they twisted shapes into giraffes and horses, into dragonflies and spiderwebs. One man loved making tollbooths for her bridges. He even painted them.

The local newspaper wanted to do a follow-up on her, and that led to a local TV station wanting to show her art on the early evening spot.

She practiced with her students so it could be done efficiently and quickly, and when the TV crew was there, they built a bridge. Of course, Nola had to show her students where to place each fold, since they couldn't see the points, but with seniors from both residences, she was able to complete it in an afternoon.

The camera crew stayed for it, shooting every fifteen minutes or so.

Nola walked across the bridge to show it was stable.

The last shot for the news program was the reporter, standing on the bridge, declaring it an impressive feat.

After the crew left, she thanked her seniors and went back home and built interlocking folded paper bridges, forming a dome. There was no rain forecast for a week. On top of the dome she built a point-to-point bridge to the peak of her house.

The neighbors she now had were better neighbors than the neighbors of her childhood. They asked if she was having a party, if she *could* have a party or, rather, would she mind if the neighbors included her yard in an impromptu block party?

She invited her seniors to the party, and they constructed paper bridges on the spot. They weren't high, so no one had a problem when children and dogs ran along them. The day was bright and sunny. The backyard domes and bridges she had built fluttered or wavered in the breeze. People pointed up and laughed in appreciation. A man approached her and asked if he could have her as a guest lecturer in a class he taught.

"What class is this?" she asked.

"It's called Aspirational Divisions. That's what the catalog calls it because they think it sounds grander. But, really, it's about dreams. It's about making your dreams come true, working toward the goal of your heart."

She could hear the faint snap of paper in the wind. She could see the points where some of the bridges landed, or sprang from. She was very close to accepting her life as it was. And so she smiled and said, "But they don't, do they? They don't come true in the way you want or in the way you think."

He nodded. "Ah, but look what you've achieved here. Look at all you've done."

At that the wind picked up and the rain began and, amid the shrieks and laughter, the paper bridges began to sheer themselves away and shred themselves on the lawns and streets.

The points held steady, however, and they were there to be discovered again just as, far away, that special point hovered. She had decided to give up on that special point, to stop thinking it was meant for her. Dreams don't come true in the way you want or in the way you think.

The neighbors liked the bridges. She showed them what she had done, explaining it as best she could. One neighbor asked if she could make a point-to-point bridge over a swimming pool, so the children could jump in. Another had a septic repair about to start, and wondered if a folding bridge would be possible so they could get around it easily. No, not a folding bridge, she said, but a small reverse-suspension bridge would work.

Most neighbors had requests. Some of them had been children when their parents complained about the strange things in Nola's yard. They had been interested but forbidden to be involved. Now they could say they liked all her bridges, and began to ask for them as ornaments on the street, useful under certain conditions. They applied for and got permits as "public installations." Soon the street sparkled and waved on sunny days. She put up bridges at both ends of the street, and the neighbors loved driving under them to their own private bridges. Another world really, they said, nodding to each other.

Nola continued to experiment. She was thinking about reverse bridges—constructions that could keep two points separated, unable to be bridged. It was a strange idea for her, thinking about deliberately creating a separation.

On her street, the bridges grew like trees, and grew into trees, and Nola created paper skywalks for the neighbors' delight; the children in particular all felt that they lived in an enchanted world. Above them, every so often, Nola paused on one of her floating bridges and felt the sheer intensity of being neither here nor there, of being suspended, of being a point in the universe that she knew and could see contained all the points there ever were.

The Café, the Sea, Deauville, 1966
Frederic Tuten

1.

NATASHA WAVED TO HIM from her high window. He blew her a kiss. He checked his watch. He was already fifteen minutes late but he decided to have a brandy at the café and burn away the rabbit-stew lunch still churning in his stomach.

2.

Seagulls whirled in long loops, their reflections smashing into her window. She waved again before disappearing behind a flimsy red curtain.

"You know," he once had said after they had made love on their third rendezvous in her cold, vast apartment, "your curtains look like the ones in brothel windows in Amsterdam."

"You speak from firsthand knowledge, I suppose," she said.

"That's beside the point. Why dress your window like a whore's?" He regretted saying that, apologized, and later bought her a large blue tin of her favorite caviar.

"I hope it cost you plenty," she said.

"Not enough for my stupidity," he answered, hoping he sounded sufficiently contrite. "You are far from a whore or vulgar," he added.

"Not as far as my curtains go, it seems."

"No need for irony. I know that you soar above me. You are the apotheosis of high culture. You are the total artwork, the *Gesamtkunstwerk* that Wagner dreamed of creating."

He was unsure about his German pronunciation but she did not correct him and he had hoped, in any case, that she would be impressed with his smattering of opera culture and he considered adding: Let me take you to see *Tristan und Isolde* the next time it comes to Paris. But he reckoned the expense would be above his means—the first-class train round-trip, the best orchestra seats, the high-class dinner after, and then a fine room at a fine hotel. She was rich enough to travel without advance planning or thought of expense.

319

But she seldom left her apartment or her street. So what good was her money? He would have loved to travel—to live—without a care. Not to have to settle for a middle-grade hotel with faded carpeting and suspect sheets, to be able to take an aeroplane anywhere, just on a whim, on a desire—what more was there to life but an elegant life?

"Thank you, for the compliment," she said. "It struck a note."

"You have your own power and beauty to pick and choose. I don't know why you even give me a tumble," he said.

She laughed. "If you think that, you know very little of life and nothing of women."

He checked his watch again—noticing a crack in its crystal—before entering the empty café, where Alfred stood waiting for no one.

3.

The Longines Conquest, with a green lizard strap, burned his wrist. His wife had given him the watch some birthdays ago—"for the man I love," she had said—and it told him the wrong time to punish him for his infidelities and it made him think of death three times a day and at night after dinner and again before slipping under the bedcovers.

He could always blame the tricky watch for his being late but Natasha would know he was lying.

4.

"Good afternoon, Monsieur Alfred," he said to the barman, who was standing by the window and looking out to the sea.

"The usual?" Alfred asked without turning and still at the window writing in a small green notebook.

He had always found Alfred polite enough, cordial enough, but never embracing of his clients, or at least the few he had ever encountered there at the bar or seated at the old-fashioned, upholstered red-leather banquettes with marble-top tables and black wrought-iron legs. He never understood what she saw in the café, why she had once said, "That's the only place I want to be other than my bedroom or my kitchen. It's my sea cave and if Alfred changes it I will die."

"It's very gloomy," he once ventured to comment. "Narrow like a coffin for a tall, narrow person," he had added for emphasis.

"I wonder," she said, "if I can make it my mausoleum?"

"It's already Alfred's," he said, thinking that she must never, never die. That he would never allow it.

320

"Not today, Alfred. A brandy will do, I think. Yes, something solid, fortifying but not medicinal. Something celebratory even."

The brandy was surprisingly rough and he thought of making a small fuss but finally he decided to say, "Alfred, what is your best brandy and will you have one with me?"

"Gladly, but in spirit," Alfred said.

5.

He swirled the brandy in the snifter, sniffed, sipped, smiled. He made a pleased face and an approving nod. But it was all show, because all he was thinking about was his watch.

6.

He sported a yellow maple-wood cane fashioned in Vermont, where he dreamed one day of visiting and seeing for himself the sweet sap ooze down from the maple trees. America, where trees bled sugar and people lived in yellow maple-wood cabins and sang hymns before dinner. He had read that. The simple life. He longed for it.

A simple life with her in her blue stone-floor kitchen and its collection of aging copper pots she never used but left hanging on hooks from the ceiling, as they were when her mother died. And the samovar too, like a fat-bellied silver god of the kitchen.

It made him uncomfortable that once, in their rush to couple, the samovar had watched them making love on the kitchen floor and he had imagined that the pots would fall down on them for punishment.

"There is a kind of sanctity to the kitchen that we should perhaps respect," he once said to her. "Everything has its place, the bedroom for love, the toilet for you know what, and the kitchen for cooking, no?"

"I never cook in the kitchen or anywhere else," she answered. "Unless you consider boiling water cooking."

He kept on his hat, a weathered Borsalino that had belonged to his father, a country doctor who made house calls even in the deepest winter and never remarried. He thought of his father every time he put on and took off the hat.

One day he would go to Milan and buy a new Borsalino and store the old one in his closet for good luck. And maybe he'd also buy a new suit; his workaday gray flannel with pinstripes sagged at the shoulders and looked tired, although his polished new shoes mirrored the sky and made him seem current. His father's shoes were always bruised and caked with mud and blades of grass from his country rounds. What good was it to be an educated doctor and look like a rustic, a farmer, a bumpkin married to the earth?

She had chosen his beautiful shoes for him on their tryst in London, in a shop on Jermyn Street, where rows of burnished leather shoes sat in the window like saints. "Those," she had said, "get those, and get a black umbrella and keep it rolled tightly as the Englishmen do."

7.

He was still lingering over his second brandy when she emerged from her building. His watch explained he was now more than thirty-five minutes late. She came close up to the window and looked in; he smiled and saluted her with his brandy. Instead of walking into the café, to him, as he had expected, she sped away toward the promenade.

8.

She took a seat at a table on the empty, chilly café terrace. She enjoyed the cold, the gray dampness of Deauville, where the old stone houses kept their winter iciness even in summer. She imagined that she would light the fireplace when she returned home and not answer the phone.

She ordered a double espresso, *bien serré*, she said, because she liked the sound of the words, and opened a newspaper someone had left on the chair beside her. It was three days old but she was glad that everything she read had already happened, as in a film or an absorbing novel by Simenon, which she regretted not having brought along with her to the café.

9.

His father would return from his house calls late at night and sit in the kitchen smoking his pipe, an encrusted briar from Algeria. Sometimes he would fall asleep at the table, his stethoscope still draped about his neck, his dinner half eaten.

"The trick," his father had once said, "is never to stop moving, so that life passes quickly and slowly at the same time."

10.

Without asking her permission, a young man sat down in the chair facing her. "May I engage you in conversation?" he asked.

She raised her newspaper higher. Then he asked the same in Italian, and again in English.

11.

"Here's what I think, Alfred," he said, "brandy flattens the appetite for love. But calvados quickens its hunger."

"After fifty, one should only drink warm milk with half a spoon of honey," the barman said.

"I still have some time then, Alfred."

"Of course. I myself have only started drinking milk recently, a decade ago."

"Do you drink alone, Alfred? Or do you have a wife?"

"A wife? No."

"Do you want one?"

"No."

"What are you attached to then?"

"The café. And the window, of course."

"Let me have a calvados then. I'll toss you for it."

The barman laughed. "A spinning coin makes me dizzy."

He looked out the window, wondering if he should leave and go after her or wait for her to come to him, whereupon he would apologize and offer her a kir royale, her favorite drink.

"Do you like your profession, Alfred?"

"It is the only one I have known or have ever wished for. And you?"

"I thought I'd be a doctor, like my father. But I came to realize there is no point in a doctor trying to keep people alive because in time we all will die anyway."

"Yes, but some people like to linger as long as possible. Anyway, there's no telling when it will come. I've witnessed two of my steady clients die before they finished their first drink. But mostly we are all leaves waiting for our season to fall from the tree."

"That's very philosophical, Alfred, the leaves, the trees, the cycle of life and death. But it's not very comforting and, forgive me, but I think I have heard all that before."

"Yes, it's an old song. As for comforts, I think there are very few. In any case, may I offer you another calvados?"

12.

She lowered the newspaper. The young man was handsome, his suntan richly even, his nose slightly bent, offsetting what would have made his good looks quickly boring. His blue blazer fit too tightly, so did his white shirt, open at the throat. He sleeked his hair back like a tango dancer in an Argentinean movie of the thirties.

13.

"Would you like another espresso?" the young man asked.
"No, thank you."
"A glass of wine?"
She folded the paper and gave him a long look from which he did not flinch or look away. "A Pouilly-Fuissé or a Sancerre," she said, adding, "No, a kir royale."
"That's an elegant choice. Of course, it would be from you."

14.

A propeller aeroplane circled overhead as if uncertain of its destination. She wished it would drop into the sea and drown along with its annoying buzz. She hated aeroplanes and hated travel. London, maybe, from time to time, because its wet grayness was like staying home. But perhaps one day she would take a train to Russia and see what all the mystery was about, all that vast gray, vast space, and drunken melancholy that she had read about in those old novels with their murky, noble souls talking without reserve to the heart of life. "When you read a Russian novel, especially Dostoevsky's *The Idiot,* you learn all you need to know about life," her mother had told her, drinking tea with a sugar cube between her teeth. She herself read the same Russian novels, keeping it a secret from her mother for fear she would say: "How dare you trespass into my private world?"
The damp sea breeze chilled her. She shivered and liked it.
"Take my jacket," he said, without removing it.

15.

"Have you," she asked the young man, "ever read Miguel de Unamuno's *Tragic Sense of Life*?"
"No need to. I know life's tragic."

"Have you ever read a book?"

"No and I never will."

"Can you read?"

"Certainly. But I have no wish to." He tapped his foot until her sharp look ordered him to stop.

16.

She wore black stockings with seams. A green skirt, a classic Chanel that her mother had left for her in its original box. The skirt smelled faintly of mothballs. Her sleeveless, straw-yellow sweater, a cashmere woven in Scotland that she had bought in London at Westaway & Westaway, loved her.

The straps of her high-heeled black shoes bound her ankles like sadistic vines. "Wear those shoes whenever we make love," he had said. She had forgotten to change them in her rush to leave the house.

17.

Earlier that afternoon, he had been taken to lunch by his colleagues at the law office to celebrate his fiftieth birthday. He ordered a frisée salad to start, followed by a rabbit stew with turnips and a crème caramel for desert. The espresso was bitter. The calvados made up for it.

A young colleague asked him, "What is the secret to a good life?" He was flattered to be asked but shrugged his shoulders as if to say, how would I know? He had thought of saying: Keep moving so life passes quickly and slowly at the same time, but was afraid of sounding sage-like and open to mockery. He was woozy when he left the restaurant and aglow with good feelings. He announced that he was the luckiest man alive to have such colleagues. But he saw that he was running late to his rendezvous and was glad to leave them chattering happily on the sidewalk and to find a taxi so quickly. A thought came to him as he stepped in the cab and for a moment he considered turning to the young man who had asked his advice and saying: Do not expect anything. Not even unhappiness.

18.

She enjoyed his thick weight on her, the apple aroma of calvados in his pores. She liked that he kept his watch on in bed while all else of him was naked white. She liked that he was neither young nor old

325

but at the moment of fullness before he turned unattractively ripe.

She liked how sometimes he would turn from tender to cruel, his voice commanding her to undress, to bend, to stand by the wall with her legs spread apart. "Do what you want to me, so long as you do it only with me," she had said, not long after they had met.

19.

"Married?" she asked, after deciding the young man was handsome.

"Yes."

"No ring?"

"No need to blazon one's life."

"May I ask your profession?"

"I'm a professor of the tango," the young man said, adding, "I would be honored to give you lessons."

"What makes you think I don't already know how to dance the tango?"

"I can tell from your legs."

20.

"Let's go for a walk," the young man said, half rising from his seat.

"Not now. Maybe some other time."

"When?"

"When it's another time."

21.

His watch also made him overeat. It made him sing like a mouse in the shower. It made him want to run from his life all expenses paid and fly to Brazil and sleep in a straw hut by a giant, frightening river and eat fish and fat corn roasted over a pit.

22.

How much time had passed since he entered the café, he did not know. His watch had stopped entirely, rigor mortis setting in at 4:07. Now he had an excuse to get rid of it and all the trouble it caused him. He was about to leave to find her when she passed by the window, glanced at him, laughing, young, immortal, on the arm of a slender, young, immortal man. At first he thought he would go after her but he quickly envisioned the vulgar scene that would ensue. It would be better to wait some while before trying to beg her forgiveness, to try first sending her flowers, white roses, nine, to make it up to her. And when he was with her again, bringing her another tin of caviar that made him grind his teeth at the expense. Or maybe he would never try, after her going off with a boy.

"Goodbye, Alfred," he said.

"Don't forget your cane," Alfred replied, walking to the window.

23.

He reached the sea and its flatness. Not a wave, not a ripple, not a crease. The sea was dozing, hoarding up its passion. There were no umbrellas, no chairs on the beach. The cabanas were boarded up; the houses shuttered and locked down, silent, bored, waiting for summer and the exciting return of their tenants. A three-legged black dog ran up and down, wheeled and wheeled and, howling, crashed into the water. Seagulls. He tightened his coat. He searched for his gloves. But he found instead a book he had bought for her, *Dirty Snow*, because she read Simenon by the dozens while smoking in bed.

"I hate Russian novels," she told him once, apropos of nothing, when he was about to enter her.

24.

"Do you still make love to your wife?" she asked, one day at the zoo.

"From time to time, as a courtesy," he said.

"To her?"

"To duty."

25.

She watched the afternoon cling to her window then fall away. The young man in her bed snored. It rained, smearing her windows, but still she could see the café below breaking into its first evening light.

It had rained like this one night when her mother had said, "When I'm gone, do what you wish with this place; it will be yours, of course. But please keep some of it the way I leave it. Above all, please keep the samovar where it is in the kitchen. As long as it is there, I am too."

"Your ghost, Mother."

"My spirit," she had answered.

The phone did not ring. She supposed that he would not call so soon, in any case, but she wished he would so that she could berate him for keeping her waiting. Tell him never to call her again. Tell him he had done her a favor because now she had found a man who knew what to do in bed and he could do it forever.

She was chilled and went to the kitchen to make tea. The Russian samovar stood atop a teak table draped with a heavy red damask cloth that fell to the edge of its portly nineteenth-century legs. She nodded to the samovar and lit the kettle on a stove with seven burners and on which her mother had stewed red meat and cabbage following a Russian recipe. Her mother had studied and spoke Russian but had never gone to Russia. Her mother read Russian novels and poetry in Russian and drank tea from a thick glass. She once said: "Only the Russians know life."

"What is it that they know?" she had asked, annoyed that her mother would believe that about a people who drank vodka without nuance and ate radishes without butter.

26.

"How much did you enjoy that?" the young man asked on waking, his eyes shut.

At first, because she did not like his presumption, his preening maleness, she thought to answer: Perhaps you are more proficient at giving tango lessons. Instead, she said: "If you want coffee or something to eat you will have to go out."

"Coffee. But let's drive to Rome, where the coffee has taste."

"Are you old enough to drive?"

"Yes, and with my own car." He had opened his eyes and was beaming like a proud boy, the teacher's pet.

"I don't like Italy. Or Spain, or England. I like it only here in this city, in this apartment. Or in the café across the street but never after five."

She was starting to dress when the phone rang and would not surrender. She lifted the receiver and let it drop. It rang again. She unplugged the phone and, for safe measure, left the receiver off the cradle. "I've decided," she said, sliding into bed beside him, "to change my routine, so there's time for coffee or a drink after."

"It's good to be flexible," he said, opening her robe.

"But I do not like to talk over coffee."

328

"Why talk anyway," he said, "now that it's been done."

27.

He looked up at his apartment window and its mellow, homey glow. Then, after a few moments of lingering in the rain, he took the stairs slowly, counting the steps. He was glad that the elevator was out of order because he feared it, not that it would fall but that, on a whim, it would decide to compress its walls and crush him like an iron maiden.

He hung his hat on the rack to dry and even before he took off his wet overcoat his wife said: "I made you your favorite for dinner, rabbit and turnips in white wine. For your birthday, my sweet wet bear."

She was wearing her black going-out dress and a cultured-pearl necklace he had given her on their tenth anniversary. He kissed her and gave her an extra hug and kissed her again. For a moment he thought to say: "That's too bad, I had rabbit for lunch." He decided instead to say: "How thoughtful of you, my dear," giving her a kiss on the cheek.

He had drunk too much wine at lunch and too much calvados at the café and he felt heavy in his bones and had wet cement for blood.

His wife was speaking to him very pleasantly but it did not matter. "You are still a young man," she said, thinking he was brooding at yet another birthday.

"Young enough still, I suppose," he said, feeling, as he said it, a breeze of time whiz by and take another year from him in its wake.

After dinner, in bed that night, he said, "Maybe we should go to the mountains this summer?"

"You hate the mountains, you always say you hate the mountains."

"Yes, but sometimes we must try new things before we dive into the winter of our life."

28.

The rain pelting the window kept him awake. It made him imagine himself dead and the rain leaching into his casket until whatever decomposed bits were left of him floated like suds in the bath. Also, the two rabbits jumped in his stomach, the lunch rabbit and the dinner rabbit. Also, he wondered if she would ever want to see him again or if this time, by keeping her waiting, he had gone too far.

His wife raised herself on her elbows and stared at him.

"Indigestion?"

He spoke in a low voice that she was not accustomed to. "Never be in love or love too much."

"Are you in love with someone now?"

"No."

She stayed silent for a long time. Finally, she said, "The mountains would be agreeable."

29.

Alfred was most happy when the café was empty and the sea was flat and biding its time to go wild. Above all, he liked to stand by the window as the afternoon light shrank into the edge of night—this light—and to write in a green notebook where he gathered up all the pieces and fragments of the day that he could recall, even the smallest thing: the sunlight on a hand as it raised a glass or the cracked crystal of a watch and the shadow it made on the dial. Or the way a man regards a woman from behind the café window as she crosses the street, as if the glass shielded his hungry gaze from being seen. Or the way a man drinks hunched at the bar, his black hat crowning the yellow cane beside him like a silent drinking partner.

He looked up at her apartment widow and was lucky. The light behind her as she stood at the rain-smeared window outlined her beauty. She was always beautiful. She never made cozy small talk and self-indulgent chatter as did most of his regulars, as if he were their friend, their confidant.

But she had overstepped only once when she was drunk, and had cried about her dead mother and rambled on about the beauty of the Russian soul. "Only the Russians understand melancholy, without which the soul starves. The falling snow, the crushing cold, the great distances, the birch trees in the moonlight—the Russian soul, who knows it better than I?" she had said.

There was more of the same until she tottered and almost fell off her stool; he half walked, half carried her to her building and to her apartment, where she collapsed in her bed. He had removed her shoes before leaving and left a light on in the hall lest she wake up frightened in the dark. He had rushed to leave: the vast apartment with its empty rooms and no furniture or carpets or standing lamps or pictures to befriend the naked walls had given him a chill that only his café and a glass of hot milk could warm. He had much to enter in his green notebook, when standing by the café window; he took his bowl

330

of breakfast coffee, as the sea swelled to meet the first morning light.

She apologized the next day, bringing him a gift. A Simenon novel about a man who, one day, telling no one, taking nothing, simply walked out of his life, leaving his small, successful business, his three employees, and faithful wife to puzzle over where he had vanished. He had enjoyed the book but wondered if it was something she had at hand and gave to him without a thought, an impromptu token of apology. If not, why would she ever have imagined he would have liked to read about a man who turned away from his life, taking the first train that pulled into the station and, without a plan, alighting in a remote village unknown to him and whose only light, at ten at night, came from a café with three drunks and a whore.

He himself was too settled, too happy in his café with its window to the sea, ever to leave. All the life that mattered flowed through that window and all the people in the world were winnowed down to the few who came to the café.

Though he was fearful of the time when he would be too old or too ill to tend to the café and stand by its window, he had a plan that comforted him. One day, he would sit himself in his club chair in his cozy room above the café and, with a warm glass of milk on a silver tray by his side, pore over all the years of green notebooks, one by one, savoring the pages line by line as if he were a stranger who had discovered them in a trunk beached from a schooner drowned at sea.

—For Danièle Thompson

NOTES ON CONTRIBUTORS

GABRIEL BLACKWELL's most recent book is *Madeleine E.* (Outpost19). His fictions and essays have appeared in previous issues of *Conjunctions* as well as in *Tin House*, *DIAGRAM*, *Post Road*, and elsewhere. He is the editor of *The Collagist*.

RYAN CALL is the author of *The Weather Stations* (Caketrain) and the recipient of a Whiting Award. He lives in Houston.

The actor, writer, and translator LOUIS CANCELMI is the founder and curator of *SIGNALS///noise*. His plays have been developed with and produced by Naked Angels, the Rattlestick Playwrights Theater, and the Orchard Project.

In 2016, longtime *Conjunctions* contributor CAN XUE was shortlisted for the prestigious Neustadt International Prize for Literature; in 2015, her novel *The Last Lover* (Yale University Press) received the Best Translated Book Award.

CHEN ZEPING has published widely in the field of Chinese linguistics. In addition, he has translated several contemporary Chinese writers into English in collaboration with Karen Gernant, including Can Xue, Zhang Kangkang, Alai, Yan Lianke, and Shi Tiesheng.

ROBERT CLARK is the author of four novels and four books of creative nonfiction, most recently *Dark Water: Flood and Redemption in the City of Masterpieces* (Doubleday). He has recently completed a book on Victorian artists and writers, doubt, eros, and obsession.

ROBERT COOVER has published more than twenty books of fiction and plays, his most recent being *A Child Again* (McSweeney's), *Noir* (Overlook), *The Brunist Day of Wrath* (Dzanc), and *Huck Out West* (Norton).

SUSAN DAITCH is the author of six books, most recently *The Lost Civilization of Suolucidir* (City Lights) and *White Lead* (Random House).

MONICA DATTA is a writer and architectural designer whose fiction has appeared previously in *Conjunctions:61, A Menagerie* and *Conjunctions'* weekly online edition.

KATHRYN DAVIS is the author of seven novels, most recently *The Thin Place* (Little, Brown) and *Duplex* (Graywolf). Among other honors, she has received the Lannan Award for Fiction and the 2016 Katherine Anne Porter Award from the American Academy of Arts and Letters. She teaches at Washington University in St. Louis.

ELAINE EQUI's latest book is *Sentences and Rain* (Coffee House). She teaches at New York University and in the MFA program at the New School.

KAREN GERNANT, professor emerita at Southern Oregon University, has collaborated with Chen Zeping in translating more than ten books of contemporary Chinese fiction, the most recent of which is Can Xue's novel *Frontier* (Open Letter).

KAREN HAYS lives and writes on the Monterey Peninsula. Her essays have appeared previously in *Conjunctions* and in such periodicals as *The Georgia Review* and *The Iowa Review*.

Aqueduct Press recently published KAREN HEULER's fiction collection *Other Places*, and in July 2017 will release her novella *In Search of Lost Time*.

Pushcart Prize–winner BRANDON HOBSON's work has appeared in *Conjunctions*, *NOON*, *The Believer*, and elsewhere. His next novel, *The Long Life*, will be out next year from Soho Press.

Ploughshares Solos recently published LISA HORIUCHI's digital novelette, *Bones*. Her contribution to this issue marks her first appearance in print.

MARK IRWIN is the author of nine collections of poetry, including *American Urn: Selected Poems 1987–2014* (AUP), *A Passion According to Green, Tall If* (both New Issues), *Bright Hunger*, and *White City* (both BOA). His collection of essays, *Monster: Distortion, Abstraction, and Originality in Contemporary American Poetry*, is forthcoming from Peter Lang.

Cover artist EUGENE IVANOV, a Russian Czech painter and book illustrator, has illustrated over a hundred books and held numerous solo exhibitions.

Contributing editor ROBERT KELLY's most recent publications include *Opening the Seals* (Autonomedia), *The Hexagon* (Black Widow/Commonwealth), *Heart Thread* (Lunar Chandelier Collective), and *The Secret Name of Now* (Dr. Cicero).

ANN LAUTERBACH's most recent books are *Under the Sign* (Penguin) and *St. Petersburg Notebook* (Omnidawn). A *Conjunctions* contributing editor, she teaches at Bard College.

LAWRENCE LENHART is the author of the essay collection *The Well-Stocked and Gilded Cage* (Outpost19) and an editor at *DIAGRAM*.

NATHANIEL MACKEY's most recent books are *Blue Fasa, Late Arcade* (both New Directions), and *Lay Ghost* (Black Ocean). He edits the literary journal *Hambone*.

JOHN MADERA's work has appeared in *Conjunctions, Bookforum, American Book Review, The Believer, Review of Contemporary Fiction*, and elsewhere. He lives in Brooklyn, New York.

ANDREW MOSSIN is the author of a book of critical essays, *Male Subjectivity and Poetic Form in "New American" Poetry* (Palgrave Macmillan), and several books of poetry, most recently *Exile's Recital* (Spuyten Duyvil). He is currently at work on a new book of poetry and a novel, from which "The Kite Room" is excerpted.

JUSTIN NOGA lives in Seattle, Washington. His contribution to this issue marks his first publication.

Longtime *Conjunctions* contributor JOYCE CAROL OATES's most recent books include the novel *A Book of American Martyrs* and the essay collection *Soul at the White Heat: Inspiration, Obsession, and the Writing Life* (both Ecco). She was recently inducted into the American Philosophical Society.

LANCE OLSEN's most recent book is the novel *Dreamlives of Debris* (Dzanc). He teaches experimental theory and practice at the University of Utah.

With Aftab Ahmad, MATT REECK has translated *Mirages of the Mind* from the Urdu of Mushtaq Ahmed Yousufi (Vintage India, New Directions) and *Bombay Stories* from the Urdu of Saadat Hasan Manto (Random House India, Vintage International). This fall Wesleyan University Press will publish his translation of *Class Warrior—Taoist Style* from the French of Abdelkébir Khatibi.

ELIZABETH ROBINSON wrote the poems included in this issue while a fellow at the Dora Maar House in Ménerbes, France. She is the coeditor, with Jennifer Phelps, of the forthcoming anthology *Quo Anima: Innovation and Spirituality in Contemporary Women's Poetry* (University of Akron Press).

JOANNA SCOTT is the author of twelve books, including *Follow Me* (Little, Brown) and *De Potter's Grand Tour* (FSG). Her new novel, *Careers for Women*, is forthcoming from Little, Brown in July.

French novelist, poet, and critic CLAUDE SIMON (1913–2005) received the 1985 Nobel Prize in Literature. His many works available in English translation include *The Grass* (1960), *The Flanders Road* (1961), *The Palace* (1963), *Histoire* (1968), *Conducting Bodies* (1974), *Triptych* (1976), *Georgics* (1989), *The Invitation* (1991), and *The Acacia* (1991). Louis Cancelmi's translations of his poems "Archipelago" and "North" in this issue are copyright © 1974, 2009 Les Éditions de Minuit.

Work by MARY SOUTH has appeared in *The Collagist*, *Electric Literature*, *The New Yorker*'s "Book Bench," *NOON*, *Vice*, and *Words without Borders*.

COLE SWENSEN is the author of seventeen collections of poetry, most recently *On Walking On* (Nightboat), and a collection of critical essays. The last two poems in this issue are based on Agnès Varda films of the same titles. Also a translator from French, Swensen teaches at Brown University.

FREDERIC TUTEN's most recent book is *Self Portraits: Fictions* (Norton). His contributions to *Conjunctions:54* and *Conjunctions:60* received Pushcart Prizes.

G. C. WALDREP's most recent books are a long poem, *Testament* (BOA), and a chapbook, *Susquehanna* (Omnidawn). His new collection, *feast gently*, is due from Tupelo in 2018. He edits the journal *West Branch*, and serves as editor at large for *The Kenyon Review*.

collections of short stories by

Joan Aiken
Jeffrey Ford
Juan Martinez
Christopher Rowe
Sofia Samatar

From classic strange to contemporary boundary breakers. Find them at

smallbeerpress.com

THE LONDON MAGAZINE

Est. 1732

Poetry Prize 2017

1ST PRIZE: £500 | 2ND PRIZE: £300
3RD PRIZE: £200

1st May - 30th June

www.thelondonmagazine.org

The Ronald Sukenick/ FC2 Innovative Fiction Contest

$1,500 & publication by FC2

Entries accepted August 15, 2017 - November 1, 2017

Submission guidelines: www.fc2.org/prizes.html

FC2 & The Jarvis and Constance Doctorow Family Foundation

present the

FC2 Catherine Doctorow Innovative Fiction Prize

Winner receives $15,000 and publication by FC2

Entries accepted
August 15, 2017 - November 1, 2017

Submission guidelines
www.fc2.org/prizes.html

Jarvis & Constance
Doctorow Family Foundation

FC2 is among the few alternative, author-run presses devoted to publishing fiction considered by America's largest publishers to be too challenging, innovative, or heterodox for the commercial milieu.

S O L I D

Samuel Amadon

Julie Carr

Thalia Field

Renee Gladman

Noah Eli Gordon

Lisa Jarnot

Miranda Mellis

Jake Bohstedt Morrill

Laura Mullen

Elizabeth Robinson

Jim Shepard

Mac Wellman

O B J E C T S

www.solidobjects.org

NOON

A LITERARY ANNUAL

1324 LEXINGTON AVENUE PMB 298 NEW YORK NY 10128

EDITION PRICE $12 DOMESTIC $17 FOREIGN

Bard's unique summer-based MFA in Writing focuses on innovative poetry but also welcomes students working in sound, performance, and other short or mixed-media forms. In this interdisciplinary program, anchored in the theory and diverse practices of contemporary art, students work with a distinguished faculty of writers, artists, and scholars, and are in close dialogue with faculty and students in Film/Video, Music/Sound, Painting, Photography, and Sculpture.

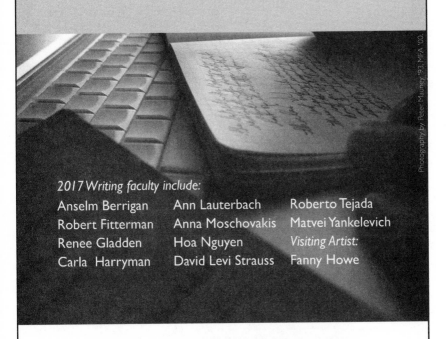

Photography by Peter Mauney '93, MFA '00.

2017 Writing faculty include:

Anselm Berrigan	Ann Lauterbach	Roberto Tejada
Robert Fitterman	Anna Moschovakis	Matvei Yankelevich
Renee Gladden	Hoa Nguyen	*Visiting Artist:*
Carla Harryman	David Levi Strauss	Fanny Howe

Bard**MFA**

MILTON AVERY GRADUATE SCHOOL OF THE ARTS

mfa@bard.edu • 845.758.7481 • bard.edu/mfa

BROWN UNIVERSITY LITERARY ARTS

HOME FOR INNOVATIVE WRITERS

Program faculty

John Cayley
Colin Channer
Thalia Field
Forrest Gander
Carole Maso
Meredith Steinbach
Cole Swensen

Visiting and other faculty

Lori Baker
Andrew Colarusso
Laura Colella
Mónica de la Torre
Joanna Howard
Erica Mena
Gale Nelson
Camille Rankine
Chika Unigwe

Since 1970, Literary Arts at Brown University has been fostering innovation and creation. To learn more about the two-year MFA program, visit us at http://www.brown.edu/cw

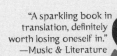

Our print issues and website are also made possible in part with the generous funding of the National Endowment for the Arts, and by the New York State Council on the Arts with the support of Governor Andrew Cuomo and the New York State Legislature.

NATIONAL ENDOWMENT FOR THE ARTS

A great nation deserves great art.

State of the Arts

NYSCA

CONJUNCTIONS.COM

Read dangerously.

@_conjunctions